D1106658

Similitude and

Approximation Theory

Similitude and Approximation Theory

Stephen J. Kline

Professor of Mechanical Engineering
Stanford University, Stanford, California

McGraw-Hill Book Company

New York · St. Louis · San Francisco · Toronto · London · Sydney

Similitude and Approximation Theory

Copyright © 1965 by McGraw-Hill, Inc. All Rights Reserved. Printed in the United States of America. This book, or parts thereof, may not be reproduced in any form without permission of the publishers.
Library of Congress Catalog Card Number 64-22193

35045

Preface

This work treats the interrelated topics of approximation theory, similitude, dimensional analysis, and modeling from the standpoint of the analytical worker in science or engineering. The relationship of these topics rests primarily on a common point of view; this view arises from the need for incomplete analyses.

Since we cannot obtain complete solutions to many problems in science and engineering, we must frequently be satisfied with a partial or fractional analysis. No single phrase seems to be available to describe such analyses as a group; therefore the term *fractional analysis* is employed. The purpose of this volume is to attempt a unified introduction to fractional analysis.

Fractional analysis is not synonymous with numerical analysis. Numerical analysis is a procedure for finding a complete answer to a particular problem in numerical form. Fractional analysis is a procedure for finding some information about the solution usually short of a complete answer. The procedure is usually analytical, but frequently employs both physical information and mathematical analysis; in addition, it

v

usually yields information about all problems in the class studied. Frequently, a fractional analysis is used to provide the approximate equation from which an approximate analytical or numerical solution can be obtained. Thus fractional analysis and numerical analysis are primarily complementary rather than overlapping methodologies.

As almost every undergraduate in engineering and science is taught today, one method for performing a fractional analysis is the procedure called *dimensional analysis*. The meaning of the term fractional analysis in the present connotation is very much in keeping with the spirit of the discussion of dimensional analysis given in the first book on the topic by P. W. Bridgman.[6]† However, at least six good books on dimensional analysis are now available in English, and they cover almost every facet and view of the subject thoroughly. Consequently, only a relatively brief résumé is given in this work, with references to more extensive treatments where pertinent. In addition to the résumé of dimensional analysis, this work covers two other methods of fractional analysis that seem to have been at least somewhat neglected in the literature; these are called respectively the *method of similitude* and *fractional analysis from the governing equations*. Neither of these methods is original with the author. However, some extensions and additions to each are included in this work.

The first chapter covers a more detailed discussion of the philosophy and uses of fractional analysis and classifies the various types of problems usually treated by such methods. The second chapter summarizes dimensional analysis. The third chapter contains a broader discussion of the method of similitude than any other known to the author; it also includes an introduction to the use of governing equations with examples employing algebraic and integral equations. The fourth chapter covers fractional analysis of differential equations with their boundary conditions. It includes not only discussion of conventional problems of dimensional analysis and modeling, but also the bases of approximation theory, construction of estimates, a brief introduction to the use of the boundary-layer concept and expansion methods for treating singular behavior, and, finally, extension of the concept of similarity by use of similarity variables and absorption of parameters. The final chapter contains a comparison of the various methods.

The level of discussion is intended to be appropriate for a current senior or first-year graduate student in engineering or science in the United States. The work is intended for use both by such students and by workers in science and engineering who must often deal with problems for which complete answers cannot be found. A working knowledge of undergraduate mathematics is presumed, and a modicum of familiarity with partial differential equations is required for Chap. 4.

† Superscripts refer to the list of references at the end of the book.

The more advanced mathematical procedures, which are naturally constructed upon the approach and analyses given, are not covered in detail, but are introduced briefly with appropriate references. In particular, the general treatment of *similarity solutions* of partial differential equations due to Morgan, the so-called Lighthill and WKBJ methods and the boundary-layer methods, are covered in this way. A more complete, integrated treatment of these topics and comparable methods for integral equations definitely seems needed, but it lies beyond the scope and intent of this work.

Examples have been drawn only from continuum analysis and include problems in fluid mechanics, thermodynamics, heat transfer, dynamics, and elasticity. However, the methods are much more widely applicable. The emphasis throughout is on methodology. No attempt has been made to provide complete coverage of any field or even to give the most modern examples. Examples have been selected solely to illustrate the methods under discussion. Some of them are made purposely trivial to provide simplicity in explanation, while others are far more complicated in order to show the types of problems which can be handled and the results achievable. In several instances the same problem is worked by different methods at different places in the text to give direct comparison of results. These comparisons are withheld until the end and are discussed together in Chap. 5.

In the process of developing the materials of Chap. 4, it becomes essential to discuss in some detail the physical meaning and content of differential (and integral) equations and to categorize and explain the meaning of different operations which can be carried out on the equations and associated conditions without actually solving them. This material, which lies between physical theory and mathematics, is conventionally missing from the standard treatments of applied mathematics; it is largely "elementary," but nevertheless of first importance to proper use of mathematics in physical theory.

The analytical worker will probably find the materials of Chap. 4 of greatest interest. The only previous systematic discussion appears to be that of Birkhoff,[5] and this is set in the language of formal group theory, which currently makes it relatively inaccessible to many engineers. In the present treatment an attempt is made to provide both simpler and firmer foundations for much of the materials on use of governing equations for fractional analysis and to provide a nomenclature, method, and conceptual framework in which these operations are better organized and clearer. It is hoped that some success has been achieved, but it is clear that much further improvement is possible.

Since problems from many fields are worked, it is not possible to define a unique list of symbols; some letters are used for several quantities.

Consequently, the nomenclature of each problem is given in a single section where the problem is introduced.   A few special symbols that are used throughout the work are listed below for convenient reference.

$\triangleq$	equal to by definition
$\stackrel{\wedge}{=}$	a dimensional equality, read "has the dimensions (or units) of . . ."
$\cong$	a close approximation
$\approx$	a rough approximation
$(^-)$	overbarred quantities are nondimensional
$0(1)$	equal to or less than order one
$U(1)$	approximately one over a finite distance and less than one elsewhere

Stephen J. Kline

Acknowledgments

The author owes a great debt to previous writers on dimensional analysis, particularly to P. W. Bridgman, E. R. Van Driest, H. Langhaar, D. H. Duncan, H. E. Huntley, and L. I. Sedov. The present work stands on the foundations they have built, and no brief statement here can include all these men nor fully discharge the debt to them.

Particular thanks are also due to: Prof. J. K. Vennard of Stanford University for his excellent introduction to the similitude method and for many helpful comments on the manuscript, to Prof. A. L. London of Stanford University for early instruction in the pi theorem and on the importance of nondimensional variables, and to Prof. A. H. Shapiro of the Massachusetts Institute of Technology for instruction on examples of the differential method and the nature of the variables in many of the illustrations. To those students in several consecutive graduate classes in fluid mechanics at Stanford University who have been subjected to earlier treatments of this material, appreciation is expressed both for many useful suggestions and for their assistance in the experiments comparing the various methods.   The very considerable assistance of Prof. G. Latta of Stanford University and Prof. G. F. Carrier of Harvard University is also gratefully acknowledged in connection with all of the underlying mathematics in Chap. 4.   Thanks are also due to Prof. Karl Klotter, formerly of Stanford University, for aid in checking the German literature.   Dr. A. J. A. Morgan of the University of California at Los Angeles has also kindly supplied much very useful material from his original work on the theory of homology solutions.   Professor D. Hudson of California Institute of Technology has supplied material relating to examples in dynamics.

Finally, thanks are due to a number of reviewers, most particularly to Dr. H. P. Eichenberger of Ingersoll-Rand Co., Prof. F. A. McClintock and S. H. Crandall of the Massachusetts Institute of Technology, Prof. D. Leigh of Princeton University, and Prof. M. D. Van Dyke of Stanford University for numerous constructive suggestions, both detailed and major, on earlier drafts of the work.   These constructive commentaries have undoubtedly resulted in a far better final volume.   The responsibility for the final work remains entirely with the author.

Contents

1   *Introduction*

The basic purpose of this volume is to explore as systematically as possible various methods of fractional analysis.   In the sense employed in this discussion, a fractional analysis is any procedure for obtaining some information about the answer to a problem in the absence of methods or time for finding a complete solution.   This fractional information may be based on anything from a list of a few of the pertinent parameters to an appropriate governing differential equation and its complete boundary conditions.   But whatever the level of sophistication and adequacy, a fractional analysis almost always uses both physical information and mathematical analysis.   The purpose of a fractional analysis is always the same: to obtain as much information as possible even though we are not able to find the complete, exact solution.

The attempt to find as much about the answer to a given problem as we can, even though a complete solution is impossible or unfeasible with the information and methodology available, forms the common basis for the entire discussion in this volume.   It will be used uniformly as the primary yardstick of adequacy for the various methods discussed, and it underlies many remarks throughout the text.

By far the most commonly known and widely employed method for such fractional analyses is the technique known as *dimensional analysis*. In one sense, most of the methodologies to be discussed might be considered as included in dimensional analysis. However, in the now considerable literature *dimensional analysis* has become more or less synonymous with the content of the Buckingham pi theorem and the developments surrounding it. Thus for clarity we shall use dimensional analysis to describe the pi-theorem methods; the broader class of methods will be referred to collectively as fractional analysis. Dimensional analysis in the narrow sense is developed in Chap. 2, but before that is done, it will be useful to discuss in more detail the types of questions we attempt to answer with all kinds of fractional analyses.

We begin by listing some of the types of applications of dimensional analysis. Among these are:

1. Unit checking to insure proper numerical procedures
2. Checking algebra and aiding memory by comparing the units of terms
3. Converting units of physical quantities in a systematic fashion
4. Reducing the number of independent parameters
5. Generalizing and correlating laboratory results and theory [including: (*a*) use of minimum amount of data, model tests, and formulas, (*b*) determination of unknown general coefficients, and (*c*) optimum choice of variables and/or parameters for simplicity and physical meaning]
6. Deriving model laws for both true models and various sorts of special models
7. Determining governing independent parameters
8. Constructing mathematical analogue techniques

In many discussions of dimensional analysis the two terms *variables* and *parameters* are used interchangeably; as already indicated in the list of uses, a distinction is made between these terms in this volume. There are a number of important reasons for keeping the terms distinct; these will become evident as various techniques are illustrated. At this point it is sufficient to define the usages employed.

Consider first an example:

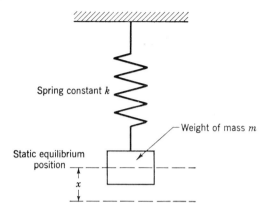

Spring constant k

Weight of mass m

Static equilibrium
position

x

FIG. 1.1

Figure 1.1 shows a simple harmonic oscillator consisting of a weight attached by a spring to an immovable ground.   In this system the variables are the displacement of the mass from its static equilibrium position x and the time t measured from some given condition.   The parameters of the problem, on the other hand, are the mass of the weight m and the spring constant k.   With this example in mind, we define variable and parameter as follows.   The independent variables are those quantities which are necessary to fix location inside a given problem.   The parameters are those quantities which are fixed for any one problem, but vary between two different problems of the same type.   In general, the dependent variable is a function of *both* the independent variables and the parameters.   Thus in the example of Fig. 1.1, the independent variable is time; it tells where we are in a given problem once the parameters are fixed.   The parameters m and k are fixed for a single system of this type, but if we want to study all possible simple oscillators of this kind, we consider variations in m and k.   For all these systems considered together, the displacement is a function of time and also of m and k.   Sometimes it is extremely useful to consider the behavior of a given system in time— that is, with fixed m and k.   At other times it is necessary to consider changes from one system to another of the same type, that is, alterations in m or k for equivalent times.   The significance of these remarks will become clearer as we progress to more complex examples and more sophisticated methods.†   When it is desirable to avoid the distinction

† Note that the word *parameter* also has another entirely different meaning in mathematics.   We speak of t as a parameter when, for example, $y = y(x)$, but we write instead $y = y(t)$, $x = x(t)$.   We will *not* use the word parameter in this sense here; in the few cases where such forms are needed we will call t a *parametric variable*.

between parameter and variable (for example, when we write a functional equation relating parameters) the word *quantity* or *coordinate* will be used to mean parameter and/or variable.

As has been correctly pointed out by Bridgman,[6] dimensional analysis does not apply to all possible equations but only to those equations that are dimensionally homogeneous and that are based on fundamental unit systems in which the formulas hold independent of the size of the fundamental unit adopted.[†] These requirements seem to cause no difficulty whatsoever in practice; therefore it will be presumed throughout this work that we are dealing with equations that satisfy these conditions.

As noted in the preface, this volume is written for analytical workers in science and engineering at a level appropriate for first-year graduate students. It is therefore presumed that the reader is thoroughly familiar with the simpler applications delineated in items 1, 2, and 3 of the list on page 2. It is hoped that the reader is also convinced that the expression of results in nondimensional form will indeed lead to a reduction in the number of independent coordinates required, and that such a process is useful, not only in reducing the amount of data, plots, experiments, and tables required, but also in correlating and generalizing results. For this reason only a very brief discussion of these topics is given in Chap. 2.

The omission of extensive discussion of these topics is in no way intended to imply that they are unimportant; it merely implies that they are normally prerequisite to present-day analytical endeavor in the fields of science and engineering.[‡] This point can be made more evident by consideration of these topics in terms of the purpose of fractional analyses in general. Fractional analyses normally take for granted the import of items 1, 2, and 3, dealing with units and dimensions. What is more, most fractional analyses employ appropriate nondimensional parameters or variables to generalize the results and to reduce the number of independent variables and parameters as far as possible. Thus, items 4 and 5 of the list of uses are employed, but they are normally accepted today without any explicit discussion of the methods. The real problems of the analyst today usually begin with determination of model laws, with formulation of the governing parameters, and with establishment of the

---

† The treatment of these underlying assumptions by Bridgman[6] is excellent and thorough; it is recommended for the reader who desires to refresh his memory. An even more extensive and very readable treatment has recently been given by Ipsen.[20]

‡ For the reader who wants to restudy any part of items 1, 2, or 3, the first three chapters of Bridgman[6] are very useful. Excellent and more modern treatments are also given by Langhaar[28] and Duncan.[13] Readers with a good background in linear algebra may well prefer the treatment of Langhaar, while those with less formal mathematics will probably find Duncan more readable. Ipsen gives a particularly thorough discussion of the meaning of units and the relations among the numerous unit systems now in actual use.

appropriate analogue techniques, that is, with items 6, 7, and 8 of the list of uses, and also with the physics (as opposed to the mathematics) of item 5.

While items 6, 7, and 8 in the list of uses of dimensional analysis above appear to be separate, they are in fact very closely related. All of them center on the question, "What are the pertinent parameters of the problem?" If the answer to this question is known, the governing independent parameters and the model laws usually follow with little difficulty. The establishment of analogue techniques requires some additional information, but, as will be shown in Chaps. 3 and 4, this information can be found by the same steps that are used to establish the independent parameters needed from the governing equations.

The foregoing discussion can be summarized by noting that the uses of dimensional analysis can be grouped into two categories: (1) establishment of the governing parameters and (2) effective management of the parameters. These two main categories can be broken down to include all the items in the list of uses on page 2 as follows:

I. Establishment and study of the governing parameters. This is central to the following uses:
   6. Establishment of model laws and similitude relations
   7. Determination of independent parameters
   8. Construction of physical and mathematical analogue techniques
II. Effective management of the parameters. This includes two subgroups:
   A. Simple manipulative and checking processes including,
      1. Unit checking
      2. Checking algebra
      3. Systematic conversion of units
   B. Rearrangement of the parameters (usually into nondimensional form) to provide:
      4. Reduction of the number of independent parameters
      5. Generalization and correlation of results

We have already noted that fractional analysis is primarily concerned with group I; it takes group IIA entirely for granted; and it usually uses group IIB more or less automatically. However, it is pertinent to examine why this is so. A given problem in dimensional analysis, when used as a technique of fractional analysis, has two primary parts: (1) finding the parameters of concern; (2) manipulating these parameters into the desired form. These parts correspond to the two main groupings above, and they have been arranged in the order in which the problem must be solved. Manifestly, it is impossible to make meaningful manipulations on the parameters of a given problem until these parameters are known.   It is a matter of common experience that finding the parameters involves most of the real difficulties in dimensional analysis.   Difficulties do occur in manipulating these parameters, but these usually are not troublesome.   To put this differently, if the average analytical worker in science or engineering is given the parameters of concern, he can be relied upon to rearrange them into at least some useful and simple form.   On the other hand, determination of the parameters required for model laws or analogue techniques is a problem requiring much more thought; they are much more frequently the source of difficulty and error.†   Furthermore, it is quite clear that any reasonable procedure in part II of the problem is necessarily based on the assumption that part I has been done correctly.   If an erroneous list of parameters is employed, only very rarely will purely mathematical manipulations ever straighten the matter out.‡

From the discussion above, it is clear that a list of the governing nondimensional parameters is in itself of great utility in the absence of other information.   However, if the purpose of a fractional analysis is to find as much information as possible about a given problem, even though the complete solution is lacking, then there is considerable information beyond the list of parameters in nondimensional form that we might also hope to find in at least some problems.   This information can perhaps be elucidated best by the following questions:

1. What is the physical meaning of each of the governing parameters and variables?   More particularly, what are the qualitative effects of an increase or decrease in any given parameter or variable?
2. Can we find the conditions under which the effects of certain parameters can be neglected either in a given region or for a particular problem?   If so, does this lead to governing equations that are more tractable so that we can solve the special case even though we cannot solve the general one?
3. Are there any combinations of two or more nondimensional parameters or variables, or transformations of variables, which lead to fewer independent quantities or which simplify the correlations achieved?
4. Can we find not only exact model laws but also distorted model laws?   Can we predict under what conditions model laws can be simplified by elimination of some of the full requirements?

The four questions just stated are clearly important, but they go beyond the confines of conventional dimensional analysis.   While there are a great number of particular problems in the literature employing

† A few data on this matter are given in Chap. 5.
‡ Some examples are available in the literature where one is saved from disaster by dimensional requirements, but such luck is rare in practice.

various methods to answer questions of this type, there seems to be very little on the methods as such, and a unified discussion seems to be lacking altogether. Thus, one of the primary purposes of this volume is to attempt at least the foundations of such a unified treatment, and to compare the utility of various procedures.

Several methods are examined, and in each instance we will be primarily concerned with the adequacy of the method in terms of the questions just posed. To expose this information, some examples are worked repeatedly by all of the methods. Finally, each method is summarized in the concluding chapter, and the adequacy of the various methods is compared on the basis of power, rigor, simplicity, accuracy, and input information required.

2   *Dimensional Analysis and the Pi Theorem Units and Dimensions*

2-1   UNITS AND DIMENSIONS

Before starting a direct discussion of the pi theorem, which is central to dimensional analysis, it is necessary to remind ourselves, very briefly, of the nature of equations, units, and dimensions.

First of all, what do we mean by the word *unit?* In the modern sense, a unit is the yardstick by which we measure the sizes of a physical characteristic of a system; both the unit and the measuring procedure must be defined by some prespecified operational procedure. Thus, the length of a bar is measured by the number of times a given scale *unit*, say an inch, can be laid off along the side of the bar. In such a procedure we must have three things:

1. a datum
2. a *unit* of measure defined by an operational procedure
3. an operational rule for interpolation and extrapolation

In the case of length, the datum is taken to be zero; the unit of measure is the inch as established by comparison with a standard inch; and the rule for interpolation is given by means of fractions which are marked on dividing machines. These operations regarding length are so well known to us that we usually take them for granted.

A dimension is the qualitative concept or idea of the characteristic measured by a given unit. Thus, in the example of the preceding paragraph, the dimension is length. The unit employed to make the qualitative idea of length quantitative may be an inch, a meter, or a mile.

In the early decades of this century, an argument still persisted in the literature concerning whether dimensions (and units) were fundamental or relative in character. Bridgman[6] discusses this matter in much detail and shows that the only tenable position is that dimensions (and units) are relative quantities. In particular, they must depend on the *specific operational procedures* employed in the measuring process. If these operational procedures are altered not only the size but also the type of dimensions and units needed will, in general, change. Bridgman also established the fact that there is no unique "best" or "fundamental" set of dimensions or units. Thus we could choose to measure geometric sizes using area, instead of length, as the unit. In a given problem this might be either more or less convenient, but it would be equally correct. We might also choose to replace temperature by color in measurements on very "black" hot bodies, but again this would not alter our final results, provided we use a consistent and proper measuring process.

Bridgman also showed what was meant by the words *proper measuring process*. In particular, Bridgman points out that the operational procedures used must be such that the physical equations are satisfied no matter what choice of units is made. This will be true, provided that the operational procedure specified requires that if the unit of measure, item 2 above, is halved, then the number of units found is doubled. Or, more generally, that the number of units measured is inversely proportional to the unit of measure. Thus 1 foot equals 12 inches and the length of a bar in feet is one-twelfth the length of the same bar in inches. This is a fact which most of us would regard as common sense because of our experience with physical systems, and it causes no difficulties in practice. We shall therefore assume that this condition is fulfilled by all unit systems discussed in the remainder of this treatment.

2-2 TYPES OF QUANTITIES APPEARING IN PHYSICAL EQUATIONS

In terms of the brief discussion just given, we can differentiate four types of characteristics of systems that enter into physical equations as follows:

1. primary quantities
2. secondary quantities
3. physical constants
4. nondimensional quantities

a. *Primary and Secondary Quantities*

A primary quantity is defined as any quantity with dimensions that can be written in terms of the first power of one unit of measure in our specified operational measuring procedures.   It must not require the use of two measuring procedures, and it must not require an expression involving any power of the dimension needed other than one.   Thus in the example above if we adopt a measuring procedure based on the usual scaling of lengths, then the length of a given bar is a primary quantity, since its dimension is just length.   However, a side of this bar is not a primary quantity, since its dimensions must be expressed as the product of two lengths or length squared.   If we add the measurement of time, say with a stopwatch, to our operational procedures, and still measure length in the usual way, then we can measure the velocity of a given mass, say of a car moving down a freeway.   The velocity of the car, in this measuring scheme, is not a primary quantity, because its dimensions involve both length and time.   We call a quantity such as the velocity of the car or the area of the bar a secondary quantity.   That is, a secondary quantity is a characteristic of a system with dimensions that must be expressed by more than one of the dimensions representing our specified measuring procedures, or by one of these dimensions to a power other than unity.

At this point it is useful to adopt a symbol due to Duncan.[13]   We define the symbol $\ominus$ to mean a dimensional equality; it stands for the words "has the dimensions (or units) of."   Thus we can say

Length $\ominus L$ primary
Area $\ominus L^2$ secondary
Time $\ominus t$ primary
Velocity $\ominus \dfrac{L}{t} = Lt^{-1}$ secondary

And we read; length has the dimensions of L, area has the dimensions of L^2, etc.   Also we would read the equations which follow as "mass has the units of pounds," or "mass is expressed in pounds."

$m \ominus \text{lb}_m$

Another way of viewing the difference between primary and secondary quantities is to observe that primary quantities cannot be subdivided in terms of the operational procedures being employed; they are the most elementary building blocks of our dimensional structure.   Thus the primary quantities in a given analysis are *postulated* by the prescribed measuring procedures.   The secondary quantities, on the other hand, are derived or built up from the primary quantities; they represent subassemblies in our analytical structure.

Two further comments on primary and secondary quantities are needed.   First, it has been shown by Bridgman[6] that the dimensions of any possible secondary quantity can be expressed as a single combination of powers (including negative and fractional powers) of the dimensions of the primary quantities.   For example, if the only dimensions of the primary quantities involved in a given operational scheme are mass, length, time, and temperature, then the dimensions of any secondary quantity q can be expressed by the form

$$q \triangleq M^a L^b t^c T^d \tag{2.1a}$$

where

$$T \triangleq \text{temperature}$$
$$M \triangleq \text{mass}$$
$$L \triangleq \text{length}$$
$$t \triangleq \text{time}$$

and a, b, c, and d are constants which may take on any real finite values including fractions, negative values, and zero.   The complete proof of this theorem is given by Bridgman[6] and Wilson.[55]   We call the dimensions of the quantity q the dimensions of the terms on the right of Eq. (2.1a) raised to the respective powers a, b, c, d.   Sometimes for brevity we also refer to the dimensions of the secondary quantity simply as the value of the exponents a, b, c, d.

Second, the use of mass, length, and time in the above example does not imply that there is anything "sacred" or "fundamental" in the nature of such a system of dimensions.   As already stated above, the primary quantities are, in effect, chosen by the investigator for a given problem by the operational measuring procedures he specifies.   There definitely is a choice; if the choice is not made explicitly, it will be made implicitly.   In the illustration above, for example, we could have chosen mass, time, temperature, and velocity as our primary quantities.   In fact, for some purposes this choice is very convenient.   In such a system length would, of course, be a secondary quantity which was made up from time and velocity.   Thus, we would write

$$\text{velocity} \triangleq V \qquad \text{primary}$$
$$\text{length} \triangleq Vt \qquad \text{secondary} \tag{2.1b}$$

The dimensions of any secondary quantity could then be expressed as:

$$q \mathrel{\hat{=}} M^a V^b t^c T^d$$

At first glance this may seem strange, since we are so accustomed to the use of primary quantities with the dimensions of length.   But if by some strange quirk we had invented a means for direct measurement of velocity, such as a police radar speed trap, before we had found a direct means for measuring length, our convention might well be the opposite.   In a measuring system based on the radar speed trap, the velocity of a car on a freeway indeed becomes a primary quantity.

Sedov[46] has extended Bridgman's point on the relative nature of secondary and primary quantities to show that even what is apparently dimensional depends on the operational measuring scheme adopted. Sedov points out, for example, that an angle measured in radians conventionally is considered nondimensional, and yet there are other possible measures of angle which give different numerical values.   Thus the numerical value of angle depends on choice of measuring units, and in this sense it can be considered dimensional.

b.   *Physical Constants and Independent Dimensions*

If we choose the units of measure for many quantities arbitrarily, then in general we will find that they do not all match.   By this we mean that the equations representing the fundamental physical principles will require introduction of constants to match up the sizes of the units we have chosen to employ.   The classic example is the constant which appears in Newton's Second Law of Motion when engineering units are employed.   In the units of physics we can write

$$F = ma \tag{2.2a}$$

where

$$m \mathrel{\hat{=}} \text{gm mass}$$
$$a \mathrel{\hat{=}} \text{cm/sec}^2$$
$$F \mathrel{\hat{=}} \text{dynes}$$

but in English engineering units we are obliged to write

$$F = \frac{W}{g_c} a \tag{2.2b}$$

where

$$F \mathrel{\hat{=}} \text{lb}_f = \text{pounds force}$$
$$W \mathrel{\hat{=}} \text{lb}_m = \text{pounds mass}$$
$$a \mathrel{\hat{=}} \text{ft/sec}^2$$

We call g_c a physical constant. Physical constants play an important role in the actual use of the pi theorem. These constants have dimensions in the same sense that the secondary quantities do. Thus in the equation above, if we take the primary quantities to be force, length, time, and mass, and we adopt engineering units of measure, namely, pounds force, feet, seconds, and pounds mass, we write:

pounds force $\stackrel{\frown}{\smile} F \stackrel{\frown}{\smile} \text{lb}_f$
length $\qquad \stackrel{\frown}{\smile} L \stackrel{\frown}{\smile} \text{ft}$
time $\qquad \stackrel{\frown}{\smile} t \stackrel{\frown}{\smile} \text{sec}$
mass $\qquad \stackrel{\frown}{\smile} M \stackrel{\frown}{\smile} \text{lb}_m$

We now solve Newton's Second Law for g_c and obtain:

$$MLF^{-1}t^{-2} \stackrel{\frown}{\smile} g_c = 32.17 \ \text{lb}_m\text{ft}/\text{lb}_f\text{sec}^2$$

A physical constant then can be defined more precisely as a characteristic whose numerical value is always uniquely fixed solely by the choice of the operational measuring procedures to be employed. If we had chosen the slug as the unit of mass, or the poundal as the unit of force, then, of course, the value of g_c would be unity, and it could have been omitted from the equation. It is noted, however, that this omission would not imply that it was correct to cancel a unit of mass against a unit of force. In terms of our operational definitions, mass and force are separate dimensions and are not interchangeable or cancelable. The fact that they happen to have the same name in some systems of measure (pounds, grams, etc.) is no excuse for performing physically improper operations. Fundamentally, there is no more justification for canceling a force with a mass than for canceling a length with a temperature. While such operations may not cause errors in some cases, they cannot aid anything and they may cause much confusion. From the point of view of dimensional analysis, the matter of canceling force against mass in a dimensional equation is clear-cut; it simply should not be done.

The use of physical constants in dimensional analysis is inextricably connected with the question of the independence or redundancy of the set of dimensions employed for the primary quantities. If none of the dimensions of the primary quantities chosen in our specified operational procedures can be expressed in terms of any combination of the dimensions of the other primary quantities, then we say the set of dimensions employed is independent; if this is not true, we say the set of dimensions employed is redundant. An example of redundancy is easily given in terms of the discussion of Newton's Second Law of Motion. If Newton's Law is relevant to the problem in hand in the sense that it gives relations between the system characteristics under study, then the use of four independent dimensions representing the four primary quantities (force, mass, length, time) is redundant. Newton's Law itself always provides a soluble dimensional equation between the four dimensions of force, mass, length, and time; it follows that the dimensions of any secondary quantity expressible in terms of only force, mass, length, and time can also be expressed in terms of any three of the four by using the dimensional equation to eliminate one in favor of the other three. There is no problem about the determinacy of such an elimination procedure; it will always go through by virtue of the form of Newton's Second Law and Eq. (2.1a), which shows that the dimensions (or units) of any secondary quantity can be expressed in terms of powers of the dimensions of units employed. [The reader can verify this determinacy for himself by combining Eqs. (2.1a) and (2.2b).]

Sedov[46] has made the role of physical constants central in discussing the problems of dimensional analysis. Sedov states that physical constants must be included whenever they are "essential." This is certainly true, and Sedov's remarks clarify such long-standing questions as those raised by Riabouchinsky[43] and Bridgman[6] regarding the analysis of Rayleigh.[42] However, the question of when the constants are essential is not simple; it is the same question as whether the given principle applies in the sense that it must be used to solve for the parameter or variable under study. This is clearly again a question of dependence and/or redundancy. We shall have more to say about this problem of redundancy in Chaps. 3 and 4.

c. Nondimensional Quantities

A nondimensional quantity† is defined as any quantity, physical constant, or any group of them formed in such a way that all of the units‡ identically cancel. Thus the exponents a, b, c, d are all identically zero in a nondimensional quantity. For example, we find the ratio of the specific heats γ has the following dimensions:

$$\gamma \triangleq \frac{c_p}{c_v} \wedge \frac{EM^{-1}T^{-1}}{EM^{-1}T^{-1}}$$
$$E^0M^0T^0 \wedge 1$$

† Also often called dimensionless parameter, pi, or nondimensional group. The four terms will be used interchangeably.

‡ To obtain constant values of a given nondimensional group it must be not only dimensionless but also unitless. Otherwise one is left with arbitrary constants depending on units such as 12 in./ft. See also in this regard the remark, due to Sedov, on angle measurement in Sec. 2-2a.

where the symbol $\triangleq$ means equal to by definition;

$E \triangleq$ energy
$M \triangleq$ mass
$c_p \triangleq \left(\dfrac{\partial h}{\partial T}\right)_p$
$c_v \triangleq \left(\dfrac{\partial u}{\partial T}\right)_v$
u = internal thermal energy
h = enthalpy
T = temperature

Since any finite quantity raised to the zero power is unity, we usually say for brevity that a nondimensional group has the units of 1. Nondimensional quantities play a central role in all of the methods of fractional analysis.

2-3 DIMENSIONAL HOMOGENEITY OF PHYSICAL EQUATIONS

As noted by Bridgman[6] and others, not all correct equations are dimensionally homogeneous. For example, one might choose to analyze a macroscopic system of fixed mass in the absence of relativity effects. For such a system the First Law of Thermodynamics can always be written:

$$Q = \Delta E + W \qquad (2.3)$$

And Newton's Second Law of Motion may be written:

$$F = ma \qquad (2.4)$$

If we add Eqs. (2.3) and (2.4) and rearrange we obtain

$$F - ma = (\Delta E + W) - Q \qquad (2.5)$$

Equation (2.5) is mathematically correct, but it is physically useless. Physically, it remains two equations, because it can be satisfied if and only if it is identically zero on each side. This follows from the fact that the dimensions of the two sides are never the same; physically, as we have already noted, it is never permissible to cancel a mass by use of a force, nor is it possible to cancel an energy (force times length) against only a force. Hence we can never combine any term on the left side of Eq. (2.5) with a term on the right side.

Thus dimensionally nonhomogeneous equations may be mathematically valid, but they are of no utility in the solutions of physical problems. Consequently, in science and engineering we can assume that all of our equations will be dimensionally homogeneous with no loss in generality.

From the example above it can be seen that dimensional homogeneity means precisely that the dimensions of each additive (or subtractive) term in the equation shall be the same.   That is, we require that each of the terms Q, ΔE, and W in Eq. (2.3) separately shall have dimensions of energy, or each of the terms F and the product ma in Eq. (2.4) separately shall have the dimensions of force in consistent units.   It is from this idea of dimensional homogeneity, together with the fact that the size of the quantity is inversely proportional to the unit of measure adopted, that Bridgman proves the results, stated in Eq. (2.1a), that the dimensions or units of any secondary quantity can be expressed as a product of powers of the dimensions or units of the primary quantities.   As we shall see in the next section, this idea also leads to the pi theorem due primarily to Buckingham.[7]

2-4   STATEMENT AND USE OF THE PI THEOREM

To give a clear statement of the pi theorem, we need to define one more term.   We will use the word *parameter* in this section to mean any of a primary quantity, a secondary quantity, a physical constant, a nondimensional quantity, or any grouping of the four.†

The pi theorem is a formal statement of the connection between a function expressed in terms of dimensional parameters and a related function expressed in terms of nondimensional parameters.   By nondimensional parameters we mean merely groups of the dimensional parameters concocted so that they are free of dimensions (and units).   It is desirable at this point to remind ourselves why it is useful to rearrange functions into such nondimensional form.

First, the use of properly chosen nondimensional parameters frequently will correlate and generalize results.   Thus, use of dimensionless groups often brings together what might appear to be separate phenomena when expressed in terms of dimensional parameters.   Employment of

† In most of the literature of dimensional analysis the term *variable* has been used for this purpose instead of parameter.   However, the word variable has a distinctly different, almost totally contrary, meaning as used in most governing equations of science and engineering.   Since later in this work we will consider governing equations in some detail, clarity demands the use of another term.   As we will see, this use of the term parameter is consistent with the definition of Chap. 1 and the usage in governing equations in Chaps. 3 and 4.

nondimensional parameters provides a better means for obtaining a grasp of the phenomena as a whole, and hence it frequently is a great aid to thorough understanding. Since this process provides correlation of a group of phenomena, it also implies that the use of dimensionless parameters may make possible predictions of untested phenomena which are covered by the correlation, but which could not have been predicted from the original dimensional form alone.

Second, the use of dimensionless parameters reduces the number of independent coordinates required. A convenient way to realize the importance of such a reduction is to recall that a function of one independent coordinate can be recorded on a single line; two independent coordinates, a page; three require a book; and four, a library. Since each point in these entries may take anywhere from a few minutes to many months to compute or measure, the utility of such a reduction is evident even without consideration of the additional mathematical complications which arise from the need for a larger number of independent coordinates.

In any given physical problem we have one or more dependent parameters, each of which is a function of some independent parameters. Let us denote any particular dependent parameter under scrutiny as q_1. If the independent parameters are $m - 1$ in number, then we may call them $q_2, q_3, \ldots, q_m$. And we may write in functional notation:

$$q_1 = f_1(q_2, q_3, \ldots, q_m) \tag{2.6a}$$

where f_1 is an unspecified function. Mathematically, Eq. (2.6a) is entirely equivalent to the relation

$$f_2(q_1, q_2, q_3, \ldots, q_m) = 0 \tag{2.6b}$$

where f_2 is some other unspecified function.

We can now state the pi theorem in the following way:

Pi Theorem†

Given a relation among m parameters of the form

$$f_2(q_1, q_2, \ldots, q_m) = 0 \tag{2.6b}$$

an equivalent relation expressed in terms of n nondimensional parameters can be found of the form

$$f_3(\pi_1, \pi_2, \ldots, \pi_n) = 0 \tag{2.7a}$$

† This theorem is usually attributed solely to Buckingham[7] and is often called the Buckingham pi theorem. However, like most results in science its foundations were laid by many other contributors including Fourier, M. Riabouchinsky, and Rayleigh (see, for example, Bridgman[6]).

where the number n is given by the relation

$$n = m - k \qquad (2.7b)$$

where m is the number of q's in Eq. (2.6b), and k is the largest number of parameters contained in the original list of parameters q_1, q_2, q_3, . . . , q_m that will *not* combine into any nondimensional form.

Following the usual practice, we shall refer to the nondimensional groups π_1, π_2, . . . , π_n as pi's.

In the original formulation of the theorem Buckingham[7] stated that k was equal to the minimum number of independent dimensions required to construct the dimensions of all the parameters q_1, q_2, . . . , q_m; this minimum number we shall denote as r.   More recently, Van Driest[50] has shown that while k is usually equal to r, there are exceptions, and the more general rule is given by the relation

$$k \leq r \qquad (2.8)$$

To clarify the matter of exceptions, as well as certain other points that are essential to proper use of the pi theorem, it is useful to attempt a clear statement of the necessary conditions for use of the pi theorem and also to discuss the reasoning underlying the theorem.   Before doing so, let us give a simple example to form a more concrete basis for discussion. We will then proceed with the discussion of the conditions, and finally give some additional examples of application.

Example 2.1. Suppose we examine a steady, fully established, laminar, incompressible flow of a Newtonian fluid through a circular tube. Let us assume, fictitiously, that we do not know the equation for the pressure drop, but we hope by use of dimensional analysis to find its form. If we believe pressure drop Δp is a function of velocity V, length of pipe L, diameter D, density ρ, viscosity μ, we would then write

$$f_2(\Delta p, L, D, V, \mu, \rho) = 0 \qquad (2.9)$$

Examining the dimensions of the six parameters in Eq. (2.9), we see that the minimum number of independent dimensions from which they can be constructed is three, for example, force, length, and time.

Hence we have $r = 3$.   We look then for three of the six dimensional parameters that will *not* form a nondimensional group, and in this case we would be successful; that is, no combination of density, diameter, and velocity alone can be made nondimensional, since neither velocity nor diameter contains the dimension mass, but density does.   We therefore conclude, for this particular problem, that

$$k = 3 = r$$

And the pi theorem then indicates that the number of nondimensional parameters we need is

$$6 - 3 = 3$$

If we had been unable to find any group of three parameters that could not be combined into a nondimensional form, then we would have looked for two of them that would not so combine, and so on, until the number k was found.

By inspection we can see in this very simple example that one form for the desired nondimensional relation might be

$$f_3\left(\frac{\Delta p}{\frac{1}{2}\rho V^2}, \frac{L}{D}, \frac{\rho V D}{\mu}\right) = 0$$

Or, since we want the pressure drop to be the dependent variable, we might write:

$$\frac{\Delta p}{\frac{1}{2}\rho V^2} = f_4\left(\frac{\rho V D}{\mu}, \frac{L}{D}\right) \tag{2.10}$$

This relation is entirely correct for the problem we stated. However, if we are shrewd enough, we can put it into still more useful form; that is, into a form which still has the same total amount of information, but which has a lesser number of nondimensional parameters or pi's. Thus we can reason *physically* as follows. For a fully established flow in a constant-area round duct, a certain symmetry is implied. In particular, we expect that the pressure drop per unit length of pipe will be constant along the pipe, since conditions do not change with length. Equation (2.10) suggests that this length should be measured in terms of the diameter of the pipe. We might seek a relation of the form

$$4f \triangleq \frac{\Delta P/(L/D)}{\frac{1}{2}\rho V^2} = f_5\left(\frac{\rho V D}{\mu}\right) = f_5(Re_D) \tag{2.11}$$

where $4f$ is the friction factor of hydraulics by definition and Re_D is the diameter Reynolds number. And, in this case, we know from an immense number of experiments that the strategy succeeds. That is, Eq. (2.11) is sufficient to correlate the pressure drop due to friction for all round pipes whatsoever under the conditions specified. This can be verified by reference to any elementary text on hydraulics. In fact, this is one of the very few cases where an exact, complete solution to the Navier-Stokes equations is known so that very adequate verification is available both theoretically and experimentally.

It is well to pause here to point out that merely because Eq. (2.11) is well verified does not automatically imply that it provides the simplest possible form any more than Eq. (2.10) does. This is an important point, and we shall return to it later on. Let us now turn again to the matter of the conditions for use of the pi theorem and the underlying reasoning upon which it rests.

With this example in mind, we now enumerate the conditions which should be fulfilled in use of the pi theorem:

1. The list of dimensional parameters must contain all of the parameters of physical significance including all independent parameters and one dependent parameter.

2. The nondimensional pi's as finally composed should contain, at least once, each of the parameters in the original list.

3. The list of dimensions used to compose the physical parameters must be independent, or else provision must be made to compensate for the redundancy.

In many treatments, the foregoing requirements are not set forth explicitly, and it is therefore desirable to discuss them briefly. Since the method makes no provision for introduction of further parameters at any stage beyond the original listing, the original list must contain all parameters of importance. Any parameters that are omitted from the original list will be omitted from the solution, and such an omission is a clear error in analysis. It is also desirable, for convenience, to have the dependent parameter appear in only one group, but this is a matter of convenience, not necessity.

As just stated, the final nondimensional form cannot contain more parameters than the original list, but there is also the possibility that it may contain fewer. However, if the nondimensional form contains fewer parameters than the original list, it must imply that either the parameters which appeared in the original list, but not in the final nondimensional form, are of significance in the problem or they are not. If they are of significance, they should be in the final nondimensional form. If they are not of significance, they should not have been in the original list of physical quantities, because this almost always increases the number of pi's unnecessarily and thus unduly complicates the solution. In other words, inclusion of unnecessary parameters in the original list is not erroneous (as is omission of pertinent parameters), but it does give added pi's. These added pi's tend to defeat one of the basic purposes of the analysis, to reduce the number of independent pi's to the lowest possible value.

The requirement concerning independence of the dimensions also is necessary. The simplest way to show this is to examine what would have happened had we used a redundant set of dimensions in the example above. Suppose that we had decided to use all of mass, length, time, and force in the analysis. Since Newton's Second Law of Motion does apply to this situation, this would be a redundant set of dimensions as already noted. We then would have found that there were only two nondimensional groups for a pipe of any length, and when we introduced the idea of pressure drop per unit length, we would have looked for a solution in terms of just one group. We would not have been able to find such a solution by proceeding in this way, and we would therefore have ultimately arrived at a contradiction. We must therefore do one of two things. Either we must work with an independent set of dimensions, or we must somehow compensate for the redundancy. The compensation is normally provided in the following manner. For each redundant dimension employed, as for example, mass in the above illustration, we introduce into the list of parameters the physical constant which shows that it is redundant. In the example of redundancy just discussed we would have simply added g_c to the list of parameters in Eq. (2.9). Of course, we could have compensated in other ways. The simplest would be to subtract one from the number of dimensions for each degree of redundancy. The choice of method in this regard is a matter of individual taste.

In the example above, it will be noted that we proceeded directly to the desired nondimensional form from the dimensional form without any intermediate algebra. There are available several formal algebraic methods for performing the intermediate steps; these methods have been treated by many authors. All of the available texts on dimensional analysis include such methods in much detail (Refs. 6, 28, 13, 37, and 19). Careful treatments are also included in most books on elementary fluid mechanics. Not only are the existing treatments of this algebra extensive, but they cover all shades of mathematical formality and elegance so that there seems to be little or no need for further treatment. There is also another, more important, reason why the author has chosen to jump over the algebra; this is as follows.

The algebra of the pi theorem is necessary for the beginner in order to grasp the process, but it is usually cut short by the experienced worker, as was done in Example 1 above. There is good reason for this short-cutting in addition to the work saved. So long as the final nondimensional form of the relation contains all of the parameters in the original list, and so long as it contains the correct number of nondimensional groups, it is correct. That is, there is always an indefinitely large number of entirely correct possible choices of the final nondimensional pi's. The analytical worker makes a choice among these possibilities based on convenience in working with the final form and convention. In solving the problem above, the matter was fixed by convention. At this stage of the game, it would be a meaningless gesture to use any dimensionless parameters except friction factor and Reynolds number in Example 2.1, since these two quantities are so widely used already in the literature of fluid mechanics.   If a formal mathematical procedure had been used to obtain the nondimensional groups, we might, by luck, have found these standard, accepted pi's.   But since there are an infinite number of possibilities, such a fortuitous outcome is very unlikely; it is much more likely that the answer obtained from the formal method would have required rearranging to make the terms agree with standard nomenclature.   Since this is the case, it is usually much more expedient simply to look for the desired form by a process of inspection, as was done in the example given.   Such a procedure will yield an answer equally correct to that of any formal procedure, provided only that all conditions for use of the pi theorem stated above are satisfied.

In the above example we have discussed briefly how to deal with secondary quantities and physical constants which appear in the list of parameters.   There is also the possibility that some of the parameters in the original list may be primary quantities or nondimensional quantities. This causes no difficulties.   As a matter of fact, two of the items in the list of the example, L and D in Eq. (2.9), were primary quantities in the dimensional system employed.   It will be noted that they were treated precisely as any other secondary quantities in the list.   It is also useful to observe that when two quantities in the list have the same units, a nondimensional group can always be formed simply by taking their ratio.

In the case of nondimensional quantities, the same comment applies. They are treated, and counted, just the same as the other parameters in the list.   If they are already nondimensional, it is not necessary to rearrange to obtain a nondimensional group.   Hence they simply appear unaltered in the final nondimensional form.

2-5   RATIONALE OF THE PI THEOREM

We now turn to a discussion of the underlying meaning of the pi theorem. To get at this we ask the question, "Why is it possible to obtain an equation in a lesser number of independent parameters simply by transforming to a nondimensional form?"   This question can be answered as follows. Any meaningful relation describing a physical situation can be assumed to be dimensionally homogeneous.   As already discussed, this implies that (1) each additive term in the equation has the same units, (2) the dimensions on the parameters from which the terms are composed can be made up of a single term containing no more than a product of powers of the independent dimensions.   These two facts constitute information about the problem in addition to the existence of a functional relation among the parameters.   By utilizing this additional information, we can achieve a simpler, more useful result.   The mathematics of this process can be viewed as follows. We have an original relation of the form

$$f_2(q_1, q_2, \ldots, q_m) = 0 \qquad (2.6b)$$

We also know that the dimensions of the m parameters in this relation can each be constructed in terms of a product of arbitrary powers of r independent dimensions. Furthermore, we know that each additive term of the relation must have the same units. If the set of dimensions used is independent, then it must follow that each additive term of the equation must contain each dimension to the same power. This is true for each dimension independently. Thus we have one additional restricting condition on the original equation for each *independent* dimension that is required to construct the dimensions of the m parameters $q_1, \ldots, q_m$. Furthermore, we can write each of these r restricting conditions in terms of an algebraic equation expressing the requirement. The algebra of the situation is thus as follows. We have $r + 1$ relations among m quantities. Consequently, if these $r + 1$ equations are *linearly independent*, then it follows immediately from the fundamental theorem of algebra that we can use r of the equations to eliminate r quantities and thus to obtain an equation among $m - r$ groups. It is the proviso of linear independence of the equations that gives rise to Van Driest's improvement on Buckingham's original theorem. More specifically, if the equations are linearly independent, $k = r$; if they are not linearly independent, $k < r$, and the difference between k and r is the same as the number of degrees of redundancy in the $r + 1$ equations.

This last point can be seen very clearly from the treatment of Langhaar.[28] Langhaar not only gives the formal algebraic treatment in terms of the Jacobian test, but he also sets forth a means for finding k in terms of formal matrix algebra. Either Langhaar's† method or Van Driest's method will overcome the difficulty regarding linear independence of the set of equations satisfactorily. The choice of method then lies with the taste and degree of mathematical sophistication of the individual worker.

2-6 HUNTLEY'S ADDITION

Recently Huntley[19] has made an important addition to the physical foundations of the pi theorem. This addition is based on the idea that a greater number of independent dimensions can, in effect, be utilized if the distinctions between various operations and concepts are very carefully maintained. Since a larger number of independent dimensions in general

† Van Driest's method is given above and used throughout the text. The reader is referred to Ref. 28 for Langhaar's technique.

implies, by the pi theorem, a smaller number of resulting dimensionless groups, a more useful answer is often obtained.

In particular, Huntley notes that there is a distinction between a length measured in the x direction and one measured in the y or z direction. He also distinguishes between the inertial property of mass and its energy-storage or heat-capacity function.

Thus, Huntley does not cancel a length in the x direction with one in the y or z direction; the net effect is to achieve up to three independent dimensions, each a distinguishable kind of length. A typical example of this idea is often used in the description of thermal conductivity which is written, for example, as

$$k \triangleq \frac{\text{Btu}}{(\text{hr})(\text{ft}^2)(^\circ\text{F}/\text{ft})}$$

It is customary not to cancel the ft in the direction of heat flow with part of the ft² term which represents the dimensions normal to the heat flow, that is, the other two cartesian coordinates. This usage has become customary, because the cancellation reduces the physical meaning in the resulting expression. The concept is almost identical to that discussed in connection with the impropriety of canceling a pound force with a pound mass, simply because they happen to have the same name. In Huntley's view, the measurement of length in the x direction is by its specification a different operational procedure from measurement of the length in the y direction, because the operations are carried out in different planes. The mathematical counterpart of this physical explanation is simply that in a vector equation it is never permissible to cancel an x component against a y or z component of any vector quantity. Similar comments apply to the energy-storage function and inertia function of mass. Huntley shows that the dimensions representing the two functions should not be canceled one against the other because they are of a different physical nature.

By maintaining such distinctions, through the use of subscripts, Huntley is able to achieve more useful results in many well-known problems.

Huntley's idea will be employed where appropriate in the following examples. The reader who is interested in examining in more detail what can be gained by this method is referred to the many excellent examples in the treatise by Huntley.[19]

2-7 EXAMPLES OF APPLICATION OF DIMENSIONAL ANALYSIS

The method of utilizing the pi theorem in Example 2.1 and those which follow has several names, none of which is universally accepted. These include: dimensional analysis, method of dimensions, the pi theorem method, Buckingham's method and Bridgman's method. In the present volume these names are used synonymously. Since dimensional analysis is the most widely accepted, this term will be preferred.

Example 2.2. Let us now examine a heat-transfer problem by the method of dimensional analysis. It is a problem for which the complete solution is known, at least for relatively simple boundary conditions, and thus it is a useful example for comparing what can be achieved by various methods.

The problem concerns the "cooking" or curing time of a portion of a homogeneous solid body of arbitrary shape. One way in which the problem can be stated is as follows. "An old housewife's rule is to cook a roast beef 20 minutes per pound. Is this a reasonable similarity law, and if not, what more correct rule can be proposed?" This problem has significance, of course, not only in preparing dinner but also in many industrial processes in which a chemical reaction or phase change requires the maintenance of a certain minimum temperature throughout an entire body for a prespecified minimum time. Thus we can reframe the question in better form as follows: "How long must we heat the body to insure that every particle in it is held above a temperature 80 percent of the way from the initial temperature to the oven temperature for at least a prespecified minimum time?"

Before using the pi theorem, we must set down a list of the parameters of concern. In this problem we might think that an appropriate list would be:

$$f(t, L, M, N, \rho, c_p, \lambda) = 0 \qquad (2.12)$$

where t = time required, L, M, and N are characteristic dimensions of the body in the x, y, and z directions, respectively, ρ is the density, c_p the specific heat, and λ the thermal conductivity of the body. One suspects that the heat-transfer coefficient for convection on the surface of the body might also enter the problem, but it is not altogether clear on grounds of this type when this effect must be considered. In the above list we are treating time as dependent, but we have omitted temperature. On the basis of this method alone, omission of temperature is a questionable procedure. The author must admit that it has been omitted primarily because one thus obtains a correct answer, and the justification can be provided from more complete analysis.† If we then assume that Eq. (2.12) contains the correct parameters, we can apply the pi theorem. There are seven parameters in Eq. (2.12). The dimensions of these seven parameters can be given in terms of four independent dimensions; mass, time, temperature, and length. Four parameters (for example,

† See Sec. 4-4.

t, L, λ, and ρ) can be found which will not form a nondimensional group. Thus $k = r$, and the pi theorem states that the nondimensional function should contain three nondimensional pi's. By inspection a set of pi's that is appropriate can be seen to be:

$$\pi_1 = \frac{L}{M}$$

$$\pi_2 = \frac{L}{N}$$

$$\pi_3 = \frac{L^2}{\alpha t} = \text{Fourier number}$$

where

$$\alpha = \frac{\lambda}{\rho c_p} = \text{thermal diffusivity}$$

This answers the problem initially set as follows. In order to have similar temperature behavior, it is necessary and sufficient to have geometric similarity and the same Fourier number. However, we want to hold the temperature above a given level for some known time. If we denote this known cooking time by t_o and the time required for the center of the body to reach the required temperature as indicated by a given value of π_3 (the Fourier number) as t_f, then for a given body the solution is:

$$t_{\min} = t_f + t_o = t_f + \text{constant}$$

And t_f is found from the condition $L^2/\alpha t_f = \text{constant}$. We can then conclude that two geometrically similar bodies will have similar temperature versus time behavior if

$$\frac{L^2}{\alpha} = \text{constant}$$

Also for fixed α, t_f varies as

$$t_f \approx L^2$$

and for fixed geometry

$$t_f \approx \frac{1}{\alpha}$$

These are the essential similarity rules for heat-conduction problems, as is well known. Thus we have found considerable information from dimensional analysis, but it does not tell us a number of other things. First, no information is given on when we might be able to neglect π_1, π_2, or π_3, or when we must include the effect of convection on the surface of the body.

A question involving whether temperature must be included in the pi's was resolved by resort to other sources of information. And, finally, we obtained the relevant physical variables on the basis of the statement "we might think that an appropriate list would be." This at least appears to be very intuitive grounds for the physical basis of our solution. These problems are considerable. However, we shall reserve further discussion of their bases for Chap. 5, when more complete information will be available.

At this point, it is well to emphasize again why the items in our list for the dimensional analysis [Eq. (2.12)] have been called parameters and not variables. They are the parameters of the problem in the sense defined in Chap. 1, and they are not the variables of the heat-conduction problem in the usual sense. Similarly, the answer to the dimensional analysis is given in terms of dimensionless parameters, not dimensionless variables. It will be useful for the reader to note that this is the case in *each* instance in the examples which follow. In a sense it is unfortunate that these quantities have been called "variables" in much of the literature, since it tends to obscure the distinction between parameters and variables; this distinction is essential to clarity in the discussion of several matters of importance in Chap. 4.

Example 2.3. As the next example, let us analyze the problem of a simple parallel-flow heat exchanger. Take as the problem the establishment of a set of nondimensional groups that will correlate the performance as measured by the effectiveness for all heat exchangers of this geometry. For simplicity, let us assume that the geometry is two concentric tubes; this does not alter the essentials of the analysis from the case of the multiple-tube exchanger normally encountered in practice. The following sketch shows the system.

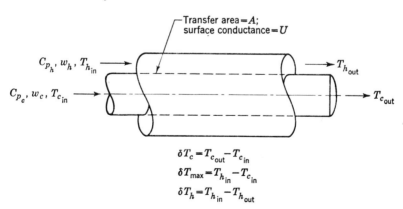

$$\delta T_c = T_{c_{out}} - T_{c_{in}}$$
$$\delta T_{max} = T_{h_{in}} - T_{c_{in}}$$
$$\delta T_h = T_{h_{in}} - T_{h_{out}}$$

Fig. 2.1

It seems relatively clear from the sketch of Fig. 2.1 that the parameters involved in this problem can be written as:

$$f(U, A, \delta T_{\max}, \delta T_h, \delta T_c, w_c, w_h, c_{p_c}, c_{p_h}) = 0 \qquad (2.13)$$

This list contains nine parameters. The dimensions of these can all be written in terms of four independent dimensions m, L, t, and T. The four parameters U, A, c_{p_c}, and δT_h will not form a nondimensional group. Thus by the pi theorem we would conclude that if the list of Eq. (2.13) is correct, there should be four independent pi's and one dependent pi. However, the answer to this problem is well known; it is two independent groups and one dependent (see for example Kays and London,[23] or McAdams,[32] where the complete solution to this problem is given in closed form and plotted on graphs). Obviously, there is something wrong with our solution. Actually, there are two things wrong.

The first difficulty is that Eq. (2.13) contains not one but two dependent parameters. Although it is not immediately evident, a careful study of the dependency relations among the parameters reveals that only two temperature differences should be included in our list. That is, given any one of the three temperature differences listed and all of the other parameters in Eq. (2.13), the other two temperature differences are both fixed. So we proceed to strike out δT_c and we obtain:

$$f(U, A, \delta T_h, \delta T_{\max}, w_c, w_h, c_{p_h}, c_{p_c}) = 0 \qquad (2.14)$$

But we still have eight parameters describable in terms of four independent dimensions. Thus the pi theorem would indicate that three independent and one dependent nondimensional groups are necessary, and hence even if we were shrewd enough to see through the rather complex dependency relations among the parameters in this problem, we would still be unable to achieve the desired result without further information. The answer found is not incorrect, but it is quite unworkable compared to the known solution.

Let us check further to see if we have obeyed the rules set down for the pi theorem above. Rule 1 says to include one dependent and all the pertinent independent parameters. This we seem to have done. Rule 2 says that the nondimensional groups must contain all of the parameters in the original list at least once. This is not the trouble here; the rule could be fulfilled if we could get that far. The list of independent dimensions used, mass, length, temperature, and time, is a well-established independent set, and thus we have followed Rule 3.

What is even more perplexing in this example is that the deviation from the pi theorem is not explicable in terms of the additions of Van Driest and Langhaar to the theory on linear independence of the restricting equations. Not only have we checked that the list contains four primaries that will not form a nondimensional group, but also the exception is in the wrong direction to be explained by linear dependence among the primary dimension equations. Specifically, if the set of equations is not linearly independent, then the actual number of groups needed is greater than that predicted by Buckingham's original statement of the pi theorem. But in this case the actual number of groups required is less than that predicted by the pi theorem in the solution above.

Thus we have found an exception to the pi theorem that seems to be inexplicable in terms of dimensional analysis alone. It then remains to be seen if other methods can explain the source of this exception and, if so, to examine whether it is reasonable to expect an able and experienced worker to have found the source of the trouble using only the procedures of dimensional analysis.

Example 2.4. We now approach a practical problem, by the Buckingham method, where the answer is not altogether known. Let us consider the correlation of the performance of centrifugal compressors. This is a more complex problem than any of the previous examples, in fact, unlike the previous cases we cannot write a single set of differential equations and boundary conditions governing the complete performance of all of the class of systems we hope to correlate.

We begin again in the conventional fashion, that is, by attempting on intuitive grounds to establish a list of parameters. We suspect that the following parameters might be of concern in this problem: flow rate Q, pressure ratio p_r, speed N, impeller inlet radius r_i, impeller outlet radius r_o, length characterizing the diffuser L, and the viscosity μ, density ρ, speed of sound a, and specific-heat ratio γ of the working fluid.

In the functional form we have:

$$f(Q,p_r,N,r_i,r_o,L,\mu,a,\gamma,\rho) = 0$$

The ten parameters in the list can be described, dimensionally, in terms of three independent dimensions: length, mass, and time. However, both the inertia function of mass m_i and the energy-storage function of mass m are required. Hence by Huntley's addition we could utilize four independent dimensions. Checking Van Driest's restriction, however, we find that there are no four parameters that will not form a dimensionless group. Several sets of three parameters can be found that will not combine into a dimensionless group, for example, Q, μ, and ρ. Hence we take $k = 3$ although $r = 4$. Thus the pi theorem suggests that $10 - 3 = 7$ groups are needed of which 6 will be independent.

However, it is clear that we cannot work effectively with six independent coordinates. It is also evident that the characterization of geometry given is far from complete. As a first step toward making the problem manageable, we might therefore restrict ourselves to consideration of geometrically similar machines. Such machines can be characterized by one length, say D, and hence the number of groups apparently needed is reduced by two. Thus we could formulate an answer to the reduced problem of homologous units as:

$$\pi_1 = p_r$$

$$\pi_2 = \frac{Q}{ND^3}$$

$$\pi_3 = Re = \text{Reynolds number} = \frac{\rho Q}{D\mu}$$

$$\pi_4 = M = \text{Mach number} = \frac{Q}{D^2 a}$$

$$\pi_5 = \gamma$$

This is virtually as far as we can go using the pi theorem alone, but it does not constitute a workable answer even for a single line of homologous units. Four independent groups are still too many to be very useful. In order to obtain a workable solution to this problem, we need to reduce the number of independent groups. It may be possible to achieve such an objective in at least two different ways.

The first method involves establishing some particular combination of two or more of the independent parameters that is characteristic of the problem at hand. This amounts to transforming the parameters into some natural form where a higher degree of generality is achieved. Dimensional analysis gives us no inkling whatsoever about how such a transformation may be found. In order to establish such a transformation it is again necessary to introduce additional experimental or theoretical knowledge.

The second method is to establish certain ranges of performance in which one or more of the independent groups have a negligible effect on the dependent group of interest, say on the pressure ratio achieved. Dimensional analysis gives no hints about where we may expect to find such a range of variables. Once again additional methodology or empirical evidence must be introduced. In this particular problem we suspect, from other known solutions, that the effect of both Mach number and γ can be largely neglected if the square of the Mach number is small compared to unity everywhere in the compressor and that the effect of Reynolds number will not be large if the square root of the Reynolds number based on the passage width and also on blade length is very large compared to unity. Thus for certain ranges of practical interest at least, we can hope to achieve a workable correlation. In practice still further information of this kind is also available, but detailed discussion of it is beyond the scope and purpose of the present volume.   The foregoing discussion is sufficient to show that dimensional analysis alone is of some utility in this problem, but that it must be very considerably supplemented before a practical answer can be found.   In particular, the inability of dimensional analysis to answer questions of the sort, "When can a given nondimensional group be neglected?" stands out clearly in this problem.

Example 2.5.   Having given several examples in which various shortcomings of dimensional analysis as a method of fractional analysis have become evident, it is useful to work a problem where the method succeeds particularly well, in order to illustrate the type of problem that can be handled.   Accordingly we consider small motions of a simple pendulum, as shown in Fig. 2.2.

Let us take as the problem the determination of the parameter(s) governing the frequency of the natural or free oscillation of the pendulum. If we consider what parameters we would use to write the equations, we would set down a list of pertinent parameters as:

$$f(\omega, L, m, g) = 0$$

where

ω = natural frequency
L = length of pendulum
m = mass of pendulum
g = local acceleration of gravity

An appropriate set of independent dimensions is mass, length, and time.   The pi theorem then suggests that there should be $4 - 3 = 1$

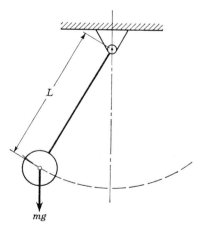

Fɪɢ. 2.2 mg

independent groups in the result.   Checking by Van Driest's method we find that the three quantities L, m, and g will not form a group so that $k = r$, and it should therefore be possible to characterize the solution by one nondimensional group.   If we try to form this group by inspection, however, we find immediately that only one of the four parameters contains mass.   Hence it is necessary to reason as follows.   Mass cannot enter the appropriate nondimensional group, since there is no way that it can be canceled by any combination of the other parameters.   We must therefore delete mass from both the list of parameters and the list of independent dimensions.   We can find two parameters that will not form a nondimensional group, say g and L, and we have a total of three parameters in our list.   The number of groups required therefore is still one, and the group needed can be found by inspection to be:

$$\pi_1 = \frac{\omega^2 L}{g}$$

Since there is only one group, it can at most be a constant.   And we can therefore write

$$\omega^2 = \frac{C \cdot g}{L}$$

This, of course, is the entire answer to the problem, lacking only the value of the constant C.   Thus we see that in this simple problem dimensional analysis works exceptionally well.   Indeed, it demonstrates that the period must be independent of the mass of the pendulum, and it also yields the explicit form of the solution.

To round out our examples by dimensional analysis we now consider a more complex problem of mechanics.

Example 2.6.† Consider a more complex mechanical system consisting of a simple beam in flexure with given loading and end conditions. We hope to find a model by which we can determine the dynamic or vibration characteristics of any beam by tests of a smaller beam or model.

In this problem, we suspect from experience that the vibration frequency ω will be a function of the following parameters:

$$\omega = \omega(E, \mu, \rho, F_j, a_i, g)$$

where

$\qquad E$ = modulus of elasticity
$\qquad \mu$ = Poisson's ratio

---

† This example is based on the excellent discussion of Prof. D. E. Hudson[18] and a suggestion from Prof. S. H. Crandall.

ρ = mass density

F_j = j conditions sufficient to fix the loading, say q in number

a_i = i lengths sufficient to fix the geometry of the beam, say n in number

g = gravity constant, weight per unit mass

The dimensions involved are mass, length, and time. It is easy to find three parameters that will not form a dimensionless group, for example, F_1, a_1, and ρ. Also we can define force ratios by normalizing on any one of the F_i, say F_1; we call these force ratios α_j. Similarly we can form length ratios by division of a length a_1; we shall call these length ratios β_i. Applying the pi theorem, we then obtain

$$\frac{\omega^2 a_1}{g} = f\left(\frac{\rho g a_1}{E}, \mu, \alpha_j, \beta_i\right) \tag{2.15}$$

where j runs from 1 to $q - 1$, and i runs from 1 to $n - 1$. The number of independent pi groups in Eq. (2.15) is then equal to the number of forces in the original load specification plus the number of lengths in the original specification of geometry, or $q + n$. [This is coincidence, not a fundamental result, since it follows from the fact that there are two other groups in Eq. (2.15) in addition to the α_j and β_i, but each of these is one less than the original list, since we have divided through by F_1 and a_1, respectively.]

Employing Eq. (2.15), we can set conditions sufficient to guarantee similar behavior of a model and the prototype in so far as frequency is concerned. Employing $(\ )_m$ for model and $(\ )_p$ for prototype we have

$$\left(\frac{\rho g l}{E}\right)_m = \left(\frac{\rho g l}{E}\right)_p$$

$$\mu_m = \mu_p \tag{2.16}$$

$$(\alpha_j)_m = (\alpha_j)_p \qquad j = 1, 2, \ldots, q - 1$$

$$(\beta_i)_m = (\beta_i)_p \qquad i = 1, 2, \ldots, n - 1$$

The conditions (2.16) demand that the materials employed have the same Poisson's ratio, and that complete geometric and loading similarity be strictly maintained. In general, this will represent such restrictive conditions that modeling on this basis would be of little practical value.

In an attempt to overcome this difficulty we might examine a more restricted class of problem. Let us assume that the body under study is a simple rectangular beam of length L, depth h, and width b; let us assume further that it is a simple cantilever beam, and the only load is the beam mass ρ per unit length. Accordingly, the list of parameters is

$$\omega = \omega(E, \mu, \rho, b, h, L, g)$$

Since we have again three independent dimensions, and eight parameters, the pi theorem requires five nondimensional groups. A solution thus is

$$\frac{\omega^2 L}{g} = f\left(\frac{\rho g L}{E}, \mu, \frac{b}{L}, \frac{h}{L}\right) \tag{2.17}$$

The model conditions then are

$$\left. \begin{array}{c} \left(\dfrac{\rho g L}{E}\right)_m = \left(\dfrac{\rho g L}{E}\right)_p \\[2mm] \left(\dfrac{b}{L}\right)_m = \left(\dfrac{b}{L}\right)_p \\[2mm] \left(\dfrac{h}{L}\right)_m = \left(\dfrac{h}{L}\right)_p \\[2mm] \mu_m = \mu_p \end{array} \right\} \tag{2.18}$$

There are still too many conditions for manageable model studies, and thus even in this relatively simple problem a correlation of workable simplicity is not achieved by use of the pi theorem alone. From the point of view of fractional analysis, we should like to be able to find a solution involving fewer conditions than Eq. (2.18). This might be distorted or approximate model laws covering the problem, it might be a grouping of parameters in improved form, or it might be a statement of the exact conditions under which some of the pi's in Eq. (2.17) can be neglected. These are essentially the same questions we encountered in Examples 2.2 and 2.4, but they are framed slightly differently, because we are seeking a solution in terms of a model law rather than a correlation. Again we will defer further discussion of these questions until other types of solutions have been developed.

2-8 SUMMARY

The examples above show that in every instance the pi theorem gives some useful information about the problem under study. In some simple problems, such as that of the pendulum, it gives remarkably complete and correct answers. The pi theorem also sets in particularly clear form the enormous utility of the use of dimensionless groups in reducing the number of independent parameters and correlating and generalizing solutions.

In addition to these useful properties, the pi theorem forms a particularly good framework for discussion of the nature of units, dimensions, and related topics, although these more elementary topics have been treated only very briefly here.

Nevertheless, the pi theorem, when used alone as a means for fractional analysis, suffers from four considerable deficiencies, as seen in the examples.

1. No direct means for finding the pertinent parameters is available. The method deals essentially with rearranging the parameters once they have been determined. As discussed in Chap. 1, this is the easier and less crucial part of the solution insofar as fractional analysis is concerned. Moreover, dimensional analysis itself provides little or no framework for incorporating or checking physical information relevant to finding the parameters beyond the original highly intuitive enumeration of a list of physical characteristics.

2. Some inexplicable exceptions to the pi theorem occur in addition to the problem of linear dependence clarified by the work of Van Driest and Langhaar. In some cases the dependent variable must be dropped from the pi's; in others, fewer parameters than indicated by the pi theorem are actually needed. The reason for these exceptions is not evident from the necessary conditions for use of the pi theorem alone or from examination of its rationale.

3. The pi theorem alone provides no means for finding or seeking conditions under which one or more pi's can be neglected. This information is particularly important, since it is central to derivation of approximate similarity rules and workable correlations for complex systems.

4. Within the framework of the pi theorem there are no means available for determining which sets of dimensionless groups may be particularly informative or useful for a given purpose, or for establishing combinations of groups for improved correlations in particular problems. In practice, of course, we almost always find decided differences between the utility of various sets of pi's among the infinitely large number of possibilities.

With these summary remarks we turn directly to the discussion of other methods of fractional analysis and defer to Chap. 5 a discussion of the reasons for the advantages, disadvantages, and exceptions to the pi theorem found, since the developments of Chaps. 3 and 4 provide considerable information on all these points.

3 *Method of Similitude and Introduction to Fractional Analysis of Overall Equations*

3-1 INTRODUCTION

In the nineteenth century a number of workers, most notably Lord Rayleigh, commonly solved problems of fractional analysis by direct use of the idea of similarity combined with the formation of force ratios. During the twentieth century this method seems to have lost favor and has been replaced almost entirely by the use of the pi theorem except in the work of a few authors in fluid mechanics (see, for example, Vennard,[52] Chap. 7). In fact, the method seems to be so little used today that no accepted name for it exists; for purposes of reference, it is called the method of similitude throughout the present volume.

This neglect of the method of similitude in modern times also extends to discussions of the method as such. No treatment known to the author provides an adequate basis of the method for use in all problems of fractional analysis. Despite this, the method of similitude has a number of useful properties of its own, and it leads very naturally into the discussion of the use of the governing equations for problems in fractional analysis. For both these reasons it seems appropriate to attempt a broader and more thorough discussion of the method of similitude.

3-2 METHOD OF SIMILITUDE

The method of similitude is basically very simple. In the nineteenth century literature and in the current applications in fluid mechanics it consists of the following basic steps:

1. The forces that are believed to be important in a given problem are enumerated, including the dependent and all the independent forces. (Force here is used in the sense of mechanics and not in the sense of a generalized force as employed in some modern work, such as in irreversible thermodynamics.) Each of these forces is then expressed in terms of the parameters of the problem by physical or dimensional arguments.

2. The pertinent nondimensional groups are constructed by forming ratios of these forces and including enough length ratios to insure geometric similarity.

The number of pi's constructed from force ratios thus equals the number of independent forces. For convenience in solution, it is also customary to use the dependent force in only one ratio in order to provide an explicit, rather than an implicit, function for the force ratio taken to be dependent.

Superficially, there would appear to be no great difference between listing the governing forces and enumerating the parameters from which these forces are composed. That is, there would seem to be no fundamental difference between the method of similitude and the pi theorem method as discussed in Chap. 2. This is certainly true, nevertheless the method of similitude has certain inherent advantages, and is a useful cross-check on results obtained by the pi theorem.

The usual physical basis for the method of similitude is some postulate like the following: "Two systems will exhibit similar behavior if geometric, kinematic, and dynamic similarity are all guaranteed; furthermore these conditions will be fulfilled if the two systems are made geometrically similar and if the ratios of all the pertinent forces are made the same in the two problems."

Probably one of the reasons that this method has lost favor in modern times is that the latter half of the postulate is not broad enough to cover all problems. Specifically, in many problems, knowledge about quantities which do not depend on forces at all, such as heat transfer or electric currents, may be sought. In fact, it would appear that the last half of the postulate rests upon a purely mechanical view of the universe. Such a view was prevalent in the nineteenth century, but is not in keeping with the modern concepts of thermodynamics. Some broader foundation is definitely needed.

One basis for such a broad foundation is given in Sec. 3-2*b*. But before this is done, it will be helpful to study one example which can be treated by use of force ratios alone in order to make clear the details of the method.

a.   Use of Force Ratios

The number of different kinds of forces found in nature is extremely large, and it is consequently impractical to deal with them all at once. Not only would this require a treatise of larger magnitude than this volume, but also it is seldom necessary to deal with more than a few of these forces in the analysis of a given physical problem. Since the purpose of this book is to develop and examine methodology, it is sufficient to take an example of one field of analysis. The field chosen is fluid mechanics, since the method is well developed in that area and since the author is reasonably familiar with the subject. A table of basic dimensionless parameters similar to that developed for fluid mechanics can be prepared for use in other fields. What is more, the preparation of such tables is very instructive both as an exercise and as a reference in any given area of science or engineering. The construction of such a table enforces a general but especially careful consideration of the basic effects to be found in the field under study; it increases the physical understanding of the dimensionless parameters normally employed; it provides for standardization of these parameters for ready reference; and, most important, it provides a firm basis for checking the possible improvement of these parameters as further data and experience are accumulated.

There are six very common forces in fluid mechanics. Fifteen independent nondimensional numbers can be formed as ratios of these six forces, taken two at a time. These forces are defined, their dimensions shown, and the fifteen independent forces systematically displayed in Table 3.1.

Examination of Table 3.1 shows that nearly all of the very commonly employed correlating groups of fluid mechanics are contained in the first six numbers. Among the very common groups only Mach number, drag

Table 3.1   Ratios of Common Forces in Fluid Mechanics

$F_V \triangleq \mu VL$	$F_P \triangleq \Delta pL^2$	$F_C \triangleq E_s L^2$	$F_S \triangleq SL$	$F_G \triangleq \rho L^3 g$	
$\dfrac{F_I}{F_V} = \dfrac{\rho VL}{\mu}$ Reynolds number	$\dfrac{F_P}{F_I} = \dfrac{\Delta p}{\frac{1}{2}\rho V^2}$ Pressure coefficient	$\dfrac{F_I}{F_C} = \dfrac{V^2}{\dfrac{E_s}{\rho}}$ Cauchy number	$\dfrac{F_I}{F_S} = \dfrac{\rho V^2 L}{S}$ Weber number	$\dfrac{F_I}{F_G} = \dfrac{V^2}{gL}$ Froude number	$F_I \triangleq \rho V^2 L^2$
	$\dfrac{F_P}{F_V} = \dfrac{\Delta pL}{\mu V}$ Stokes number	$\dfrac{F_C}{F_V} = \dfrac{E_s L}{\mu V}$	$\dfrac{F_S}{F_V} = \dfrac{S}{\mu V}$	$\dfrac{F_G}{F_V} = \dfrac{\rho L^2 g}{\mu V}$	F_V
		$\dfrac{F_C}{F_P} = \dfrac{E_s}{\Delta p}$	$\dfrac{F_S}{F_P} = \dfrac{S}{\Delta pL}$	$\dfrac{F_G}{F_P} = \dfrac{\rho Lg}{\Delta p}$	F_P
			$\dfrac{F_S}{F_C} = \dfrac{S}{E_s L}$	$\dfrac{F_G}{F_C} = \dfrac{\rho Lg}{E_s}$	F_C
				$\dfrac{F_G}{F_S} = \dfrac{\rho L^2 g}{S}$	F_S

The six forces most often encountered in fluid flow:

		These forces may be expressed dimensionally:
Inertia forces $\triangleq F_I$		$F_I \triangleq \rho V^2 L^2$
Viscous forces $\triangleq F_V$		$F_V \triangleq \mu VL$
Pressure forces $\triangleq F_P$		$F_P \triangleq \Delta pL^2$
Compressive forces $\triangleq F_C$		$F_C \triangleq E_s L^2$
Surface tension forces $\triangleq F_S$		$F_S \triangleq SL$
Gravity forces $\triangleq F_G$		$F_G \triangleq \rho L^3 g$

where

ρ = mass density
L = length
V = velocity
μ = viscosity
E_s = isentropic bulk modulus of compression
S = coefficient of surface tension
g = local acceleration of gravity

coefficient, and the ratio of specific heats appear to be missing. It is readily shown that Mach number is merely the square root of the Cauchy number, which does appear in the table, and that drag coefficient is the same type of number as pressure coefficient or Euler number; that is, the ratio of forces acting on the surface to the inertia forces.† Specific heat ratio apparently cannot be found from force considerations alone. It is also interesting to note that even among the fifteen simple numbers in

† The distinction normally lies only in the direction of the force considered.

Table 3.1, only six are apparently widespread enough in use to have acquired generally accepted names.

The appearance in Table 3.1 of all of the most common correlating groups of at least incompressible flow is, of course, not a coincidence. These groups are widely used not only for historical reasons, but also because the direct ratios of the governing forces express the correlating groups in a particularly useful, simple, and readily interpreted form. Indeed, although the Mach number is normally used for correlation purposes, the quantity that almost always appears in the governing equations is the square of Mach number, or the Cauchy number; and in Table 3.1 it is the Cauchy number that appears. Far more often than not, the use of M^2 rather than M as a variable simplifies the equations, and historically we would probably have been better off had M^2 been adopted as the conventional correlating group. However, the difference is not great and is hardly worth discussion except to illustrate why the use of direct force ratios so frequently yields, apparently fortuitously, a particularly useful combination of parameters.

Example 3.1.   We turn again to the problem of the fully established laminar flow in a tube which was solved by the use of the pi theorem in Example 2.1. The answer obtained in Chap. 2 was that the friction factor could be expressed as a function of the Reynolds number. However, it was found necessary to introduce a type of symmetry condition in addition to the pi theorem to bring the answer this far. This answer is correct in the sense that the variables can be plotted on a graph of friction factor versus Reynolds number, and for the laminar range, all the data do fall on a single line. (See, for example, Moody[34] or any standard work on elementary fluid mechanics.)

Using the method of similitude we can carry through the solution for a correlation of the pressure drop in the round pipe using nothing but Table 3.1 as a source of information.

Inspection of our catalogue of forces for fluid mechanics suggests that in this problem gravity force, surface tension force, and compressive force will be unimportant. This leaves inertia force, pressure force, and viscous force. One of these forces is dependent. Thus two pi's are required, one independent and one dependent. From Table 3.1 these pi's would be Reynolds number and pressure coefficient. The pressure coefficient is readily transformed into friction factor by using the defining equation for friction factor. Thus we observe that once we have constructed the necessary table of forces for fluid mechanics, we can obtain the answer found by the pi theorem for the present problem with the same input information and less effort. The answer obtained is also automatically found in terms of the standard parameters in this instance, and will in general occur in at least a very useful and readily understood form. We also automatically find that a smaller Reynolds number suggests relatively increased frictional effect, hence increased friction factor.

b. Generalization of the Method of Similitude

In Section 3-2*a* it was shown that some fractional analysis problems in fluid flow can be solved by considering the forces of importance in a given problem without applying any other ideas. This type of solution is based on the hypothesis that complete similarity will be obtained in a flow field if geometric, kinematic, and dynamic similarity are all achieved and that these three types of similarities will occur if the geometry is similar and all the forces are similar.

However, as already noted, this approach is not sufficient to solve all types of problems. In fact, it is not even sufficient to solve problems of compressible flow, since in that case it is frequently necessary to introduce at least the ratio of the specific heats in addition to the force ratios in the list of independent pi's. It is therefore pertinent to ask "Under what conditions can we, in general, guarantee similar behavior of two systems?"†

One sufficient answer to this question can be given by the following postulate:

If two systems obey the same set of governing equations and conditions and if the values of all parameters in these equations and conditions are made the same, then the two systems must exhibit similar behavior provided only that a unique solution to the set of equations and conditions exists.

This postulate is sufficient but not necessary, since it is entirely possible for two different sets of equations to have the same solution and thus for some systems to have similar behavior under other conditions. Such behavior would be rare, and could in general be found only if the solutions were known. Since there is no need for fractional analysis when the solutions are known, the sufficient conditions stated in the postulate are those we normally need in fractional analysis.

The phrase *equations and conditions* is employed rather than merely *equations* alone in order to imply specifically that the boundary conditions must also be the same if one or more of the equations involved are differential in form. The questions of existence and uniqueness of solutions are also involved in the postulate stated above. However, we will defer detailed discussion of these questions to Chap. 4 and continue here with the line of argument needed to develop the method of similitude.

---

† Some readers may find the general remarks in this section regarding the relation between the governing equations and similitude hard to follow completely at this reading since a number of different points are involved. If this occurs, it is suggested that the reader continue through Chap. 4 and then read this section again; many of the points discussed can be made entirely clear only in terms of examples.

The existence of a set of equations and conditions which are the same for two systems can be established on either of two bases.   First, the two systems can be physically of the same class, such as two tubes with fully established flow.   We then *assume* a priori that the governing equations express some immutable laws of nature and will therefore always have the same form provided only that we specify sufficient information about the two systems.   Second, we may know the governing equations from prior experiments, so we can compare them directly whether or not the two systems are the same.   This second basis is broader and includes the first, but it can be used only when the governing equations have been explicitly developed.

In terms of this discussion we can now see that the classical method of similitude based on force ratios employs a basis of the first type; it implicitly assumes that some set of governing equations based on immutable laws of nature exists; it further assumes that the terms in these equations can be expressed in terms of forces alone; and it then moves directly to a solution of the problem by dealing with the ratio of forces to guarantee that the parameters in the governing equations will have the same values.   Since it does not employ the governing equations explicitly, in a sense it implies that, while they exist, they are not available in usable explicit form.†

However, in the present state of physics, it is very rare that we encounter a problem for which we cannot write at least a set of overall or "black-box" governing equations based on the known macroscopic laws of nature.   This suggests that examination of some general list of governing equations should tell us what other types of parameters in addition to forces must be fixed, if any, in order to guarantee equal values of the nondimensional parameters in an appropriate set of governing equations and conditions.   No two workers would employ quite the same list of fundamental equations, but a sufficient list for problems in continuum analysis, that is, fluid flow, elasticity, classical electromagnetism, heat transfer, and thermodynamics, is the following:

1. Conservation of Mass
2. Stoichiometric Principle (conservation of atoms, molecules, etc.)
3. Newton's Second Law
4. Equation of State (state principle)
5. First Law of Thermodynamics
6. Second Law of Thermodynamics
7. Rate Equation Theory (Fourier's law, Fick's law, Ohm's law, etc.)
8. Maxwell's Laws of Electromagnetism

† This remark applies in the same sense to all of dimensional analysis as summarized in Chap. 2.

9. Conservation of Electrical Charge

10. Newton's Laws of Gravity

This list includes only principles that give rise to working equations. Thus the concept often called the Zeroth law of thermodynamics is omitted since it only defines a concept, temperature, but does not provide a working equation. Similarly, Newton's first and third laws are omitted as are the axioms of statics since these concepts lead respectively to the definition of force and of mechanical equilibrium which are inherent in the complete equations of motion derived from Newton's Second Law. Item 4 in the list includes not only the familiar relation for gases, but also all other independent functional relations among the properties of a system. This includes the most general form of Gibbsian-type equation for the open system with chemical reaction and the familiar expressions of Hooke's law for solid bodies, as well as equivalent relations for more complex systems.† Similarly, item 7 includes all rate equations such as Fick's law, Ohm's law, etc., and the generalization of these inherent in the Onsager reciprocity theorem of irreversible thermodynamics.

We now examine the fundamental equations one by one to see what types of effects can occur. It is useful to begin with a general form of the first law of thermodynamics applicable to a control volume (open system). Such an equation is:

$$ q \;+\; \Sigma(h_F w)_{\text{in}} \;=\; \left(\frac{\partial E}{\partial t}\right)_{\text{inside}} \;+\; \Sigma(h_F w)_{\text{out}} \;+\; \frac{dW_x}{dt} $$

Rate of heat transfer in	Rate of energies entering with mass including reversible flow work of transport	Rate of energy storage inside	Rate of energies leaving with mass including reversible flow work of transport	Rate of delivery of work excepting reversible flow work of transport

$$(3.1)$$

† If the reader is unfamiliar with this point of view, a more thorough discussion is given in Ref. 24. It should also be noted that some recent authors, particularly in rheology, have begun to call item 4 and item 7 taken together *the constitutive relations;* this term is understood to include the stress strain and stress rate of strain relations. It should be noted that these relations are not always known either theoretically or empirically in their entirety. For simple substances, such as pure crystalline solids and perfect gases, almost all the desired information can be calculated from kinetic and statistical molecular models. In some other systems, most notably water, the statistical theories are inadequate, but quite precise data is available over wide ranges. In more complex and less studied substances, such as high polymers, very little is yet known about the constitutive relations in either integrated or differential form.

For these reasons and perhaps others, workers in various fields will probably want to modify the exact list of fundamentals to make it more suitable to their purposes. Such modification is appropriate and a highly valuable study. However, the list as given will be sufficient for the problems we will discuss in this volume and for most problems in continuum analyses.

where the summation signs imply addition of all inflows and outflows, respectively, and

> q = all forms of heat transfer at boundary of control volume
> E = all stored energy forms inside the control volume
> $h_F = e + pv$, where $e = E$ per unit mass of flow
> w = mass flow rate
> W_x = all mechanical work done except reversible flow work

Equation (3.1) merely shows that the energy of a given macroscopic system under analysis can be altered in three ways: heat transfer, work, and mass transport. We must include in the heat term all modes, namely, radiation, convection, and conduction. In the work term we must include all interactions with the surroundings not included in the heat-flow or mass transport terms; this would include not only any mechanical terms but also field interactions such as electromagnetic effects, gravity effects, and the flow of electric current. (Electric current can also be treated as a mass flow of charged particles; either view will suffice here.) In the mass-transport terms we must also include all energies associated with mass crossing the boundaries of our system, including energy associated with chemical configuration if such are pertinent. If these things are done, then Eq. (3.1) is sufficient to enumerate all of the ways in which the energy of a macroscopic control volume can be altered, and thus it should be sufficient for a discussion of all possible energy effects unless our present scientific knowledge is less complete than we believe.

We now set down a similar equation for Newton's Second Law in the form of the momentum theorem.

$$0 = \int \rho V_i V_R \, dA + \frac{\partial}{\partial t} \int \rho V_i \, d\mathbf{V} + F_{\text{body}} + \int d\,A\sigma \qquad (3.2)$$

(entire control surface)	(material inside control surface)		(entire surface)
Forces due to transport of momentum across control surface	Forces due to change of momentum inside control surface	Forces due to fields such as gravity and magnetism	Surface forces; shear and pressure

where

> $V_i \triangleq$ velocity in any arbitrarily defined set of inertial coordinates
> $V_R \triangleq$ velocity relative to bounding surface of control volume
> ρ = density
> t = time

σ = stress
A = area
V = volume

Equation (3.2) applies to any macroscopic control surface in the absence of relativity effects.†

We now inspect Eqs. (3.1) and (3.2) to see whether they contain partly the same or entirely independent information.   Examination of the momentum equation (3.2) shows that it contains the same forces that occur in the mechanical terms of Eq. (3.1).   Such mechanical terms occur as the result of the action of forces of the sort enumerated in Table 3.1.   Thus it seems reasonable to state that so long as these forces are unaffected by the other terms in the energy equation, the two types of action can be viewed as independent, and problems which deal only with the force terms can be solved by the use of Table 3.1 or other suitable tables of force ratios alone.   This is the case for incompressible flows, and it probably accounts for the widespread use of the method of similitude based on force ratios alone in problems of that kind.   Such solutions date back at least to Lord Rayleigh in the mid-nineteenth century.   For more general problems, however, Eq. (3.1) suggests that it will be necessary to introduce other types of effects even if one is seeking only correlations of the forces, since the other forms of interactions may then affect the force terms. Apparently, if the heat flow, the thermal energy associated with mass transport, or the thermal energy stored in the system are believed to affect the variable one is seeking, then some appropriate energy ratios must also be included in the pi groups formed.   Thus, a possible tentative conclusion is as follows.   The force ratios, if complete, will account for the mechanical-energy terms in the energy equation; this includes the work term, the flow work, and any mechanical energies, such as those due to gravity or kinetic energy (inertia), that are associated with mass transport or motions inside the system.   However, it is necessary to avoid including some specific single effect, such as the hydrostatic pressure change caused by motion in a gravity field, twice in a given solution. Since the energy equation contains the mechanical terms, but the momentum equations do not contain the thermal terms, the best place to check the independence of various effects would seem to be the energy equation (3.1) or its equivalent.   However, in doing so it must be remembered that it is not sufficient merely to lump all force effects into a work term as is frequently possible in a conventional thermodynamic analysis.   That is, the mechanical-energy terms must be carefully reduced to their ele-

---

† Equation (3.2) reduces to the more conventional form when $V_i = V_R$ if the control volume is nonaccelerating and the reference of coordinates is fixed on the control surface.

ments by use of force diagrams, and a table, such as Table 3.1 for fluid flow, must be employed to find the ratios of forces needed for similarity. After this has been done, the results can be compared with the governing overall energy equation to determine the totality of energy and force ratios required to specify overall similarity of the two systems with regard to both external interactions and detailed similarity of the energies and forces inside the system.

This then provides a possible method of specifying the force and energy ratios that will be required in order to insure complete similarity. However, we must still ask, "Are there any other categories of quantities or effects that can occur?" To answer this question we proceed to examine the remaining physical principles in the list given above, checking, in each instance, to see if any new items must be added beyond the pertinent force and energy ratios to specify solution of each equation and thus to ensure similarity.

Taking the principles in the order of the list, we have first conservation of mass and of atoms. These introduce no new requirements, since the equations of momentum and of energy, in the form given, both employ the continuity equation and thus inherently include mass conservation.

The notion of the state principle does introduce a new possible set of parameters, namely, those based on the properties of the system or its surroundings. Dimensionless groups based on the ratios of properties do play an important role in some problems. The concept of a functional relation between the properties is independent of the other principles involved, and if such an equation is needed to link the variables or parameters occurring in the other equations, then one or more pi's involving appropriate ratios of properties will in general be required. This point will be made clearer by example below.

The next principle, the Second Law of Thermodynamics, does not add any new parameters or variables to fractional-analysis problems. Physically, this is due to the fact that the function of the Second Law, in any analysis, is to prescribe the possible direction of real processes and to locate steady-state or equilibrium situations in configurational problems. This function does not add any new effects; it provides additional knowledge about the energy terms already present. Mathematically, this can be seen by noting that the variable introduced by the Second Law, entropy, is fixed if the energy fluxes are fixed and the equation of state for the system is prescribed.

Similarly, rate-equation theory and the laws governing electric, electromagnetic, and gravity effects do not appear to introduce the need for any new types of quantities. The rate equation merely specifies the magnitude of some of the terms in the energy equation in terms of properties of the system and surroundings. The electrical and gravitational equations are concerned with force and energy terms that appear in the momentum and energy equations. If the force and energy equations are complete, these terms will be included.

At this point, it is well to emphasize that the governing equations employed are redundant and nonunique. They contain overlapping information (for example, the force terms in the energy equation and the mass-conservation concept in both energy and momentum equations). They can be replaced, at least to the extent of rearranged form, by other sets of governing equations that are equally valid. The precise equations needed depend on the definition of the system to be studied; in many simple problems there is a choice of governing equations to be used depending on the tastes of the analytical worker, because of the redundant information contained in the equations.†

The foregoing discussion and the sufficiency postulate for similarity stated in Sec. 3-2b seem adequate to provide a firm foundation for similitude methods. However, some questions regarding the independence of the parameters employed will almost always arise. These questions can be vexatious indeed, and they clearly depend on the amount of redundance in the governing equations set down (or visualized). We can ignore the redundancies and simply set down all the dimensionless parameters that might possibly be included; such an answer will be correct, but it will normally also be almost totally useless, since it will contain such a large number of groups. Nor is it possible, at least at present, to resolve these redundancy problems in general form. To do so we would have to set down the most general form of each of the governing equations explicitly, and examine the relations among them. But this we cannot do, since we are unable to write some of the principles, as for example, the state principle, in anything but undefined functional form, and this is not sufficient for the purpose. Moreover, the form of the equations depends on the station of the observer in some cases. Nevertheless, it is quite possible to obtain some general results, as noted above, and it is much easier to find specific results in any given case by examining the governing equations applicable to the particular problem.

But what is even more pertinent is that the use of the governing equations in the fashion just discussed raises a logical paradox in regard to the whole framework of fractional analysis as we have developed it up to this point. In the resolution of this paradox lies the basis for considerable further improvements in methodology and understanding.

The entire discussion, up to this section, has been based on the pi

† This point seems to trouble many analysts, but the remarks made should clarify it provided one accepts the idea that "nature is never inconsistent to itself" and thus that the alternatives must give the same answer provided the solutions are properly carried out.

theorem or on the use of force ratios. There is therefore an implicit assumption that we do not have available more information than the respective inputs for those methods, that is, a list of parameters or a list of forces.† However, in order to broaden the similitude idea beyond use of only force ratios we have had to introduce the relation between the similitude ideas and the governing equations. In so doing we have invoked the idea that these equations, at least in overall form, apply to each and to all macroscopic processes, provided only that we have no nuclear or relativity effects (and even in such cases we would not discard the equations shown, but would modify them and add a few more). This is tantamount to stating that we believe we can now write some governing equations for almost any problem in science or engineering. We may not be able to solve these equations in many instances. In others we may not even be able to get down enough equations to make a complete solution theoretically possible. (For example, in highly irreversible processes we cannot yet write adequate expressions for the irreversible changes, but only for the end states when we stop the irreversible action.) Thus it at least appears‡ that man's knowledge of his physical surroundings, while far from complete, has reached the point where even this last type of difficulty only occurs in a minority of technically significant problems.

The logic of the situation thus impels us to ask why we do not make use of the very considerable information inherent in the governing equations explicitly. That is, in addition to using them to illuminate the dependency relations in specific problems of interest in order to apply the method of similitude, why not also try to use these governing equations to see how much we can get out of them, even if the equations are incomplete or we cannot find a complete solution? In terms of the objectives of fractional analysis, the answer is that we should certainly make such an attempt to see what additional information, if any, we can obtain!

A word of caution about the types of pi's that may be needed here. It is stated above that several of the governing equations do not introduce any new types of pi's. This does not mean that any one of the governing overall equations is irrelevant in fractional analysis. On the contrary, precisely what is being suggested here is that the pertinent governing equations, that is, those that would normally be required to solve a problem of the type under study, should be explicitly set down and examined in the most detailed form available. Each of these equations may or may not introduce new parameters or variables needed in the solution, but this

---

† If we had more information, normally we would use it; this is particularly true if we adopt the spirit of fractional analysis as discussed in the introduction.

‡ This appearance may be illusory; it has been before in the history of science. But even if this is so, the search for systematic methods almost invariably leads to a gain in understanding.

is not known in advance, and each contains information relevant to a complete solution. However, if the argument above is correct, then it is possible to express all of the pi's needed, from whatever equation or condition they arise, as a ratio of forces, of energies, or of properties occurring in or affecting actions upon the system (or as some combination of these three types).

In the previous section, the force ratios normally employed in one field of analysis were developed. Before discussion of the use of governing equations directly for fractional analysis, it is pertinent to extend the method of similitude by illustrating the use of energy and property ratios.

c. *Some Energy Ratios of Heat Transfer*

With energy, as with force, the total number of forms occurring in all macroscopic problems is unmanageably large, but it is very seldom necessary to deal with all of these forms of energy simultaneously. Thus, it is again appropriate to study a more restricted field to illustrate the type of reasoning employed and the types of parameters found. In this instance, heat transfer will be used.

There are three well-known modes of heat transport: conduction, radiation, and convection. In addition, in some heat-transfer problems two other energy terms are significant: thermal-energy storage in solids and in fluid streams. Taking the five forms of energy in pairs, ten nondimensional groups can be formulated. These groups are shown in Table 3.2.

A few comments on Table 3.2 are pertinent. It is common in heat transfer to represent radiation by use of an effective convection coefficient, since the two modes of action, radiation and convection, are so commonly found in parallel. This allows addition of the two groups $h_r L/\lambda$ and hL/λ to form a single Nusselt number,† or similarly to combine the two groups $h_r L^2/wc_p$ and hL^2/wc_p to form a single NTU.† The group hL^2/wc_p is not in the conventional form of a Stanton number,† which is usually written as h/Gc_p. However, the identity is easily demonstrated since G is defined as $G \triangleq w/A \triangleq w/L^2$.

Table 3.2 contains most of the common dependent groups of heat transfer and would be sufficient for solving many problems. However, it is clear that some groups that are usually employed in convection heat transfer are absent. These additional groups include some ratios of properties, some of the groups listed in Table 3.1, and some combinations of the groups in Tables 3.1 and 3.2. The reasons for the appearance of these additional groups are readily explained by study of the dependencies among the equations for the particular type of problems involved. The

---

† Definitions of these groups are given in Table 3.2.

Table 3.2   Ratios of Common Energy Forms in Heat Transfer

$q_c \triangleq \lambda LT$ Conduction	$q_r \triangleq h_r L^2 T$ Radiation	$q_v \triangleq hL^2T$ Convection	$E_s \triangleq \dfrac{\rho c_v T L^3}{t}$ Storage in solids	
$\dfrac{\lambda L}{wc_p}$	$\dfrac{h_r L^2}{wc_p}$	$\dfrac{hL^2}{wc_p}$ Stanton number or NTU	$\dfrac{\rho L^3 c_v}{wc_p t}$	$E_f \triangleq wc_p T$ Storage in fluid streams
	$\dfrac{h_r L}{\lambda}$	$\dfrac{hL}{\lambda}$ Biot number	$\dfrac{L^2 \rho c_v}{t\lambda} = \dfrac{L^2}{\alpha t}$ Fourier number	$q_c \triangleq \lambda LT$ Conduction
		$\dfrac{h}{h_r}$	$\dfrac{\rho L c_v}{h_r t}$	$q_r \triangleq h_r L^2 T$ Radiation
			$\dfrac{\rho c_v L}{ht}$	$q_v \triangleq hL^2 T$ Convection

The five forms of energy expressed as an energy rate:

Conduction $= q_c \triangleq \lambda LT$

Radiation $= q_r \triangleq 6\epsilon L^2 T^4 \triangleq h_r L^2 T$

Convection $= q_r \triangleq hL^2 T$

Storage in solids $= E_s \triangleq \dfrac{\rho V c_v T}{t} = \dfrac{\rho L^3 c_v T}{t}$

Storage in fluid streams $= E_f \triangleq wc_p T$

where

V = volume

ϵ = emissivity

6 = Stefan-Boltzmann constant

λ = thermal conductivity of solid

k = thermal conductivity of fluid

w = mass flow rate

C_p, C_v = specific heats at constant pressure and constant volume

L = characteristic length

h = convection coefficient

h_r = apparent convection coefficient for radiation

$\alpha = \dfrac{\lambda}{\rho c_v}$ = thermal diffusivity

NTU = number of thermal units; defined as quantity shown. See Kays and London[23]

ρ = density

T = temperature

t = time

The very common Nusselt number $\triangleq \dfrac{hL}{k}$ does not appear as a natural energy ratio, but can be shown to be the product of an energy ratio, a force ratio, and a property ratio.

key factor is the complex nature of the apparently simple convection coefficient h.

Unlike the conduction coefficient λ, the convection coefficient is not a simple thermodynamic property of the system. The convection coefficient is actually a function of the velocity field about the body in addition to the properties of the fluid. Thus it depends on the solution to an underlying problem in fluid mechanics and also possibly on properties relating the thermal and flow-field characteristics. Consequently, the parameters fixing the flow field and its relation to the thermal field may be needed for a complete correlation.

In a problem of heat conduction, the rate equations show, it is sufficient to specify the material and the time and temperature boundary conditions. This fixes the conductivity and the specific heat of the solid; thus it is sufficient to fix the two significant energy rates, the conduction rate and the storage rate. Therefore Table 3.2 is in agreement with the solution found in Chap. 2, that is, if we specify geometric similarity and fixed Fourier number, the solutions to two problems will be similar.

Similar remarks can be made about a problem in which we are concerned with energy storage and convection heat transfer. That is, it would be sufficient to ensure geometric similarity and a fixed value of the parameter $\rho L c_v / h t$ in order to ensure complete similarity. In the conduction problem, it was enough merely to specify the temperature and time boundary conditions and the materials involved to fix h; but here we must also fix the detailed characteristics of the flow field. This means that we must introduce the equations of momentum and continuity in addition to the equations for energy. Or to put this in terms of similarity, we must guarantee similarity of properties of the fluid and of the forces in the flow field in addition to geometric similarity in order to ensure that the velocity fields will be similar and that the parameter $\rho L c_v / h t$ will be fixed. Thus we see that in heat-transfer problems involving convection and energy storage effects, it is necessary to ensure similarity of property ratios, of forces, and of energies in addition to geometric similarity of the bodies. The details for a given case can best be found by examining the pertinent equations, as in the following example.

Example 3.2. Using Table 3.2, let us first consider a purely thermal conduction heat-transfer problem. We take again the cooking problem of Example 2.2. Here we need to find a similarity rule governing the cooking time of arbitrarily shaped solid bodies in an oven.

We note that all three modes of heat transfer may be important. Radiation and convection occur at the surface of the body and conduction occurs inside, as shown in Fig. 3.1. We now construct the simplest pos-

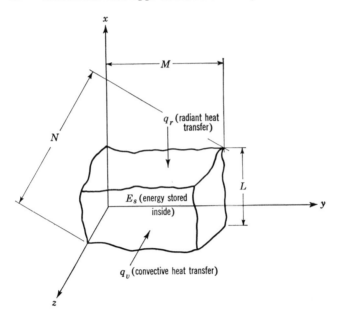

Fɪɢ. 3.1

sible thermal circuit† to represent this problem (Fig. 3.2).   Figure 3.2 is
not sufficient to solve the complete problem, but it will suffice to determine
what energy effects act independently.

We see that the sum of the radiation and convection heat transfer act
as a single energy effect in this problem, as is often the case, but that conduction is a separate effect.   That is, the ratio of the radiation to the
convection is unimportant; only the sum of the two is pertinent, but
the ratio of conduction to convection plus radiation heat transfer is im-

† A thermal circuit is conventionally drawn using standard symbols for electrical
circuits which imply thermal elements by analogue.

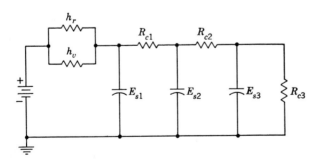

Fɪɢ. 3.2

portant.   We also observe that we need a term representing energy storage in the body in addition to factors specifying geometrical similarity of some kind.   Thus from Table 3.2 an appropriate set of pi's for the thermal factors is

$$\pi_1 = \frac{L^2}{t_c \alpha} = \frac{E_s}{q_c}$$

$$\pi_2 = \frac{(h_v + h_r)L}{\lambda} = \frac{q_v + q_r}{q_c} = \text{Biot number}$$

And the geometrical specification we can take as before to be

$$\pi_3 = \frac{L}{M}$$

$$\pi_4 = \frac{L}{N}$$

Thus we obtain the following answer.   The cooking time will be the same if all of π_1, π_2, π_3, and π_4 are fixed.   Again we must interpret the time for complete cooking in terms of $t_{\min} = t_f + t_o$ as in Ex. 2.2.   Clearly we would also get the similarity rules for conduction.

By inspection of Table 3.2 we also see that increasing π_1 increases the importance of the transient conduction effect and that increasing π_2 increases the importance of the heat transfer to the surface.   Thus we can see that if π_1 is large and π_2 is small, we would expect to have primarily a conduction problem; while if π_1 is small and π_2 is large, we would have primarily a convection and radiation problem.   Although we are unable to make these conclusions quantitative by this method, they are nevertheless useful information we were unable to achieve by use of the pi theorem on this same problem in Chap. 2.   For later reference it should be noted that an added conclusion arises not so much from the method itself as from the fact that the method allows us to use physical information that we could not bring to bear within the framework of the pi-theorem methods.

3-3   DIRECT USE OF GOVERNING OVERALL EQUATIONS

In developing a general method of similitude in Sec. 3-2*b*, we were led to an examination of the crucial dependency relations among the governing equations, and this virtually forced attention onto the idea of explicit use of the governing overall equations, in some form, for fractional analysis. As we have already seen, both by example and by discussion, the more physical information we can bring to bear, the better answers we can obtain from fractional analysis.   We would thus expect that more detailed equations will give more complete results; this is, of course, true.   However, the amount of information obtainable from even the least detailed forms of the governing equations is frequently very surprising.   Furthermore, it is often useful to employ extremely simple equations in direct conjunction with tables of dimensionless ratios, such as those of Tables 3.1 and 3.2.   For both these reasons, as well as for the sake of clarity, we begin with an illustration using only the most rudimentary governing equation.

Example 3.3.   Consider the correlation of drag and heat transfer on a body falling through a fluid under the action of gravity.   To simplify the matter, we shall assume that the body is a sphere.   Let us presume that the body enters some medium, such as the atmosphere of an unspecified planet, with an arbitrary velocity.   We are interested in determining the acceleration and also the rate at which the body will be heated by friction.

For purposes of studying further the matter of dependence of the physical quantities and the representation of this dependence inherent in the overall equations, it is useful to examine first a simpler related problem, namely, the same drag problem in the case where the fluid is incompressible.

If the medium is incompressible and if we are concerned only with the drag, then it is sufficient to specify geometric similarity and constancy of all force ratios involved, for the reasons given in Sec. 3.2b.   In all analyses

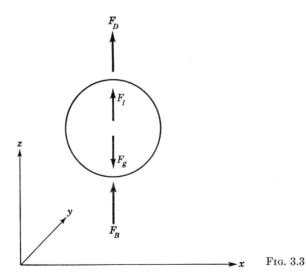

Fig. 3.3

of this type, we begin with some type of system diagram, in this case a free body diagram of the forces.

In Fig. 3.3, it is seen that four forces affect the fall of the body: gravity, drag, buoyancy, and inertia. The equation for the overall dynamic equilibrium of the body is very simple; it is

$$F_g = F_I + F_B + F_D \tag{3.3}$$

where

F_g = gravity force
F_I = inertia force
F_B = buoyant force (hydrostatic pressure forces)
F_D = drag force

However, if the body is bluff, the drag force will have two causes, namely, a pressure force and a viscous force. Thus we have for some cases at least five forces; we will require four pi's, three independent and one dependent. Three of these can be selected from Table 3.1; appropriate groups include: Reynolds number, Froude number,† and drag coefficient. In addition we need a group representing buoyancy force. This we can formulate very simply as follows:

$$F_B = \rho_f \mathbf{V}$$
$$F_g = \rho_B \mathbf{V}$$
$$\frac{F_B}{F_g} = \frac{\rho_f}{\rho_B}$$

where

ρ_f = density of fluid
ρ_B = density of body
$\mathbf{V}$ = volume of body

Thus we have found four pi's which will serve our purpose. However, if instead of merely extracting similarity rules from these pi's, as we have done previously, we choose to express them as an equation, we can find further results.

We note that the Froude and Reynolds numbers and the drag coefficient all involve an inertia force. Thus we could produce them, or their reciprocals, by the simple expedient of dividing Eq. (3.3) by F_I.

$$\frac{F_g}{F_I} = 1 + \frac{F_B}{F_I} + \frac{F_D}{F_I}$$

† Froude number is used in a different sense here than is usual for problems restricted to systems on earth.

Upon inserting

$$F_D = F_{\text{pressure}} + F_{\text{viscous}} = F_p + F_v$$

we have

$$\frac{F_g}{F_I} = 1 + \frac{F_B}{F_g}\frac{F_g}{F_I} + \frac{F_v}{F_I} + \frac{F_p}{F_I} \tag{3.4a}$$

On rearranging and noting $\dfrac{F_B}{F_g} = \dfrac{\rho_f}{\rho_B}$

$$N_p = \frac{1}{N_F\left(1 - \dfrac{\rho_f}{\rho_B}\right)} - \frac{1}{N_R} - 1 \tag{3.4b}$$

where

$$N_F = \text{Froude number} = \frac{F_I}{F_g}$$

$$N_R = \text{Reynolds number} = \frac{F_I}{F_v}$$

$$N_p = \text{pressure coefficient} = \frac{F_p}{F_I}$$

Here we must note that we have defined the pressure coefficient, the Froude number, and the Reynolds number in the step between Eqs. (3.4a) and (3.4b). That is, we define them to be the force ratios appearing in Eq. (3.4a). This procedure is permissible since, as shown in Table 3.1, the form of the ratios is appropriate.

Equation (3.4b), although based on a very rudimentary analysis, nevertheless provides considerably more information than could be obtained from knowledge of the pi's alone.

In particular, we see immediately from Eq. (3.4b) that if the term ρ_f/ρ_g is small compared to unity, it can be dropped from the solution, since it will be insignificant. Similarly, we can establish from Eq. (3.4b) over what ranges other parameters may be neglected. In an algebraic equation, such comparisons of magnitude are obvious and always valid; in a differential equation, the matter is more subtle, as we shall see in Chap. 4.

At this point, we must be extremely careful about what we mean by such terms as Reynolds number or Froude number. As already noted, we can define a parameter which is the ratio of two forces in the problem, say the inertia to viscous force. This ratio will have the form of a Reynolds number, as shown in Table 3.1; but *it is not necessarily the standard form*. That is, we cannot simultaneously define Reynolds number in some arbitrary standard way, and also define it as the ratio of inertia to viscous forces without checking to see that the two definitions agree for the problem at hand. As a matter of fact, they often disagree. It then follows that we can neglect a term which is small in the sense of the example above, but it does *not* follow that a given force ratio is small merely because a standard form of a parameter takes on a very small (or large) value. Again, using the ratio of inertia to viscous force as an example, it does not follow that this ratio will be small simply because some arbitrary standard form of Reynolds number is large. Indeed, some of the worst blunders in the history of fluid mechanics have been based on a failure to make this distinction clearly. This particular example (inertia and viscous forces) has become notorious in fluid mechanics, but the difficulty is not isolated to that example or indeed to that subject. The logical trap of the double definition for a single term exists whenever we establish standard forms for the common parameters and also try to attribute to these forms direct physical meaning for a very wide range of problems. Since we do this in almost all technical fields as they advance, it is important to be very clear about this point. That is, we must never assume that we can judge magnitude on the basis of an arbitrary standard form, no matter how useful that form has proved to be in the past, until we have demonstrated that the form employed does indeed give the pertinent energy, force, or property ratio for the particular problem at hand.

In cases where the standard form and the form giving the pertinent ratio of forces, energies, or properties are not the same, then the parameter actually giving the ratio is almost always far more useful and relevant. Moreover, if the reasoning regarding force, energy, and property ratios above is correct, then it is always possible to form these more pertinent ratios, provided we know enough about the problem in hand; in Chap. 4 we shall see in more detail what information is needed for this purpose.

With these remarks in view both the limitations and the uses of a table of parameters, such as Table 3.1 or 3.2, can be further clarified. The parameters of Tables 3.1 and 3.2 suggest the forms of parameters which we should seek in a given problem. The tables thus can be used as a checklist. They also form a starting place from which parameters that do give more information about specific problems can be sought. But we must always remember that the parameters of Tables 3.1 and 3.2 lack specificity in the sense that the particular scales or values of physical quantities best representing a given problem are not stated; we cannot use the parameters as they stand in Table 3.1 or 3.2 for comparison of magnitudes without further checking. Moreover, the establishment of the proper scales is a *research* problem; sometimes it is an easy, almost trivial task, but in some cases it is a difficult and subtle problem.

Returning to the falling-body problem we see that by use of the equation for the most elementary free-body diagram in addition to our table of force ratios, we are able not only to find the governing pi's in a very simple way, but also to determine when one or more force ratios can be neglected in the solution. In addition, we can see at a glance what the physical meaning and qualitative effect of the various pi groups will be. Thus for the incompressible case our strategy works quite well, and we now attempt to extend it to the case of the compressible fluid, which is of more interest.

In the case of the compressible medium, there is a considerable temptation to reason that if the medium is made compressible, then it is sufficient merely to introduce a term which accounts for the compressive forces in the fluid as it flows around the body. That is, the drag force may now have three parts: a viscous portion, a pressure portion, and a portion due to the formation of waves by compression of the fluid medium. Thus, reasoning by the older method of similitude based on forces alone, we would conclude that we need only add one more group. If we make the groups nondimensional by use of inertia force, this will be the Mach or Cauchy number. If we hope to obtain an answer that will work for *any* compressible medium, however, this solution is not sufficient. In order to show this, we set the governing overall equations. Since we are concerned with forces and accelerations, it is appropriate to commence with the equation of momentum. We understand the nature of inertia forces from the most elementary considerations of dynamics. It is the drag forces that are under question. To see these clearly, we adopt a set of coordinates fixed in the falling body; to avoid the necessity for discussion of accelerating control volumes, which is complex, we shall assume for the moment that the body is falling steadily. This is sufficient to illustrate the question involved. For this set of coordinates the control surface can be taken as a portion of the fluid with the sphere cut out. (See Fig. 3.3*a*.)   The equation of momentum is

$$\int p \, \overrightarrow{dA} + \int \rho V^2 \, \overrightarrow{dA} = \overrightarrow{g} \int \rho \, dV - \overrightarrow{F_B} - \overrightarrow{F_V}$$

(whole sur-   (bottom   (over
face, includ-   surface)   control
ing that   volume)
of sphere)

$$+ \frac{d}{dt} \int \rho \overrightarrow{V} \, dV + \int \rho V^2 \, \overrightarrow{dA}$$

(inside)   (top
                     surface)

The momentum equation contains the pressure and compressive forces in the four integral terms. These terms contain five dependent variables:

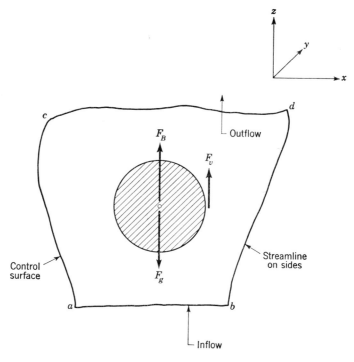

Fig. 3.3a

pressure, density, and three components of velocity. If we fix these five quantities, the pressure and compressive forces are fixed. In addition, if we know the velocity field and the viscosity, the shear force is fixed. Thus we observe that we have five dependent variables and the parameter viscosity to deal with. But we have only three equations representing the three components of the vector momentum equation. Clearly then we must introduce two more equations. The obvious choices are the continuity equation and the energy equation:

Continuity

$$\int \rho V \, dA = \int \rho V \, dA + \frac{\partial}{\partial t} \int \rho \, d\mathbf{V}$$

(bottom surface)   (top surface)   (inside)

Energy

$$\int \rho V h_F \, dA = \left(\frac{dE}{dt}\right) + \int \rho V h_F \, dA$$

(bottom surface)   (inside)   (top surface)

The continuity equation contains only variables that also appear in the momentum equation, but unfortunately the energy equation contains, in addition to these variables, a new dependent variable, internal thermal energy.† Thus we must find still one more equation linking internal energy, density, and pressure. Such an equation is given by the equation of state. If we are dealing with one pure Newtonian fluid substance, then by suitable transformation of coordinates we can always find an equation of state that has no more than two independent intensive properties and we may therefore write:

$$e = e(p,\rho)$$

To complete this discussion of the dependence of the variables on one another, it is very helpful to use a more explicit equation of state. Let us therefore assume that we are dealing with a medium that satisfies the perfect-gas equation of state. For this type of substance we have the very simple relation:

$$e = c_v T$$

Also the enthalpy h is

$$h = e + pv = c_p T$$

And thus for a perfect gas

$$\frac{p/\rho}{e} = \frac{pv}{e} = \frac{h - e}{e} = \frac{c_p - c_v}{c_v} = \gamma - 1$$

where

$$\gamma = \frac{c_p}{c_v}$$

$$v = \frac{1}{\rho}$$

Thus we see that the advent of a properties ratio in this problem is a direct consequence of the nature of the dependency relations among the pertinent overall equations. More specifically, if we examine the equations set forth above, we find that the forces depend on the density; to find density we must solve the energy equation which in turn involves internal energy. Hence we need the equation of state which links internal energy to the other properties among the dependent parameters. The physical reason for this mathematical structure is as follows. The compression of a fluid involves not only mechanical transport work but also

---

† Since $h = u + p/\rho$ and p,ρ were already counted, only one new variable is introduced.

storage of energy in the form of internal thermal energy. This can be seen from the appropriate Gibbsian equation.

$$de = T \, ds - p \, dv$$

which applies to any pure single fluid substance of the sort under discussion. More specifically, for the perfect gas the ratio of the net mechanical energy of transport in a pressure field to the concomitant and unavoidable storage of thermal energy is precisely

$$\frac{d(pv)}{de} = \gamma - 1 = \frac{\text{change in flow work}}{\text{change in internal energy}}$$

as has just been shown. Thus we see again the crucial role of the explicit dependency relations among the governing equations.

It is now possible to complete the fractional analysis by reasoning as follows. The equations set forth above for momentum, energy, continuity, and the equation of state are sufficient to determine the dependent variable sought. Thus if we can ensure that all of the variables and parameters in the equations are fixed and are the same in two given cases, then we can assert that similarity will be achieved on the basis of the first grounds given in Sec. 3-2*b*, provided a unique solution to the equation exists. This is true whether we can solve the equations or not, and in this case guaranteeing fixed values for the variables is easier by at least several orders of magnitude than solving the complete equations. In fact we have already enumerated the forces needed and shown that the equations also involve one property ratio which fixes certain significant energy terms. We can proceed to obtain the desired fractional analysis in either of two ways. We can simply set down the force ratios found in the solution of the incompressible problem plus the Mach number and the ratio of specific heats as a solution, or we can normalize the governing overall equations and extract the pi groups that appear in the various terms. The first method is easier and is in fact completed by the remarks just made. The second method requires additional work, but will in general yield more information.† Since it is quite complicated for the case just given, we shall not complete such an analysis in this instance but will give other examples below.

It is worth noting that the number of parameters in this problem is unduly large, and the more complete analysis of the governing equations to determine what terms might be neglected would certainly be in order if we were seeking the most possible information about this problem rather than attempting to illustrate methodology. Similar remarks apply to

---

† As we have just stressed, formal use of Tables 3.1 and 3.2 does not in general give magnitudes.

the heat-transfer portion of this problem as originally set. It is left to the reader to demonstrate that the overall equations are sufficient to guarantee that the groups given above plus the Prandtl number $c_p\mu/\lambda$ are sufficient to provide similarity in the heat-transfer problem.

Example 3.4. To further illustrate the utility of the use of overall equations, take again the problem of correlation of the pressure drop in a pipe with laminar, fully established, incompressible flow (Example 2.1). In the present solution we again draw a sketch of the forces on a relevant control surface. The sketch shows that three types of forces appear in

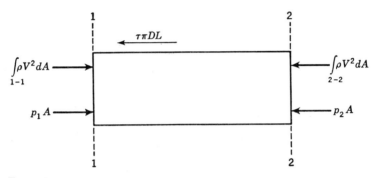

Fig. 3.4

the momentum equation: pressure, shear, and inertia. When we solved this problem by reference to Table 3.1 in Example 3.1 and by the pi theorem in Example 2.1, we found an independent pi and thus took the friction factor as a function of the Reynolds number. This is entirely correct; however, we now write the actual momentum equation without attempting to solve it. This yields

$$\underbrace{\int_{1-1} \rho V^2\, dA}_{F_I} + \underbrace{p_1 A}_{F_p} = \underbrace{p_2 A}_{F_p} + \underbrace{\tau\pi\, DL}_{F_V} + \underbrace{\int_{2-2} \rho V^2\, dA}_{F_I}$$

If the flow is *truly steady and fully established*, we see immediately that the two terms representing inertia forces cancel out, since ρ and V are the same in any given element dA at the ends of the control surface. Thus we obtain

$$\underbrace{(p_1 - p_2)A}_{F_p} = \underbrace{\tau\pi\, DL}_{F_V}$$

This asserts that for a truly steady flow we should be able to obtain a solution for the governing groups by dividing by F_v; that is,

$$\frac{\Delta p\alpha^2}{\mu V\beta} = \frac{\Delta p}{\tau} = \frac{F_p}{F_v} = \text{Stokes number} = \text{constant}$$

where α and β are appropriate length scales.   This is indeed a proper and, for many purposes, a very useful solution,† although it is not in the form to which we are accustomed.   It is readily verified from the actual known complete solution‡ as follows:

$$\frac{\Delta p/(L/D)}{\frac{1}{2}\rho V^2} \triangleq 4f = \frac{64}{Re} = \frac{64\mu}{\rho VD}$$

which, on rearranging, yields

$$4fRe = \frac{\Delta p/(L/D)}{\frac{1}{2}\rho V^2}\frac{\rho VD}{\mu} = \frac{\Delta p \cdot D^2}{\mu VL} = 64$$

Note $\alpha = D$, $\beta = L$; Table 3.1 does not give scales.   Moreover, too-early cancellation of lengths causes a loss of information; Huntley's addition (Sec. 2-6) applies here.

This simplification will not work for the turbulent regime; the Reynolds number appears to a different power in the expression for friction factor, and the density will not cancel through the equation.   Nor would we expect it to do so, since the inertia is important in the turbulent regime inasmuch as it affects the fluctuating forces expressed by the Reynolds stress§ even though the mean flow is steady.

Example 3.5.   We now apply the same method to the problem of the heat exchanger discussed in Example 2.3, where we found some inexplicable difficulties in application of the pi theorem.

Take again the same figure as in Example 2.3.

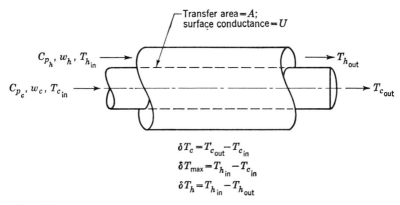

FIG. 3.5

---

† For example, it leads directly to the useful result that the Nusselt number is constant in a fully established laminar flow in a tube.

‡ See any standard work on fluid mechanics, for example, Vennard.[52]

§ The relevant Reynolds stress is given as $\tau = \overline{-\rho u'v'}$, where ( )′ indicates the instantaneous deviation from the mean velocity and (‾) indicates a time average.

We now set the overall rate and energy equations sufficient to determine the behavior without attempting to solve them. The energy equations are:

$$q = (wc_p)_h \, \delta T_h \qquad (3.5)$$

and

$$q = (wc_p)_c \, \delta T_c \qquad (3.6)$$

The overall rate equation is

$$q = UA \, \delta T_m = \int_0^{A_t} U(T_h - T_c) \, dA \qquad (3.7)$$

where A_t = total heat-transfer area. Since q is inside the control volume, we eliminate it between Eqs. (3.5) and (3.6). In addition we define non-dimensional variables indicated by $(^-)$ as follows:

$$\delta \bar{T}_c = \frac{\delta T_c}{(\delta T)_{\max}} \qquad \delta \bar{T}_h = \frac{\delta T_h}{(\delta T)_{\max}} \qquad \bar{A} = \frac{A}{A_t}$$

where $(\delta T)_{\max}$ = maximum temperature difference between hot and cold fluid at any points inside the control volume. This gives

$$(wc_p)_h \, \delta \bar{T}_h = (wc_p)_c \, \delta \bar{T}_c \qquad (3.8)$$

and

$$(wc_p)_h \, \delta \bar{T}_h = A_t \int_0^1 U(\bar{T}_h - \bar{T}_c) \, d\bar{A} \qquad (3.9)$$

We can now eliminate either $\bar{T}_h$ or $\bar{T}_c$ from Eqs. (3.8) and (3.9) by differentiating (3.8) once and (3.9) twice with respect to area $\bar{A}$. We choose to eliminate $\bar{T}_c$, and on differentiating obtain:

$$\frac{(wc_p)_h}{A_t} \frac{d^2 \bar{T}_h}{d\bar{A}^2} = U\left(\frac{d\bar{T}_h}{d\bar{A}} - \frac{d\bar{T}_c}{d\bar{A}}\right) = U\left(1 - \frac{d\bar{T}_c}{d\bar{A}} \frac{d\bar{A}}{d\bar{T}_h}\right)\frac{d\bar{T}_h}{d\bar{A}}$$

and

$$(wc_p)_h \frac{d\bar{T}_h}{d\bar{A}} = (wc_p)_c \frac{d\bar{T}_c}{d\bar{A}} \qquad \frac{d\bar{T}_c}{d\bar{A}} \frac{d\bar{A}}{d\bar{T}_h} = \frac{(wc_p)_h}{(wc_p)_c}$$

on combining and dividing by $\dfrac{(wc_p)_h}{A_t}$, we obtain

$$\frac{d^2 \bar{T}_h}{d\bar{A}^2} = \frac{UA_t}{(wc_p)_h}\left[1 - \frac{(wc_p)_h}{(wc_p)_c}\right]\frac{d\bar{T}_h}{d\bar{A}} \qquad (3.10a)$$

Similarly eliminating $\bar{T}_h$ yields

$$\frac{d^2 \bar{T}_c}{d\bar{A}^2} = \frac{UA_t}{(wc_p)_c}\left[\frac{(wc_p)_c}{(wc_p)_h} - 1\right]\frac{d\bar{T}_c}{d\bar{A}} \qquad (3.10b)$$

Integration of Eq. (3.10a) or (3.10b) is possible and can readily be carried out if we know U as a function of A. However, U is an extremely complex function of the geometry and flow conditions. Moreover, we can find a great deal of information from Eqs. (3.10) even though we do not know U as a function of A and thus cannot integrate explicitly.

First of all, we observe that we could cast any problem of the type considered in the form of Eqs. (3.10); in such a form the variables $\bar{T}_h$, $\bar{T}_c$, and $\bar{A}$ will always be the same. The difference between one problem and the next will lie in the value of the two parameters $A_t U/(wc_p)_h$ and $(wc_p)_h/(wc_p)_c$. Thus, if we fix the value of these two parameters, a single solution for the dependent parameters $\delta T_c/(\delta T)_{\max}$ and $\delta T_h/(\delta T)_{\max}$ should exist in the form:

$$\frac{\delta T_c}{\delta T_{\max}} = f\left[\frac{UA_t}{(wc_p)_c}, \frac{(wc_p)_h}{(wc_p)_c}\right]$$

and

$$\frac{\delta T_h}{\delta T_{\max}} = f\left[\frac{UA_t}{(wc_p)_h}, \frac{(wc_p)_h}{(wc_p)_c}\right]$$

This is clearly an explicit solution for the dimensionless groups needed to provide a correlation and, unlike the solution by dimensional analysis in Example 2.3, it provides the number of groups used in the literature.

Further inspection of Eqs. (3.10) shows why we had difficulty in Example 2.3. In this particular problem, the separate values of c_p and w are irrelevant; only their product wc_p is pertinent. In fact, most modern references on heat exchangers, such as Kays and London,[23] define a single symbol for the product wc_p. Thus while it is physically possible to vary w and c_p independently, and while both w and c_p are important and thus relevant secondary quantities, it just happens that the form of the governing equations is such that the two quantities never appear except as a simple product. If either w or c_p appeared singly in some term of the equations, or if w and c_p also appeared in any other combination besides a simple product in the equations, then each would be needed independently in the dimensional analysis. Since this applies to both hot and cold fluid, inclusion of the four quantities w_c, c_{p_c}, w_h, and c_{p_h} yields two groups too many. Again we will reserve discussion of the implications of these remarks to Chap. 5, where the various methods are compared.

From Eqs. (3.10) we can also find much more information. For example, if the ratio $(wc_p)_h/(wc_p)_c$ is small compared to unity, Eq. (3.10a) shows that the solution depends only on the parameter $UA_t/(wc_p)_h$. Similarly Eq. (3.10b) shows that if $(wc_p)_h/(wc_p)_c$ is very large compared to unity, the solution will depend only on the parameter $UA_t/(wc_p)_c$. Taken together these results lead directly to the dual definition of performance parameters utilized so effectively by Kays and London[23] as a means for providing compact solutions in graphical form for all possible problems of this class.   Thus derivation of the dimensionless parameters from the governing equations yields, as we anticipated, not only a correct, but also a particularly useful set of parameters.

3-4   CONCLUDING REMARKS

The examples given are sufficient to demonstrate the utility of the method of similitude as a means for finding governing parameters of the problem. The construction of the relevant tables provides a most instructive means for systematizing and improving correlation parameters.   Although the original developments of the methods were based on too narrow a foundation, it has been shown that this basis can be broadened to include at least any macroscopic system when the equations of state of the substances are reasonably well understood and when there are no relativity or quantum effects.   Further generalization is probably possible, but has not been attempted here.

An important weakness of the method of similitude is that it gives only the standard forms of the parameters and does not tell us directly the appropriate scales; thus without further analysis we cannot tell whether or not these standard parameters indicate the magnitude of terms in a specific problem.

In discussing the broadened basis for the method of similitude, we were led directly to a more important conclusion about problems in fractional analysis.   In particular, both the discussion and the examples given show the very considerable power of fractional analysis employing the governing equations in some form.   Not only is it useful to assume the existence of immutable governing equations in order to provide a broader and more complete basis for similitude, but actual use of the governing equations, even in a very rudimentary form, leads immediately to more information, to more useful parameters, and to more general solutions to similitude problems.   All of these points are evident in the examples given above.   These examples also show that the equations are useful whether they are complete or incomplete and whether they are algebraic, integral, differential, or combinations of all three.   Examination of the examples given also suggests three important conclusions about the direct use of governing equations for fractional analyses:

1. The more complete and detailed the equations and conditions we use, the more information we are able to derive.
2. The direct use of governing equations for fractional analysis relies upon a clear understanding of the physical information implied

by the equations—as distinguished from the mathematical content per se. To use the method effectively it is necessary to have a clear understanding of the meaning and limitations of mathematical models of physical reality as embodied in governing equations.

3. The final example suggests the inherent power in transforming the variables to nondimensional form and standard magnitude. As we shall see, such transformations are the basis for a number of important procedures.

In Chap. 4 we will then explore the implications of these remarks in some detail.

Since the preparation of the first draft of this work, the book by Sedov[46] has appeared in English translation. Sedov advocates use of dimensional analysis in conjunction with the governing equations. He states that to perform dimensional analysis properly, it is necessary to diagram the system just as if one were preparing to solve the problem completely, and then to set down enough parameters and variables† to determine the solution for the dependent quantity. Sedov has clearly shown that one can obtain important information by simultaneous use of the governing equations together with dimensional analysis, but that there are important limitations on the method. His work is strongly recommended for any reader who wants to form a picture of what can be achieved by dimensional analysis in a broader sense than it has usually been used in technical literature in the English language. Sedov gives many excellent examples which augment those given in Examples 3.2 to 3.5, and the viewpoint of Sedov's work is apparently quite close to that of the present work; there is, however, one important difference.

As pointed out above, and as noted by Sedov himself, the governing equations contain far more explicit information than can be used within the framework of dimensional analysis. Thus the real need does not seem to be further refinement or extension of dimensional analysis as such. The real need seems instead to be the formulation of systematic methods for obtaining information directly from the governing equations without actually solving them. The underlying logic of the situation has already been discussed in Sec. 3-2; specific suggestions for suitable methodology are given in the examples and summarized in items 1 to 3 above. Accordingly, we turn directly to an attempt to construct systematic methods of fractional analysis using the governing equations in Chap. 4.

† Sedov uses the terms parameter and variable interchangeably; the usage of this volume is followed here.

4 *Fractional Analysis of Governing Equations and Conditions*

4-1 INTRODUCTION

This chapter is concerned primarily with the construction and illustration of systematic procedures for the direct use of governing equations and conditions as a basis for similitude and fractional analysis. The preliminary discussion and examples in the previous chapter suggested three important ideas about such procedures.

First, the more complete and detailed the governing equations and conditions employed, the more information can be obtained. The most detailed governing equations are usually the differential equations for the system. Moreover, the bulk of problems in which we cannot find complete analytic solutions are those described by one or more partial differential equations. Thus, fractional analysis is most useful on just this kind of problem. We will stress the idea that it is important to examine

68

all of the equations and conditions necessary to provide a solution, preferably a unique solution.

Second, to carry out fractional analyses based on governing equations we must have a clear understanding of the physical information inherent in governing equations and of the limitations of mathematical models of physical reality. We will accordingly stress the "physical information" inherent in the governing equations which has been much less extensively treated in the literature than the purely mathematical aspects of how to solve the equations once the necessary physical information has been put in.

Third, it is appropriate to use a standard procedure for transforming the variables to nondimensional form and standard magnitude. As noted in concluding Chap. 3, it is not sufficient, for many purposes, to make the governing equations nondimensional in any arbitrary way. If the maximum information is to be obtained, both form and magnitude of variables must be studied carefully. Unless the magnitudes of the variables as well as the parameters are considered, misleading information is usually obtained in certain classes of problems. Thus, it is often essential to discuss magnitudes systematically (even though this is usually the hardest part of the problem). The form of the variables when reduced to standard magnitude is also important. The amount of information obtained always depends directly on the care and insight used in choosing the form of the variables, and study of several different forms often yields more information than can be found from any one form alone.

In transforming to various nondimensional variables three different, but related, procedures are employed. Each has a distinct, useful physical meaning. Unfortunately, different names have been used for them by different authors; often the same name has been used for more than one, and the names have been interchanged by various authors. We shall call these three procedures:

1. Normalization
2. Absorption of parameters
3. Combination of variables

The terms *absorption of parameters* and *combination of variables* describe the process implied and should be in general agreement with the reader's understanding; detailed definitions are given in context below. *Normalization* has been used to mean many different things in the literature. We shall use it to mean making the equations and conditions nondimensional in terms of nondimensional variables of standard magnitude. Normalization is the most important of these three processes for fractional analyses. The implications stemming from the physical information inherent in a complete set of governing equations and conditions in normalized form are the basis for almost all the procedures that follow.   The discussion accordingly begins with a detailed discussion of a standard procedure for normalization, even though its full implications will not be immediately obvious.   Before we turn to discussion of this procedure one more remark is necessary.

Some of the procedures that will be based on normalized equations are rigorous and accurate; in many cases they are entirely rigorous and as accurate as the description of physical reality provided by the governing equations and conditions employed.   Other procedures discussed are definitely approximate and must be viewed as trial methods in which results should be checked against data.   An attempt is made throughout to distinguish rigorous results from trial methods, that is, to state explicitly the degree of approximation in each case.   However, no apology is made or intended for the trial methods; all too often they are the only recourse in difficult problems.

4-2   NORMALIZATION OF THE GOVERNING EQUATIONS

a.   A Procedure for Normalization

We have defined normalization to mean making the governing equations and conditions nondimensional in terms of nondimensional variables of standard magnitude.   In some problems one normalization is sufficient to give all the information needed for similitude and approximation theory studies; in others no one transformation of variables will do, and several must be used to provide the needed information about all problems in the class and/or regions of interest in a given problem.   Since the methodology developed here is to some extent new, we will begin in this section by studying a problem where one normalization is sufficient and defer until later sections the more difficult problems in which more than one transformation of variables must be used.

To carry out a normalization two steps are required; these are:

1. Make all the variables nondimensional in terms of the appropriate scales of the problem; this will be discussed in much more detail below.
2. Divide through the equation by the coefficient of one term to make the equation dimensionless term by term.†

---

† Actually one makes the equation unit-free or unitless as noted in Sec. 2-2c, but conventionally the term dimensionless is used; this practice will be followed here.

As noted in Sec. 4-1, the precise choice of scales in step 1 is very important. The method for choice of scales we will now suggest more or less automatically provides a form in which all desired similitude information can be obtained in those problems where one normalization is sufficient, and it forms a very good starting point in those problems where ultimately further transformation of variables is required. We will therefore use it as a standard procedure; it will form the basis of almost all the remainder of the discussion. This procedure is as follows:

1. Attempt to define all dependent nondimensional variables so that they are approximately unity over a finite distance and nowhere exceed approximately unity in the domain of concern.
2. Attempt to define all independent nondimensional variables so that their increment is approximately unity over the same domain of concern. (This means that the extent of the domain will run from 0 to 1, 1 to 2, etc., in the new variables.)

The term approximate is used here in the engineering sense, that is, the closest estimate which can be provided with reasonable effort. Usually it means within a factor of 2 or closer to the true value, and it would not normally differ from the true value by as much as a factor of 10.

We now give an example to form the basis for further discussion and to make the ideas clear.

Example 4.1.   Illustration of Normalization.   The system analyzed in Example 2.2 is shown again in Fig. 4.1. Once again the problem is to determine a similarity rule for cooking such a solid body. The governing differential equation for conduction inside the body is the well-known "heat" equation.

$$\frac{\partial^2 T}{\partial x^2} + \frac{\partial^2 T}{\partial y^2} + \frac{\partial^2 T}{\partial z^2} = \frac{1}{\alpha}\frac{\partial T}{\partial t} \qquad (4.1a)$$

where

T = temperature difference
x,y,z = cartesian coordinates
t = time
α = thermal diffusivity

and the boundary conditions are:

at $t = -0$: $T = T_i$
at $t = +0$: $\left.\begin{array}{l} x = 0,L \\ y = 0,M \\ z = 0,N \end{array}\right\}$ at the surface $T = T_a$

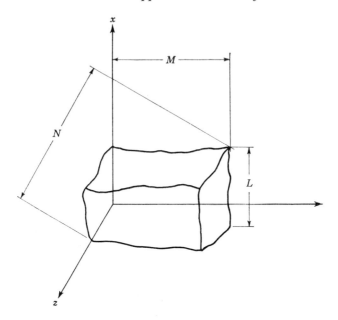

FIG. 4.1

These boundary conditions are sufficient for the problem discussed in Example 2.2, but are not sufficient for the extended problem discussed in Example 3.2.

The dependent variable appearing in the differential equation is a temperature difference. According to the procedure above we attempt to nondimensionalize the dependent variable in such a way that it approximately equals unity over a finite region but nowhere exceeds approximately unity in terms of the boundary conditions. In this example we must define a nondimensional temperature as follows:†

$$\bar{T} = \frac{T}{T_i}$$

where both T and T_i are measured from T_a as datum.

The suggested procedure also states that we should make the independent variables nondimensional in terms of the boundary conditions in such a way that each one runs from zero to approximately unity over its interval of integration. In the case of the length variables x, y, and z we define these nondimensional variables:

$$\bar{x} = \frac{x}{L} \qquad \bar{y} = \frac{y}{M} \qquad \bar{z} = \frac{z}{N}$$

† Throughout the remainder of the text, the symbol ($^-$) will always mean a non-dimensional variable.

For other geometries, of extreme types, different characteristic lengths may be needed to fulfill the requisite conditions; these may be either fewer or greater in number than three. However, for most bodies the dimensions L, M, and N will suffice, provided they are the longest dimensions in the three coordinate directions. Almost any shape can be subdivided into parts which can be characterized by three dimensions in this way.

The time variable is somewhat more difficult to handle. Since time runs from zero to infinity, it is not immediately obvious how the normalization should proceed. However, if we remember that the effects under study will occur in a finite time, then we can handle time in the following way. Define a time constant of the body t_c as the time required for every particle to change in temperature at least two-thirds† of the difference between initial body temperature and applied oven temperature. We can then define a nondimensional time in terms of this time constant, and the necessary condition on the time variable will be given for at least one time constant.‡ If necessary, we could then repeat the analysis for further time constants, but since the equation will be the same in this case, we will not encounter new results. It therefore suffices to define a nondimensional time variable as $\bar{t} = \dfrac{t}{t_c}$.

To complete step (1), it is now necessary merely to substitute the nondimensional variables into the differential equation. This amounts to a transformation of variables from T, x, y, z, and t to the nondimensional variables $\bar{T}$, $\bar{x}$, $\bar{y}$, $\bar{z}$, and $\bar{t}$. This transformation yields:

$$\frac{T_a}{L^2}\frac{\partial^2 \bar{T}}{\partial \bar{x}^2} + \frac{T_a}{M^2}\frac{\partial^2 \bar{T}}{\partial \bar{y}^2} + \frac{T_a}{N^2}\frac{\partial^2 \bar{T}}{\partial \bar{z}^2} = \frac{T_a}{\alpha t_c}\frac{\partial \bar{T}}{\partial \bar{t}}$$

Now performing step (2), divide through the equation by the term T_a/L^2; this yields the nondimensional equation

$$\frac{\partial^2 \bar{T}}{\partial \bar{x}^2} + \left(\frac{L}{M}\right)^2 \frac{\partial^2 \bar{T}}{\partial \bar{y}^2} + \left(\frac{L}{N}\right)^2 \frac{\partial^2 \bar{T}}{\partial \bar{z}^2} = \left(\frac{L^2}{t_c \alpha}\right) \frac{\partial \bar{T}}{\partial \bar{t}} \tag{4.1b}$$

The boundary conditions of Eq. (4.1b) are:

at $\bar{t} = -0$: $\quad \bar{T} = 1$

at $\bar{t} = +0$: $\quad \begin{rcases} \bar{x} = 0,1 \\ \bar{y} = 0,1 \\ \bar{z} = 0,1 \end{rcases}$ $\bar{T} = Ta/T_i = 0$ (since T_a has now been taken as the reference temperature)

† Or more precisely $1 - 1/e = 0.628$.

‡ This is equivalent to stating that we define the domain of concern to extend over one time constant.

The steps carried out on the differential equation above are not modified in any essential way for integral or algebraic terms. It is only necessary to note that the same steps can be carried out under an integral sign provided we take proper account of changes in the limits of integration. The parameters can then be extracted, since they are constants.

b.   *Meaning of Normalized Governing Equations*

A normalized equation, such as (4.1*b*), generally contains two distinct kinds of quantities, dimensionless *variables* and dimensionless *parameters*. In the following discussion the parameters will again sometimes be called dimensionless groups or pi's. The dimensionless variables can be identified by the superscript bar in each case; they are the variables of the original equation in normalized form. For example, in equation (4.1*b*) the four nondimensional independent variables are $\bar{t}$, $\bar{x}$, $\bar{y}$, $\bar{z}$, and the nondimensional dependent variable is $\bar{T}$. The dimensionless parameters in Eq. (4.1*b*) are each enclosed by parentheses for purposes of identification.† Inspection shows they are composed from the boundary conditions;‡ from the characterizing sizes, or scales, of the body; and from the physical parameters of the original equation. These physical parameters may be system properties, physical constants, or both. In the case of Eq. (4.1*b*) the pi's consist of

$$\left(\frac{L}{M}\right)^2 \qquad \left(\frac{L}{N}\right)^2 \qquad \text{and} \qquad \frac{L^2}{t_c\alpha}$$

It should be noted that although these pi's are composed from the system scales, boundary conditions, and physical parameters, their *form*, i.e., the combinations appearing, is explicitly dictated by the structure of the variables and parameters in the governing equation and boundary conditions.

It is very important to understand thoroughly the meaning of variation in one or more of the variables as opposed to changes in values of the parameters. To make this point entirely clear, we define a *class of problems* as follows. Any group of problems which obeys the same normalized governing equations and boundary conditions will be called a *class of problems*. It is specifically noted that this need not imply identical or even geometrically similar systems; both physical details and the gross nature of the systems can vary as long as they can be adequately repre-

---

† Parentheses are used for clarity in this first example only; they will not be used in later equations.

‡ In this case the boundary value T_a cancelled out, but this does not usually happen. Such cancellation has, in fact, a useful physical meaning, which we will discuss shortly.

sented by identical normalized equations and boundary conditions. It is also clear that geometrically similar or even physically identical systems will not satisfy the condition stated unless the boundary conditions can be expressed in the same way. Since the symbols employed in the normalized equation are irrelevant, any problems for which the equations can be brought to identical normalized equations and boundary conditions by trivial transformations of variables, such as $\bar{T} = \bar{S}$, etc., also belong to the same class. Finally, two problems can be made to belong to the same class, even though they initially do not, if transformations of variables can be found which bring the *normalized equations and boundary conditions* to an identical form.

If we examine a *single problem* in a class of problems, the dimensionless parameters normally† will have a certain numerical value, since they are composed of the boundary conditions, system properties, sizes, and physical constants. Having fixed the values of the parameters, we can still allow the value of nondimensional variables to change. *Such changes in value of the variables then imply moving through the domain of concern inside a given problem.* For example, as $\bar{x}$ runs from 0 to 1 in Eq. (4.1*b*), we move through the body from one side to the other in the x direction. In this process, the parameters which involve the characterization of x (those containing L) do not change, since L is an overall scale fixed by the size of the body.

In order to change the value of the parameters in a given class of problem, we must change either some property of the system, such as α or the size of the system given by L, M, or N. *Thus a change in the value of the parameters implies a change from one system to another within the given class of problem.* For example, if we increase L and hold M constant, we change to a new problem with different geometrical shape.

It is useful at this point to recall the method by which governing equations are derived. Consider the heat-conduction equation as an example. The important steps and assumptions leading to the heat equation (4.1*a*) are:

1. Define a system—in this instance an infinitesimal cube.
2. Write the governing equations. An energy-balance and Fourier's rate equation for conduction are required here.
3. Make the necessary idealizations—in this instance assume that there are no sources and the material is isotropic; that is, the conductivity is the same in all directions.
4. Combine and simplify the equations based on 3; this yields Eq. (4.1*a*).

† Exceptions can occur if the boundary conditions are expressible only in terms of implicit functions of the variables.

The purpose of applying this procedure to an infinitesimal element is, of course, to make the results as general as possible by requiring that the equations apply to each and every point in the system in detail. The solution to such detailed differential equations is often very complex, but this complexity in no way alters the fact that the equation has been constructed to be a mathematical model of a certain physical problem and that normally each term or set of terms in the equation represents a definite physical effect.† In this instance the four terms of Eq. (4.1a) represent, respectively, from left to right, the increments of energy flow due to heat conduction in the three directions x, y, z, and the energy storage inside the cube, all per unit time.

Moreover, if we hope to obtain complete answers from this mathematical model, all the relevant variables and parameters must be contained in the governing equations and boundary conditions; since no new variables or parameters are introduced by the processes of integration, only those which appear in the governing equations or boundary conditions will appear in solutions found from them. Integration cannot add physical effects, that is, missing terms or boundary conditions. The mathematics may suggest that we have insufficient boundary conditions; it may suggest the type of boundary conditions we should seek, but it cannot tell us what the missing boundary conditions actually are, nor can the mathematics alone tell us we have forgotten terms representing some physical effect. Only comparison of the solution with real system behavior, i.e. data, can do so.

In order to get on with the discussion of similitude based on the governing equations, let us assume for the moment that the equations and boundary conditions are complete and appropriate, that is, that they are a good model of physical reality and are mathematically consistent. This allows us to draw the needed conclusions and to postpone until the next section the detailed consideration of how we decide whether a given set of equations and boundary conditions is indeed complete and appropriate.

Examination of the derivation of Eq. (4.1b) from Eq. (4.1a) shows that normalization in no way modifies the physical content of the equations or boundary conditions. We also observe that normalization leads to a single parameter modifying each set of terms‡ representing a distinct physical effect, less one. (The less one arises from dividing by one coefficient in order to make the entire equation nondimensional.)

The normalized equations and boundary conditions contain all the governing parameters, provided that a complete and appropriate set of

---

† Sometimes one term is used to represent several effects.

‡ In Eq. (4.1b), each set has only one term, but this need not be so, as later examples will show.

governing equations and conditions is employed. As already noted, under these conditions all the variables, all the parameters, and all the relevant physical information needed for a solution must appear in the equations and boundary conditions. That is, the normalized dependent variable(s) can be expressed as a function of the *normalized independent variables and the parameters.* This is what we mean by a solution. For example, we can express the solution to Eq. (4.1*b*) in functional form as

$$\bar{T} = \bar{T}\left[\bar{x},\bar{y},\bar{z},\bar{t}; \left(\frac{L}{M}\right)^2, \left(\frac{L}{N}\right)^2, \frac{L^2}{t_c\alpha}\right] \tag{4.1c}$$

Equation (4.1*c*) expresses only the nature of the solution and not its form. We do not need to actually solve Eq. (4.1*b*) to obtain Eq. (4.1*c*). Nevertheless, we observe immediately from Eq. (4.1*c*) that the parameters of the normalized governing equations are the same as the parameters of the solution. Indeed, if the argument above is correct, this must be so for all such equations. Thus we do not need to write the equivalent of Eq. (4.1*c*). *It is sufficient to normalize the governing equations and boundary conditions and extract the dimensionless parameters by inspection.*† *If the governing equations and conditions employed are complete and appropriate, the parameters found must be a necessary and sufficient set for modeling procedures.* To clarify this assertion, consider its implications in the present problem. Equation (4.1*b*) was purposely formulated so that it has the same form for all problems of this class. Since the boundary conditions in the normalized coordinates contain no parameters, the solution depends only on the parameters

$$\left(\frac{L}{M}\right)^2 \qquad \left(\frac{L}{N}\right)^2 \qquad \text{and} \qquad \frac{L^2}{t_c\alpha}$$

and the dimensionless variables $\bar{x}$, $\bar{y}$, $\bar{z}$, and $\bar{t}$. If we examine a fixed point in a particular system (given by fixed values of $\bar{x}$, $\bar{y}$, $\bar{z}$, and $\bar{t}$), we must obtain a unique value of $\bar{T}$ under the conditions assumed, provided only that the values of

$$\left(\frac{L}{M}\right)^2 \qquad \left(\frac{L}{N}\right)^2 \qquad \text{and} \qquad \frac{L^2}{t_c\alpha}$$

† Many workers have used this or closely related procedures to solve specific problems. The earliest formal treatment known to the author is that due to Ruark,[44] who calls the procedure *inspectional analysis.* Ruark's discussion has been expanded by Birkhoff.[5] However, Ruark gives only a small fraction of the many types of results which can be achieved, and Birkhoff states the procedure is merely "suggestive." Neither Ruark nor Birkhoff provide a discussion of when and how the procedure can be made rigorous, nor do they provide systematic procedures covering use of the boundary conditions or consideration of the magnitude of terms.

are fixed. Accordingly, we define *equivalent points* in two systems of a given class as points given by equal values of the nondimensional variables $\bar{x}$, $\bar{y}$, $\bar{z}$, and $\bar{t}$. It follows that equivalent points in any two systems of the same class will exhibit similar behavior under the conditions stated, provided the value of

$$\left(\frac{L}{M}\right)^2 \qquad \left(\frac{L}{N}\right)^2 \qquad \text{and} \qquad \frac{L^2}{t_c\alpha}$$

are the same for the two systems. If we denote the nondimensional temperature at any arbitrary point in the body as $\bar{T}_j$, we can then express this result as

$$\bar{T}_j = \bar{T}_j\left(\frac{L^2}{M^2}, \frac{L^2}{N^2}, \frac{L^2}{t_c\alpha}\right) \tag{4.2}$$

Since Eq. (4.2) holds for every point in the body, it is possible to state an explicit answer based on the normalized equation for the similarity and dimensional-analysis problems. To solve the dimensional-analysis problem, it is necessary only to read off the parameters from the normalized governing equation and boundary conditions. Thus from Eq. (4.1b) one finds the pi's to be

$$\pi_1 = \frac{L^2}{M^2}$$

$$\pi_2 = \frac{L^2}{N^2}$$

$$\pi_3 = \frac{L^2}{t_c\alpha}$$

To obtain the similarity rule, we again recall that the problem stated that all points in the body were to be held above a certain minimum temperature for a specified time to insure cooking. From Eqs. (4.1) and (4.2) we can conclude that $\bar{T}_j$ for any two bodies of this type will reach the same value when π_1, π_2, and π_3 have the same values. Since the least cooking will take place at the center of the body, we write Eq. (4.2) for the center point. We again observe that for geometrically similar bodies the specific requirement for total cooking time is that which yields a given π_3 plus a fixed cooking time t_o. Thus, as in Ex. (2.2), we obtain $t_{\min} = t_f + t_o$; t_f is found from the condition that $\pi_3 = $ constant and from the values of L and α for the body. As already noted, bodies described need not be totally geometrically similar. The pi's given are sufficient for any problem in this class and hence for any body whose appropriate thicknesses can be characterized by the dimensions L, M, and N alone.

This remark is useful, since we can readily find explicit mathematical solutions to Eq. (4.1) only when the boundary conditions can be expressed in quite simple form. If the outline of the body is even moderately irregular, computation of the complete temperature-time history will usually require considerable computer time. In such instances the similarity properties just developed, unlike those found in Chaps. 2 and 3, are sufficient to provide many answers without detailed computations.

We have already stressed that the form of the nondimensional variables chosen for normalization is important. It is instructive in this connection to pursue the cooking problem a little further using another form of the variables. Suppose we make only the simplest change in the variables, a shift in the datum temperature to some value other than T_a. Call the new datum temperature T_d. If we retain the same definition of $\bar{T}$, $\bar{x}$, $\bar{y}$, $\bar{z}$, and $\bar{t}$, the differential equation (4.1b) is unaltered, since it involves only derivatives of $\bar{T}$ and hence is independent of datum. This can be checked by direct substitution. The boundary conditions, however, become:

$$
\begin{aligned}
&\text{at } t = -0: & \bar{T} &= 1 \\
&\text{at } t = +0: & \left.\begin{array}{l} \bar{x} = 0,1 \\ \bar{y} = 0,1 \\ \bar{z} = 0,1 \end{array}\right\} &\text{at the surface} \quad \bar{T} = \frac{T_a - T_d}{T_i - T_d}
\end{aligned}
$$

The solution will now depend on the parameter $(T_a - T_d)/(T_i - T_d)$, as well as on the three parameters found previously. Thus a simple shift in datum complicates the solution to the similarity problem; only carefully chosen coordinates yield optimum answers. Usually there is a physical motivation for such choices. In this instance, one measures temperature from the equilibrium, or steady-state, value T_a. However, there are no general rules, and in many cases it helps to try more than one set of coordinates to see which set gives the most useful results.

In the example above we have shown that when a complete, appropriate set of governing equations and boundary conditions is known, normalization can provide a rigorous solution to the canonical problem of dimensional analysis or similitude. This procedure provides more explicit forms of the parameters; it also provides a basis for one type of distorted model and includes the definition of permissible distortions. This by no means exhausts the possibilities inherent in study of the governing equations without explicit solution. However, before additional procedures are discussed, it is important to make clearer what is meant by complete and appropriate governing equations and boundary conditions. This problem is discussed in the following section.

4-3 CONDITIONS REQUIRED FOR RIGOROUS SOLUTION OF THE CANONICAL PROBLEM OF SIMILITUDE AND DIMENSIONAL ANALYSIS USING NORMALIZED GOVERNING EQUATIONS

In Sec. 4-2, a "rigorous" solution to the cooking problem was given; however, this solution rests on the assumption that the governing equations and conditions employed are complete and appropriate. It is now necessary to give operational meaning to this phrase. We shall use the the term *complete* to describe the requisite physical conditions and the term *appropriate* to describe the required mathematical conditions. Each of these has two parts. The mathematical and physical conditions must parallel each other in many ways, and they often give hints or information about each other. Nevertheless, it is convenient to discuss them separately.

The word complete implies first that enough independent equations have been set so that a solution for the dependent variable(s) is possible. Thus the number of independent equations must, in general, equal the number of dependent variables.

The word complete also implies that the mathematical model inherent in the equations employed does represent the physical problem with sufficient accuracy in the region of interest. It must be emphasized that the equations always deal with a mathematical model, not reality. Some models are better than others, but all retain some degree of uncertainty and inaccuracy. The degree of inaccuracy we can accept depends on the circumstances; thus complete implies that all the really important physical effects are contained in our mathematical model. For example, the effects enumerated in connection with Eq. (4.1*a*) in Sec. 4-2 must include all the relevant energy terms, and the terms, as written, must be accurate expressions of these effects. It would seem at first glance as if this is begging the question, but such is not the case, provided we are willing to admit the validity of the scientific method. The scientific method is founded squarely on the idea that nature, not man, is the ultimate arbiter. In order to check any scientific hypothesis—be it a logical proposition, concept, or a mathematical equation—the scientific method admits of only one course of action. We must compare the hypothesis, or its deductive consequences, with measured performance of the actual systems to which it relates. Thus, if the equation we are using is one we have newly derived, we should have considerable doubt about its adequacy. If, on the other hand, it has been available in the literature for a long time, and if it has been verified by many careful observers at a number of different places within the domain we are considering, then we can be relatively certain that it is reliable. Since the method is inductive, we can never reach complete certainty, but we can almost always distinguish whether we have a high or a low plausibility of accurate prediction. Indeed, in relatively well-established fields the governing equations and the boundary conditions bring to bear a truly vast body of accumulated evidence. Consider the heat equation employed in Example 4.1; this equation has a long history going back to Fourier. When first published it was very properly subjected to scientific skepticism and argument, but over the years the conditions under which it holds have been systematically refined and checked by comparison with many, many experiments by many independent observers, and have been cross-checked and verified over and over again. Since the method is inductive, it is always possible that exceptions may be found, and the region of validity for Eq. (4.1a) will, accordingly, have to be further redefined or narrowed. However, this is no longer likely. We know today with considerable assurance the kind of system for which Eq. (4.1a) governs the behavior; this includes even the accuracy with which we can measure the physical parameters involved, and hence the accuracy with which theoretical predictions will compare to measurements.

The term appropriate has been used in Sec. 4-2 to imply what many mathematicians call a "well-posed" problem; it refers particularly to the boundary conditions. It is well known that certain types of equations require certain kinds and numbers of boundary conditions in order to obtain a unique solution or even any solution at all. We say that a problem is well posed if (1) a unique solution exists for the equation with the boundary conditions as set and (2) the solution is continuously dependent on the boundary conditions, that is, small alterations in the magnitude of the boundary conditions create only small changes in the solution.

The requirement for existence of a solution is important, since if no solution exists to the equations and boundary conditions as set, then we cannot conclude that the parameters involved are correct. This remark has nothing to do with the existence of a physical solution. We have a physical problem and some physical action results; thus we are forced to the belief that some physical solution does exist. But if the *equation* with the boundary condition set does not have a solution, then it cannot describe the real physical problem to which a solution (that is, a behavior of the dependent variable) does exist. If the equations are known to be complete on the grounds just described, we normally expect that there will be a solution which describes the dependent variable(s) in terms of the independent variables of the equations alone.† The primary question then becomes, "Have we chosen appropriate boundary conditions?"

† This is merely an expectation based on experience; it is by no means a proof.

Unfortunately, these questions of existence of solutions in the case of most interest (nonlinear partial differential equations) are by no means simple. It is not possible to cover the available theorems in this book, and in many cases they are lacking entirely. The reader who is concerned with specific problems of this type should turn for assistance to the standard works on advanced partial differential equations† or to consultations with applied mathematicians. However, we can, where appropriate, cite the required proofs or the lack thereof in specific examples.

For instance, in the case of the heat equation (4.1*a*) with the boundary conditions given in Eq. (4.1*b*), an existence theorem is known.†

It is appropriate here to recall that in some of the examples of Chap. 3 we employed linear algebraic governing equations. In such cases a unique solution exists, provided (1) the number of equations is equal to the number of unknowns and (2) the equations are independent. The second condition is given explicitly in terms of the nonvanishing value of the Jacobian. Independence of the equations can also be expected, but not proven, from the physical independence of the ideas they describe.

One other factor operates in our favor: the complete equations for macroscopic systems, in general, involve terms describing forces, energies, and properties. The values of these quantities are nearly always continuous and differentiable; accordingly, we expect that the complete mathematical models will have these properties. This argument is clearly only an expectation, not a proof, since the term complete is always relative. Moreover, even this expectation frequently fails if we simplify the complete equations by dropping terms, as we shall see in Secs. 4-6 and 4-7.

Nevertheless, it is a matter of common experience that the worst forms of mathematically "pathological behavior" seldom occur in what we have called complete equations describing the macroscopic behavior of nature. This makes it very profitable for the researcher to try solutions under the assumption that the mathematical conditions he needs are fulfilled and then check later. In our case, what this implies is that we can seek model laws by the procedures of normalization even when existence theorems are not known, with the expectation that the procedure will give correct results a very large percentage of the time if our equations are complete. In such cases, we must bear in mind that the laws so found must be checked against experiment before final acceptance.

Similar remarks apply to the question of uniqueness of the solutions. To guarantee from mathematical grounds that two systems will have similar behavior, we must show that the solution not only exists but also is unique. However, this is often difficult, and few theorems for nonlinear partial differential equations are available. Moreover, if more than

---

† See, for example, Courant and Hilbert[11] or R. V. Churchill, "Fourier Series and Boundary Value Problems," chap. 6, McGraw-Hill Book Company, New York, 1941.

two solutions exist, then we must determine which solution is more stable and what initial conditions are needed to guarantee similarity.

Again it is often desirable to rely on an expectation based on physical knowledge. In this question of uniqueness we rely on the close relation between the stability of physical systems and the uniqueness of mathematical solutions. There are two cases of particular interest.

Suppose first that we can actually establish from mathematical considerations that more than one solution is possible. Then we can usually assume that the most stable solution will be the one found in nature. Indeed, we can often purposely perturb the system to insure that this will be so. If the actual solutions, or even their general form, is known, then we also have a number of minimum principles, based primarily on the Second Law of Thermodynamics, which can be used to show which solution is the most stable. However, in fractional analysis we do not usually know the solution, and we must then fall back on the expectation that the most stable solution is the one which will almost always be found in nature.

Second, consider cases in which we cannot establish uniqueness from mathematical grounds at all, that is, we cannot establish a theorem to tell us whether a unique solution is to be expected. However, if the equations are known to be complete, we again expect that a solution does exist, and we can then ask the necessary question directly of nature by an experiment. That is, we observe directly whether two systems do exhibit the same general type of behavior. This is particularly important when we are comparing systems of the same class but of a different physical nature. Usually, the amount of physical data needed is quite small, since gross changes in the behavior normally occur between one solution and another. Consider, for example, the question of phase stability of a pure fluid; it takes only minimal observation to determine whether the liquid or gas phase is more stable and actually occurs at a given temperature and pressure. Thus a few crude observations are often sufficient. As we shall see in Sec. 4-6, this same type of crude data is often of crucial importance in approximation theory, for much the same reasons.

In summary, we can guarantee similar behavior of systems from the governing equations only when the equations are physically complete and mathematically appropriate. Since establishment of the physical completeness is inductive, we can never be completely certain about it; however, we can be certain to precisely the same degree that we can predict any solution at all about the class of problem discussed. In many cases, the outcome can be predicted with a very high degree of assurance. Indeed, all we are really saying here is that nothing is a dead certainty in science; everything is subjected finally to the ultimate test of a check against performance. In some cases, this check is more crucial than in others, since the degree of assurance which can be provided by past checks and by the general theorems available from mathematics both vary from one case to another.

In the cases where both the physics and the mathematics are well known, we can predict model laws from normalized equations with as much rigor as we can achieve in predicting anything. In cases where the completeness of the equations is in more doubt or where the necessary mathematical theorems are lacking, we can still seek such laws with the expectation that they will usually be correct, but more checking will be needed. In either event, if we use the best available equations, we should expect to get the most reliable answers that can be furnished on the basis of current knowledge. Like all expert knowledge, it may turn out to be wrong once in a while, but the probability is in our favor compared to other procedures.

Thus the sensible course of action seems to be to normalize enough equations and also enough boundary conditions to provide a well-posed mathematical problem. This procedure also provides several important bonuses, as we shall see. It requires the analytical worker to consider just what is needed to obtain a rigorous similarity or model law; this suggests what additional information should be sought and also advises about the urgency of a check. The procedure also almost automatically discloses other information of importance about the physics and mathematics of the problem and provides the basis for many other useful procedures in fractional analysis. We turn next to the study of these other matters.

4-4   BASIS OF IMPROVED CORRELATIONS

a.   *General Basis*

As a first application of the ideas developed in Secs. 4-2 and 4-3, we will consider the general problem of how correlations can be improved by study of the governing equations and conditions and then apply the ideas to the special case of homogeneous equations.

We have already seen in the example of Sec. 4-2 that different choices of nondimensional variables give results of differing utility. We do not know in advance which will be the most useful set to choose. However, it is obvious at the outset that the fewer parameters required to specify similar behavior the more useful the result will be.† We also know from the discussion of Secs. 4-2 and 4-3 that the parameters contained in a complete and appropriate set of governing equations in standard normalized form must be sufficient to describe the similarity behavior of the class

† If this is not entirely clear, see Sec. 2-4.

of systems described over the domain of interest. This is true no matter how we transform the variables in the equation; this fact leads to a very important idea that we will use in many of the procedures that follow.

> If we can find transformations of the governing equations in standard normalized form that reduce the number of parameters in the equations and conditions, then more useful similarity laws can be expressed.

Indeed, this idea can be carried further. If we can find transformations of variables that reduce the number of variables or reduce the number of variables and parameters together in both the equations *and* the conditions, then we have established useful simplifications that can be used to express other types of similarity. We have not yet dealt with these types of similarity, but will do so in Sec. 4-10.

To clarify the idea expressed we again use the example of Sec. 4-2.

b. Homogeneous Equations

In solving the cooking problem by the pi theorem a troublesome matter arose. We found that we did not need a parameter representing the dependent variable, temperature, even though the general pi theorem procedure suggests that we do. Examination of the procedures used to solve this same problem in Sec. 4-2 shows why this is so and leads to useful theorems covering this behavior in other cases.

Normalizing the equations and conditions in Sec. 4-2 involves a special case of improved correlations by reduction in number of parameters. In the original physical equation (4.1a) the parameter T_i appears in the boundary conditions. However, if we normalize on properly chosen coordinates, T_i does not appear in either the equation or the boundary conditions in the normalized form; this is shown explicitly by Eq. (4.1b). As we showed in the example, this will not occur in all coordinates, but there is at least one set of coordinates in which a solution can be expressed independent of the magnitude of T_i; such a set is given explicitly by Eq. (4.2), and it leads directly to the solution of the similitude problem.

Examination of the steps of normalization between Eqs. (4.1a) and (4.1b) shows that the parameter representing the dependent variable will in fact cancel from the equation in the normalization process whenever the equation is homogeneous in the dependent variable. Indeed, this is just the test for homogeneity in the mathematical sense.† It is useful to state this result in the form of a theorem.

---

† Homogeneity is usually defined as follows. If upon insertion of the quantity λx for x in a given equation, λ identically cancels, then the equation is said to be homogeneous in x. In our example we need only set $\lambda = 1/T_i$ to observe Eq. (4.1a) homogeneous in T.

Theorem 1

If the governing equations are homogeneous in a given variable, and if the boundary conditions can be expressed in standard normalized form independent of a parameter representing this same variable, then similitude laws can be found which are independent of the scale of that variable.

The proof of this theorem has already been given by the reasoning in Sec. 4-4a and the definition of homogeneity. A similar theorem can be given for physical parameters and dependent variables; its proof has also, in effect, been given.

Theorem 2

If a given parameter appears to the same power in each term of the governing equations, and if this parameter does not appear in the boundary conditions of the normalized equations in standard form, then the solution for the dependent variable is independent of the given parameter, and such a parameter can be excluded from the specification of similarity in appropriate coordinates.

A few remarks concerning these theorems are in order.

Homogeneity is far more common in the dependent than independent variables because of the usual form of differential equations (look, for example, at the form of x, y, z, and t in Eq. 4.1a).

It is specifically noted that homogeneity, not linearity, is the sufficient condition for the purpose of Theorems 1 and 2. For example, if a constant term, not including temperature, were added to Eq. (4.1a), then the requirements of Theorem 1 would not be fulfilled and we would not find similarity laws independent of the scale of T. On the other hand, Theorem 1 can be fulfilled in nonlinear equations if, for example, each term contains products of the dependent variable to the second or some higher power.

Regarding Theorem 2, we can see that it specifically covers the cancellation of mass in the pendulum problem of Example 2.5. In that problem mass occurs to the first power in each term, since the restoring force, gravity, is proportional to the mass of the pendulum. It must also be observed that Theorem 2 will cover such behavior in instances where it would not be found from the pi theorem alone. Such cases may occur whenever all the dimensions of the parameter also appeared in other parameters and/or variables in the governing equations or boundary conditions. In this case, the parameter might still cancel because of the form of the equations and conditions, but the cancellation would not be found by the pi theorem.

Finally, the discussion of Sec. 4-4*a* and Theorems 1 and 2 clearly emphasizes important reasons for normalizing the governing equations and conditions and then extracting the parameters from them to solve problems in similitude, rather than merely inspecting the original physical equation as has sometimes been suggested. If inspection of the original physical equations is employed, the improvements, that is, the reduction in number of parameters and/or variables made possible by special circumstances such as homogeneity, will, in general, be overlooked. The results thus obtained will not be wrong, but they will contain more parameters than are necessary. This largely defeats the purposes of correlations and the use of nondimensional variables. By performing more than one normalization, we also bring out, explicitly, the advantage of one set of nondimensional coordinates over another.

4-5 RELATIONS AMONG ELEMENTARY PROCESSES

a. Model Laws, Similitude, and Analogues

The discussion of Secs. 4-3 and 4-4 shows that we can employ the governing equations and boundary conditions to find the governing parameters and similarity rules. While we cannot guarantee that the solutions found in this way always will be rigorous, they usually will be in a particularly useful and relatively complete form, and they are the best we can do with currently available knowledge. Moreover, these processes make particularly clear the nature of model laws and similarity. It is accordingly helpful to recapitulate the relations between model laws, similarity, governing parameters, and analogues, keeping in mind these processes relating to the governing equations.

Solving a similitude problem is virtually the same as finding the governing parameters. The only distinction is the form of the two results. Finding the governing parameters, in general, requires the following approach.

The governing independent pi's in this problem are π_2, π_3, and π_4. The value of these pi's is sufficient to fix the value of the dependent group π_1 at any given point in the domain of the solution.

In comparison, the similarity rule requires this sort of statement.

In order for the solution to two problems of the same class to be the same (similar), it is sufficient that the value of all the independent pi's π_2, π_3, and π_4 be the same in the two problems.

In both cases, in order to prove the statement is correct, the conditions enumerated in Sec. 4-3 must be satisfied. Moreover, it is relatively easy to find what adjustments must be made among the parameters to provide similar behavior once the structure of the pi's is known in detail in either of the statements above.

Model problems and analogue methods are essentially the same problem set in still another guise. In model work, one tries to predict the performance of some final system called the *prototype* from tests on the performance of some other actual system called the *model*. For such work to be useful, two conditions must be fulfilled: (1) it must be easier and/or cheaper to determine the desired results on the model than on the prototype, and (2) it must be possible to predict the performance of the prototype from that of the model accurately. The first condition is normally fulfilled, otherwise there would be no point in using a model. However, the second point needs further discussion.

A model may be an alternative version of the same system built on a smaller scale. For example, in the cooking problem it might be a smaller solid body which would have a quicker response and could therefore be tested with greater ease. However, a model can also be a completely different type of system. In this case, it is usually called an *analogue*. For example, in some cases of the cooking problem an electric transmission line could be used. There are many ways in which such models or analogues can be found; however, we are concerned at the moment with whether the normalized equations can be used for the establishment of rules predicting prototype behavior from model or analogue behavior. This can be accomplished readily as already shown; the following reasoning demonstrates the basis more specifically.

If the equations and conditions are complete and appropriate in the sense of Sec. 4-3, the normalized governing equations and boundary conditions must contain solutions which will predict the behavior of the system accurately for all problems of interest. Since the only change from one problem of the class to another is in the value of the pi's, it follows that any two problems which have the same value of the pi's in the normalized equations and boundary conditions will have the same behavior. Thus to employ a model it is sufficient to find a convenient problem in the class considered which can be made to assume the same values of each of the pi's in a complete and appropriate set of normalized equations and boundary conditions. This does not mean the same value of each quantity found in any pi, but merely equality of each of the overall pi's, since the solution can be given in terms of them alone. In the problem above this would mean that the model and prototype must have at least the same value of Fourier number, and also of $(L/M)^2$ and $(L/N)^2$ (if these length ratios are sufficient to describe the body).

Such a model law depends on the same factors as the similarity problem, so it can also be made as rigorous as the knowledge of the complete equations and boundary conditions for the problem. That is, the remarks of Sec. 4-3 on rigor and assurance of solution are again directly applicable. In addition, such model laws are not restricted to geometrically similar systems or to other requirements of this type. If a means can be found for ensuring that two systems will have the same normalized equations and boundary conditions with the same value of the pi's which appear in these equations, then similarity of behavior is assured up to the extent indicated in Sec. 4-3.

b. An Alternative Procedure

A number of authors have used a "scaling" procedure† to determine similarity laws from differential equations. It can be shown that this procedure yields similar results but is weaker than the one suggested in Sec. 4-2; the demonstration follows.

In scaling, one tries to find scale factors that will make two systems in a given class of problems behave in a similar fashion. One assumes each variable in one system can be written as a scale factor times the same variable in the second system. Each scale factor is initially taken as independent. The requisite ratios among them are then determined by requiring that a substitution into the differential equation for the first system by the variables representing the second system result in no change in the differential equation. For example, in the cooking problem we have discussed in Examples 2.2 and 3.3, we would define

$$\lambda_T T_1 = T_2$$
$$\lambda_t t_1 = t_2$$
$$\lambda_x x_1 = x_2$$
$$\lambda_y y_1 = y_2$$
$$\lambda_z z_1 = z_2$$

where the subscript 1 stands for the first system, 2 for the second system, and the λ's are the scale factors. The DE for the first system is:

$$\frac{\partial^2 T_1}{\partial x_1^2} + \frac{\partial^2 T_1}{\partial y_1^2} + \frac{\partial^2 T_1}{\partial z_1^2} = \frac{1}{\alpha}\frac{\partial T_1}{\partial t_1}$$

Formal substitution of the variables for the second system into the equations yields

$$\frac{\lambda_T}{\lambda_x^2}\frac{\partial^2 T_2}{\partial x_2^2} + \frac{\lambda_T}{\lambda_y^2}\frac{\partial^2 T_2}{\partial y_2^2} + \frac{\lambda_T}{\lambda_z^2}\frac{\partial^2 T_2}{\partial z_2^2} = \frac{\lambda_T}{\alpha\lambda_t}\frac{\partial T_2}{\partial t_2}$$

dividing by λ_T/λ_x^2 gives

$$\frac{\partial^2 T_2}{\partial x_2^2} + \frac{\lambda_x^2}{\lambda_y^2}\frac{\partial^2 T_2}{\partial y_2^2} + \frac{\lambda_x^2}{\lambda_z^2}\frac{\partial^2 T_2}{\partial z_2^2} = \frac{\lambda_x^2}{\alpha\lambda_t}\frac{\partial T_2}{\partial t_2}$$

† See, for example, Refs. 37, 18, and 20.

The requirements for similarity are then

$$\left(\frac{\lambda_x}{\lambda_y}\right)^2 = 1 \tag{4.3a}$$

$$\left(\frac{\lambda_x}{\lambda_z}\right)^2 = 1 \tag{4.3b}$$

$$\left(\frac{\lambda_x^2}{\alpha\lambda_t}\right) = 1 \tag{4.3c}$$

Scaling procedures usually stop at this point. However, the λ's represent the scale factors between system 1 and 2, and if we recall that the scales for each should be measured in terms of the boundary conditions and system size, then the Eqs. (4.3) result in

$$\left(\frac{L_1}{L_2}\frac{M_2}{M_1}\right)^2 = 1 \qquad \text{or} \qquad \pi_1 = \text{constant} \tag{4.4a}$$

$$\left(\frac{L_1}{L_2}\frac{N_2}{N_1}\right)^2 = 1 \qquad \text{or} \qquad \pi_2 = \text{constant} \tag{4.4b}$$

and

$$\left(\frac{L_1}{L_2}\right)^2 \frac{t_{c2}(\alpha)}{t_{c1}(\alpha)} = 1 \qquad \text{or} \qquad \pi_3 = \text{constant} \tag{4.4c}$$

Thus Eqs. (4.3) give the same results as normalization but in less complete form because the scale factors are left undefined. In order to translate the results into a form in which they actually can be applied to a given system, the scale factors must be determined. Moreover, the scale factors used must really characterize the system; if arbitrary scales are used, even though they appear in the problem, all problems of the class may not be represented in the same way. Under these conditions, there is no assurance that similarity will really be achieved.

Another difficulty in examples of scaling procedures in the literature is that in many cases such procedures have been applied to the governing equations but not to the boundary conditions. As has been emphasized repeatedly, the boundary conditions must also be brought to standard size, and parameters sometimes occur in the boundary conditions in addition to those arising from the equations.† Serious errors in important technical problems have occurred in at least one field due to the use of scaling procedures on governing equations without concomitant study of the changes occurring in the boundary conditions. It is, of course, possible to study the boundary conditions also using scaling procedures, but the suggestion to do so is not implicit in the scaling procedure as it is in the normalization suggested in Sec. 4-2.

† The importance of this point becomes even clearer in Example 4.7, where more complex boundary conditions for this problem are examined.

While the choice between the method of Sec. 4-2 and a test for invariance of both the equation and boundary conditions is thus in part a matter of preference, normalization brings out additional information on such matters as cancellation of homogeneous parameters. It is also preferred by the author, since it provides a form of the governing equations which is immediately useful for several other purposes as shown below.

c. *A Remark on Force Ratios*

A number of workers have raised a question regarding the interpretation of governing parameters as force ratios as employed in Chap. 3. For example, Dr. L. H. Smith[48] has very properly objected to the interpretation of the conventional Reynolds number as the ratio of inertia to viscous stresses.† In discussion of these remarks, Prof. G. F. Wislicenus attributed to L. Prandtl[40] the following opinion: Reynolds number does not always equal the ratio of inertia to viscous stress, hence it is correct to say only that when two systems are geometrically similar and have the same Reynolds number, the ratio of inertia to viscous stress is the same in both flows.

In his notes Smith[48] has posed the question of whether a stronger statement can be made. As we have already stated in Chap. 3 (pages 56 and 57), this can be done under the proper conditions. The appropriate conditions follow from the results of Secs. 4-3 and 4-2.

Two remarks are pertinent. First, as was stressed in Chap. 3, unless the Reynolds number is formed properly, it assuredly will not represent the ratio of inertia to viscous stress, and what is proper for one problem may not be for another. The mere selection of proper units may not even guarantee similarity, as indicated by the statement of Wislicenus. If, to take an absurd example for emphasis, we form the Reynolds number with the length of the left foot of King Henry VIII, the form of the dimensionless group will be that of a Reynolds number, but it will not tell us very much about any problem in fluid mechanics.

Second, if we follow the procedure suggested in Sec. 4-2, or some equivalent procedure, to bring the terms in the variables of the governing equations to approximately unit magnitude and divide by the coefficient of one term, then the parameters must represent the ratios of the important effects, whether they are forces, energies, or other quantities. This follows from the fact that the governing equations express the magnitude of these terms by construction. Moreover, if the magnitudes hold for all points in the domain under consideration, then the parameters must express the ratio of forces or the other relevant quantities at all points

† Reynolds number is a typical enample; analogous remarks apply to governing parameters in general.

within the domain. Note that the parameters so formed will involve the specific boundary conditions and system sizes, hence they will vary in form from one problem to another. It cannot be expected that they will always be in some conventional arbitrary form. However, when the parameters found by this type of normalization do differ from the conventional forms, they will tell us more about the problem in hand than the conventional forms. Further examples as well as a discussion of the validity of estimates of magnitude appear in Secs. 4-6 to 4-9.

d. Relation among Dimensional Analysis, Governing Equations, and Boundary Conditions; Internal and External Similarity

It has been repeatedly shown that it is necessary to employ not only the differential equations but also the boundary conditions and system sizes to find complete, rigorous solutions to problems in similitude. It has also been emphasized that some kind of governing groups can be found by use of any characteristic quantities to nondimensionalize the governing equations, but that the utility of the results is crucially dependent on the particular choice of characteristic quantities. The more closely the chosen quantities represent the system in kind and magnitude, the better the results achieved. From this point of view it is then not surprising that the boundary conditions of the problem and the size of the system domain are logical starting places to seek the characteristic quantities for normalization.

Inspection of the example of Sec. 4.2 will, in fact, show that the nondimensional parameters are not composed of the variables in the sense used here, but rather are made up from system sizes, boundary values, and the physical constants of the system. Since it is the parameters which are of concern in dimensional analysis, it is clear that dimensional analysis in the sense of Chap. 2 is closely related to the boundary data and system sizes, and any procedure which omits this information is not likely to prove fruitful in similitude problems. In this context the reason we avoided the use of the word *variables* in discussing the pi theorem can be seen. If the word variable is used in connection with the pi theorem, a semantic confusion is unavoidable in relating the pi theorem method to methods based on governing equations.

The importance of boundary conditions is also evident from the purely mathematical viewpoint. Since we are dealing with partial differential equations, a change in boundary conditions means a change in the form of the solution and may involve a change in solution magnitudes. In this case, the normalization appropriate for a given problem may not be appropriate for another problem with changed boundary conditions. Indeed, if we fail to reduce all problems in the class to standard magnitudes, we cannot even guarantee similar behavior based on the parameters found in the equation. Moreover, in many instances a change in boundary conditions gives rise to new parameters, since we must include parameters appearing in the normalized boundary conditions as well as those in the governing equations.

All these remarks again emphasize that studying the governing equations alone without concomitant study of an appropriate set of boundary conditions will be very limiting in any similitude problem. Unfortunately, this point has been overlooked in many discussions. This has led to a much poorer appraisal of methods based on the governing equations than might otherwise have occurred. A notable exception on this point is the discussion of L. I. Sedov.[46] Sedov has achieved many useful and advanced results in part because of his explicit recognition that the necessary and sufficient number of parameters is always those needed to solve for the dependent variables and/or parameters of interest; he consequently routinely sets appropriate initial and/or boundary value data in the sense of Sec. 4-3.

At this point, it is useful to discuss the difference between *internal* and *external* similitude. All the procedures we have discussed in Chaps. 2 and 3 deal only with external similitude, in the sense that they relate performance in one system to performance in another system of the same class. As we have seen, external similitude can be given in terms of the parameters alone.

Use of the governing equations and conditions provides a framework in which the rigor, or lack thereof, can be better established for such external similitude. Moreover, it also allows study of the variables and hence of fruitful combinations of the variables and/or parameters. This possibility leads us to several more advanced topics, including a consideration of magnitudes (approximation theory) and the search for improved correlations through absorption of parameters and reduction in the number of variables and/or parameters. As will be shown in Sec. 4-10, the establishment of governing equations and conditions containing a reduced number of variables immediately provides relations between certain points within the system and hence leads to the establishment of *internal similarity* properties of the system. The reduction in the number of parameters by combining with variables leads to a rigorous basis for distorted models, that is, models that do not obey geometric similarity. Sections 4-6 to 4-9 deal with approximation theory and necessarily involve more difficult mathematics than has been required thus far. The reader who is primarily interested in model theory and/or similitude and who desires to avoid the mathematical complications of approximation theory may want to turn directly to Sec. 4-10, which contains discussion of two other types of similitude and modeling which are different from the external similitude thus far discussed.

4-6   APPROXIMATION THEORY

Frequently in engineering work it is not feasible to model all aspects of the behavior of the prototype; it then becomes important to determine under what conditions some pi groups can be neglected.   Similarly, in many instances we are able to write the governing equations and appropriate boundary conditions but are unable to find a desired analytical solution.   In both these situations it is very helpful to employ a normalized equation to examine the order of magnitude of the individual terms either for a particular problem or for various special assumptions defining groups of problems.

Again using the cooking problem as an example, we recall that we tried to make each term in the nondimensional *variables* in Eq. (4.1*b*) approximately unity in magnitude.   Assuming we were successful, it then would be possible to compare the magnitude of the terms by examining the magnitude of the pi groups.   If any of these are small compared to the others, we can attempt to drop them from our model correlation. We also drop the associated terms from the equation to see if we can find a simpler approximate equation that still gives a satisfactory solution. This procedure with its limitations and conditions is called *approximation theory*.   Approximation theory is a very powerful tool for many engineering and scientific problems; on the other hand, it is also mathematically notorious for the many pitfalls which may be encountered.   Instead of considering these pitfalls at the outset, we will proceed once again to give a simple illustration using the cooking problem; this problem is free from serious mathematical difficulties.   After this illustration is completed, a more systematic discussion of the bases of the subject is given.

a.   Extension to New Classes of Information by Approximation Theory

Example 4.2.   Consider again the cooking problem shown in Fig. 4.1. Again we seek to model the cooking time after the body is placed in an oven. It is required that all parts of the body be held above a given temperature for a specified time.   The initial temperature of the body is T_i throughout, and the oven temperature is constant at T_a.   We insert the body into the oven at time $t = 0$.   The temperature at any point on the surface of the body is denoted as T_s.   The governing differential equation for the temperature distribution in the body is well known; it is the Fourier equation of heat conduction

$$\frac{\partial^2 T}{\partial x^2} + \frac{\partial^2 T}{\partial y^2} + \frac{\partial^2 T}{\partial z^2} = \frac{1}{\alpha}\frac{\partial T}{\partial t}$$

Boundary conditions applicable are:

at $t = -0$: $T = T_i$

at $t = +0$: $\left.\begin{array}{l} x = 0,L \\ y = 0,M \\ z = 0,N \end{array}\right\}$ at the surface $T = T_s$

But T_s is itself unknown and must be determined from the rate equation for convection from the oven air to the surface of the body. Since the surface cannot store energy, the heat rate by convection to it must equal the rate of conduction into the body. This condition gives

$$hA(T_a - T_s) = kA \left(\frac{\partial T}{\partial n}\right)_{\text{surface}} \tag{4.5}$$

where n = normal to the surface.

Defining as before

$$\bar{x} = \frac{x}{L}$$

$$\bar{y} = \frac{y}{M}$$

$$\bar{z} = \frac{z}{N}$$

$$\bar{T} = \frac{T - T_a}{T_i - T_a}$$

and also

$$\bar{T}_s = \frac{T_s - T_a}{T_s - T_i} \tag{4.6}$$

$$\bar{n} = \frac{n}{l/2}$$

where l = smallest of L, M, and N. Then on normalizing we obtain the rate equations for heat flow at the surface

$$\tau \triangleq \frac{T_a - T_s}{T_s - T_i} = \frac{2k}{hl}\left(\frac{\partial \bar{T}_s}{\partial \bar{n}}\right)_{\text{surface}} \tag{4.7}$$

Equation (4.7) defines τ, the temperature ratio of interest in determining T_s. Moreover, we have constructed $(\partial \bar{T}/\partial \bar{n})_{\text{surface}}$ to be the same for all problems of this class and of magnitude unity.† Consequently, if the

---

† Justification for the remarks on magnitude appears in Sec. 4-6b. In this problem our attempt to make all terms in the variables approximately unity does succeed over the whole domain of interest; this is what makes the problem free of pitfalls.

Biot number $= hl/2k \gg 1$, then the temperature at the surface immediately approaches T_a and the problem is essentially one of pure conduction. If $hl/2k \ll 1$, then the problem is primarily one of convection. Finally, if $hl/2k \simeq 1$, then both convection and conduction are important. These are the same conclusions reached in Example 3.2, but they have been made quantitative in terms of the nondimensional parameter of concern $hl/2k$.

In order to continue the solution further, it is useful for the moment to suppose that the Biot number is large compared to unity on all faces of the solid. This reduces the problem to one of pure conduction; the appropriate equation and boundary conditions then become

$$\frac{\partial^2 \bar{T}}{\partial \bar{x}^2} + \left(\frac{L}{M}\right)^2 \frac{\partial^2 \bar{T}}{\partial \bar{y}^2} + \left(\frac{L}{N}\right)^2 \frac{\partial^2 \bar{T}}{\partial \bar{z}^2} = \left(\frac{L^2}{t_c \alpha}\right) \frac{\partial \bar{T}}{\partial \bar{t}} \tag{4.1b}$$

$$\text{at } \bar{t} = -0: \qquad \bar{T} = 1$$
$$\text{at } \bar{t} = +0: \qquad \bar{T} = 1$$

except at the surface where $\bar{T} = 0$, that is, at

$$\bar{x} = 0,1$$
$$\bar{y} = 0,1$$
$$\bar{z} = 0,1$$

We are assuming that Eq. (4.1b) was constructed so that each term containing only variables in the normalized equation is approximately unity. If this is true, then the magnitude of each term is given solely by the nondimensional parameter. Moreover, since each term has a physical meaning, and since we made the equation nondimensional by division on the coefficient of one term, each parameter gives the magnitude of the ratio of two important effects. Thus, for example, $(L/M)^2$ represents the ratio of net heat conduction in the y direction to net heat conduction in the x direction; we also note that L/M raised to any power but 2 does not have this significance. Similarly the Fourier number $L^2/t_c \alpha$ which appears in Eq. (4.1b) represents the ratio of net heat conduction in the x direction to storage of energy in the solid, and in the form set gives the magnitude of this ratio to a first approximation.

If, as we also assumed in deriving Eq. (4.1b), the estimates of the nondimensional variables, hence the nondimensional terms in the governing equation, are valid over the entire domain of interest, then only the larger terms in the equation will be of concern. Consequently, we consider systematic variations in the values of the pi's in the normalized equation. First, suppose that L is small compared with both M and N

in Eq. (4.1); it then follows that

$$\left(\frac{L}{M}\right)^2 \ll 1 \tag{4.8a}$$

$$\left(\frac{L}{N}\right)^2 \ll 1 \tag{4.8b}$$

If we recall that each term in the differential equation represents a given physical effect or part of one (otherwise it should not be there), then it is clear that logically the size of the terms represents the size of the relevant physical effect. Thus we can conclude that we can drop the terms with small parameters as insignificant. In this case we obtain

$$\frac{\partial^2 \bar{T}}{\partial \bar{x}^2} = \left(\frac{L^2}{t_c \alpha}\right) \frac{\partial \bar{T}}{\partial \bar{t}} \tag{4.9}$$

This equation contains only one parameter $L^2/t_c\alpha$, hence if the value of this parameter is the same, the solution to the problem will be the same. Thus, as before, we conclude it is the governing parameter. This amounts to reducing the problem from a three-dimensional to a one-dimensional transient-heat-conduction problem, but the reduction has not been done arbitrarily. On the contrary, we have found explicitly the criteria under which such an approximation is allowable, these are the conditions (4.8a) and (4.8b), and $hl/2k \gg 1$. There are several further points of interest in this reduction.

First, if only one of conditions (4.8a) and (4.8b) is satisfied, then only one term can be dropped and the problem is two-dimensional. Secondly, if L is large compared to M or N, then Eq. (4.1b) can be reformulated upon multiplication by either $(M/L)^2$ or $(N/L)^2$ so that the small dimension appears in the Fourier number in place of L. This is equivalent to normalizing on M^2 or N^2 instead of L^2.†

Multiplication by $(M/L)^2$ or $(N/L)^2$ results in an equation similar to (4.1b) but with the terms reorganized slightly. The reader can readily verify that exactly the same line of reasoning as that applied to drop terms from Eq. (4.1b) will go through for this modified equation. This implies that the critical Fourier number in all cases is $l^2/t_c\alpha$, where l is defined as the smallest of the three dimensions L, M, and N. Thus we can divide *all* problems falling in this class into two groups (1) one of the

† It is almost always instructive to examine the various equations which arise from division by the different parameters in step 2 of the normalization. Often one of them is more useful for a particular problem, and sometimes other definitions are useful for different ranges of the parameters. A good example of this latter point is given by the heat exchanger plots of Kays and London;[23] in this case use of an alternative set of definitions for effectiveness and heat-capacity rate ratio greatly simplifies charts and design procedures.

three dimensions L, M, and N is small compared to the other two, (2) two or three of the dimensions L, M, and N are of approximately the same size. In either case, study of the normalized equation leads to the Fourier number $l^2/t_c\alpha$ and thus shows the following useful result about the similarity behavior of this class of problems.

> The transient portion of the cooking time t_f is proportional to the square of the minimum dimension to the center of the body.

This result follows from Eq. (4.1*b*) and from the fact that the terms with larger dimensions can be neglected, while those with equal dimensions will not change the result. This answer is a very explicit, simple, and useful similarity rule. It is a more complete answer than that obtained by other methods in Chaps. 2 and 3. It provides a rigorous answer to the question originally posed in Chap. 2 concerning whether the housewives' cooking rule is correct. Clearly, the stated housewife's rule (20 minutes per pound) is wrong, since it implies proportionality to the product of all three characterizing length dimensions. This is dimensionally improper, and it also ignores the crucial shape factors and exponents embodied in the ratios $(L/M)^2$ and $(L/N)^2$.†

The result we have found so far holds only for the case where conduction is the controlling process; $hl/2k \gg 1$. This assumption implies physically that the resistance to heat flow due to conduction is large compared to that due to convection even for the shortest path to the center $l/2$. It is quite possible that this condition is fulfilled for the larger lengths but not the shortest. It is also fairly common that the value of h is different on the different sides owing to insulation or different contact conditions. It is left as an exercise for the reader to examine the various cases which can arise and to determine numerical criteria in terms of governing parameters, showing when various terms can be neglected and which cases are essentially one-dimensional when h takes on different values on the various sides. The results have interesting implications regarding the assumption of "one-dimensional flow."

b. *Classification of Problems and Difficulties in Approximation Theory*

As the example of Sec. 4-6*a* shows, approximation theory is a tool which can lead to useful results. However, unless the procedure is very carefully employed, it can easily give misleading information. Indeed,

---

† The newly married reader is cautioned at this point that domestic tranquility may be better preserved if it is remembered that the technical accuracy of this result is not necessarily well correlated with the reaction of the nonmathematically inclined housewife; she may justifiably prefer meat thermometers to differential equations.

mathematicians sometimes call such procedures *experimental mathematics*, by which they mean to imply that answers so obtained are experimental and must be checked. This is generally correct, but there are some conditions under which we can obtain approximations with reasonably good assurance; the purpose of this section is to discuss some of the physical and mathematical bases for these conditions and to see where some of the difficulties lie.

In Sec. 4-6a we saw one example where we did find accurate estimates for each term in a differential equation in terms of the boundary conditions and system sizes in a finite region. Where this can be done it is possible to define dimensionless variables in such a way that approximation theory will provide criteria for derivation of approximate governing equations and less stringent similarity requirements. There are several ways in which these estimates can be established, as we shall see. In the conduction problem of Sec. 4-6a, we tried to define nondimensional quantities such that all terms in the variables of the normalized governing equations were made order one or less throughout the domain of the solution and the boundary conditions were brought to constant unit size. Since the equation in normalized form contains only nondimensional variables and nondimensional parameters, we can then judge the importance of each set of terms by the magnitude of the parameter which stands in front of the terms containing variables. This procedure appears very straightforward; however, so far we have only *assumed* that the necessary estimates can be provided. We shall now have to discuss when this can actually be done. In this process a number of difficulties and complications will become apparent.

It is useful to recall the remarks of Sec. 4-2b regarding the derivation of governing equations which show that each set of terms which is multiplied by a pi in the normalized governing equations ordinarily represents some distinct physical effect. Thus if the governing equations are algebraic, direct comparisons can be made between terms; any set of terms which is small can immediately be dropped, and a good approximation must always result. See, for example, the treatment of density ratio in the problem of the falling body (Example 3.3).

If, however, the governing equations are differential in form, they apply only locally and not to the system as a whole in the form set.

If we are concerned with a "local" effect described in the equation, say a comparison of two forces at a particular point, and if we can show that a given set of terms really is small compared with others at the point of interest, in a complete differential equation, then, again, this set of terms can be dropped without difficulties arising. However, this seldom does us much good. We are usually concerned with the solution, that is, the dependent variable, and it is usually a "global" effect in the sense that it depends on the differential terms over some whole region. In this latter case, justification for dropping terms then becomes much more difficult, because we must guarantee that they are uniformly small throughout the whole domain before we can safely drop them. If a given term is large at even one point, this may contribute appreciably to the overall effect of concern. Moreover, even a small effect can appreciably alter the solution if it acts over a sufficiently long span. Thus we must demonstrate not that the effect is small locally, but that it has a small effect on the integrated overall quantity we are studying. Hence, to proceed with mathematical arguments, we must necessarily discuss the relation between the magnitude of the terms in the differential equation and the magnitude of terms in the integrated solution; this can be very complicated.

In the case of integral equations, the situation is the same as that just stated for differential equations. This follows from the fact that the governing integral equations can be visualized (for this purpose) merely as the differential equations with enough integrations to eliminate all derivatives indicated formally by integration signs; in fact we will use this form to discuss differential equations at some places. Thus, for present purposes, remarks about integral and differential equations are essentially the same.

It is convenient to study the mathematical problems of approximation theory in two parts: (1) the provision of estimates for the terms in the governing equations, (2) the connection between these estimates and the integrated solution in the case of differential and integral equations. In both parts it is helpful to distinguish between *uniform* and *nonuniform* behavior.

A problem is said to have uniform behavior if it is possible to supply a single estimate for each variable in such a way that each term containing variables in the governing equation is made approximately unity over a finite range in the domain of interest and equal to or less than unity throughout the remainder of the domain. A problem is said to have nonuniform behavior if it is not possible to satisfy these conditions.

It is noted that a problem which is nonuniform in one set of coordinates (variables) may be uniform in other coordinates. Again, we use the phrase *set of terms* to mean one or more additive terms in the equation which are multiplied by a single parameter in the normalized equation.

Nonuniform behavior can arise in two ways. First, one or more terms can change rapidly in a narrow zone, but change little or not at all everywhere else. This situation is called a *boundary-layer* problem (after the treatment of such a problem by L. Prandtl, see Example 4.8). Second, a differential equation may contain singular points where one or several terms become very large; then it may not be possible to give estimates of these terms that apply near the singular point and also in other regions. These two problems are often closely associated, but are not identical; one can occur without the other.

If a given problem exhibits uniform behavior, and if we are concerned with a domain of finite extent, then the procedures illustrated in Sec. 4-6a go through without difficulty and approximation theory is extremely useful. If a problem displays nonuniform behavior, has singular terms, or requires an infinite interval of integration, then we must expect mathematical difficulties and will need additional special considerations. In particular, we must always bear in mind possible nonuniform behavior of the solution in the limit of very large and very small values of the parameters, that is, the behavior of the solution with one or more of the parameters small may be entirely different from that with the same parameter set identically zero.† Consequently, we must (1) discuss means for discovering when uniform behavior can be assured, and (2) discuss what steps can be taken when the behavior is nonuniform. These are both complex problems, and in the present state of mathematical theory of differential and integral equations it is not possible to give complete answers. Some useful procedures, rules, and comments can nevertheless be provided.

In general, previous discussion of these problems has been primarily mathematical, and considerably less attention seems to have been given to the use of physical information. In the present discussion, more emphasis is placed on the use of physical information, for two reasons. First, the present discussion is centered on fractional analysis and hence is most concerned with those cases where complete mathematical theory is not available. Second, the use of physical information, even in very crude form, in conjunction with mathematical analyses of the present type can be a very powerful tool and has in fact often been employed. More explicit discussion of the places and ways where it should be used (or sought) seems desirable.

c. *Conditions Required for Approximation Theory*

We commence by discussing the usual mathematical conditions invoked as a basis for approximation theory. For precision in our statements we use the term *approximately* and the symbol $\approx$ to indicate very nearly equals, and the word *order* and the symbol $O(1)$ to mean roughly equal to or less than 1. We will also find it convenient to use the term *unity order* to mean approximately 1 over a finite range and less than 1

---

† It is emphasized that this nonuniform behavior is associated with limiting values of the parameters and not the variables, even though it may arise owing to infinite extent of one or more independent variables.

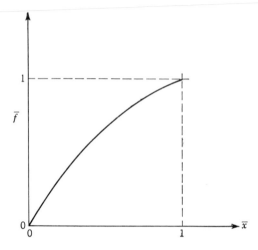

Fɪɢ. 4.2

everywhere else in the domain of interest.   We denote *unity order* by the symbol $U(1)$.

The conditions usually stated are that the function and its derivatives must be continuous and differentiable up to an order one lower than that appearing in the differential equation in a finite domain.   This means that the function can be normalized, since it is bounded, and that the domain of integration can be made approximately unity by normalization. These are sufficient, but not necessary, conditions to guarantee that we can make approximations term by term.   There are often good grounds for assuming these conditions, as we shall see.   However, these conditions are not enough to tell us what the approximations should be.†

The easiest way to show this is by example.   Consider a problem in which a function f is given by an ordinary differential equation of the second order in x.   Examine three possible types of solution as shown in Figs. 4.2 to 4.4.

Since we assume that the function is bounded and that the domain is finite, we can normalize to bring the function to unity order and the domain to unity, provided we have some idea about the magnitude of the function.   This has already been done in Figs. 4.2 to 4.4.   Now consider only figure 4.2; the slope of $\bar{f}$ can be estimated as

$$\frac{d\bar{f}}{d\bar{x}} \approx \frac{1 - 0}{1 - 0} = 1 \tag{4.10a}$$

† In earlier drafts of this work, a few of which are extant as dittoed notes, the author attempted more exact general mathematical conditions. Unfortunately, these attempts had loopholes, which were pointed out by friendly reviewers.   In the present discussion the conditions have been weakened to meet these difficulties; this section of the earlier versions should not be used.

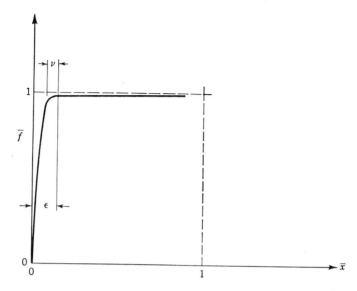

FIG. 4.3

If $\bar{f}$ looks more or less like Fig. 4.2, then the second derivative is not larger than

$$\left| \frac{d^2\bar{f}}{d\bar{x}^2} \right| \leq \frac{\left| \frac{d\bar{f}}{d\bar{x}} \right| - 0}{1 - 0} = \frac{1 - 0}{1 - 0} = 1$$

$$\frac{d^2\bar{f}}{d\bar{x}^2} = 0(1)$$

For higher order derivatives we get estimates of the same type,

$$\frac{d^n\bar{f}}{d\bar{x}^n} = 0(1)$$

that is

$$\frac{d^n f}{dx^n} \leq \frac{f_m}{L^n}$$

where

$$\bar{f} = \frac{f}{f_m} \approx (1)$$

$$0 \leq \bar{x} \leq 1$$

$$\bar{x} = \frac{x}{L}$$

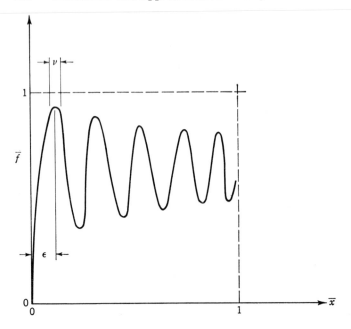

Fɪɢ. 4.4

The estimate that we use in this case can be expressed in general as

$$\frac{d^n f}{dx^n} \approx \frac{f_m}{L^n} \tag{4.10b}$$

We shall call an estimate using Eq. (4.10b) a *smooth* estimate. Estimates of this type are often employed; it is, for example, what we used in Sec. 4-6a. However, smooth estimates are highly restrictive, and they are by no means always correct. We can readily see this by examining Figs. 4.3 and 4.4. Suppose that in these figures $\epsilon \ll 1$. (The symbol $\ll$ is used here to indicate that we can make ϵ as small as we like compared to 1.) In this case no estimate of the sort given above can be correct over the entire range $0 \leq \bar{x} \leq 1$, since the average slope in the region $0 \leq x \leq \epsilon$ is

$$\frac{d\bar{f}}{d\bar{x}} \approx \frac{1 - 0}{\epsilon - 0} = \frac{1}{\epsilon}$$

and we can make ϵ as small as we choose. The estimate for $d^2\bar{f}/d\bar{x}^2$ in the range $0 < \bar{x} < \epsilon$ is

$$\left| \frac{d^2\bar{f}}{d\bar{x}^2} \right| \approx \frac{df/d\bar{x} - 0}{\epsilon - 0} = \frac{1}{\epsilon^2}$$

In fact if df/dx changes very rapidly at the "corner," even this estimate is too small. We then have to make an estimate of the extent of the corner in $\bar{x}$. If, for example, the corner extends from say $\bar{x}$ to $\bar{x} + \nu$, where $\nu \ll \epsilon$, then we have

$$\frac{d^2\bar{f}}{d\bar{x}^2} \approx \frac{(\partial f/\partial x)_{\max} - 0}{\nu} = \frac{1}{\epsilon\nu} \gg \frac{1}{\epsilon^2}$$

Repeating the procedure in the same range, we obtain

$$\frac{d^n\bar{f}}{d\bar{x}^n} \approx \frac{1}{\epsilon^n} \qquad \text{or possibly} \qquad \frac{d^2\bar{f}}{d\bar{x}^n} \approx \frac{1}{\epsilon\nu^{n-1}}$$

Hence for functions like those shown in Figs. 4.3 and 4.4 the smooth estimates applicable to Fig. 4.2 get worse and worse as we go to derivatives of higher and higher order.

We can summarize these results in the form of a rule.

Rule 3†

1. Uniform estimates of a function f and its derivatives up to order n can be given over a finite region if the function and its derivatives up to order $n - 1$ are continuous and differentiable and if the function is smooth (that is, has a general nature like that of Fig. 4.2).
2. If also f is normalized to be $U(1)$ and the variables x_i to run from 0 to 1, then

$$\frac{\partial \bar{f}}{\partial \bar{x}_i} \approx 1 \qquad \text{and} \qquad \frac{\partial^r \bar{f}}{\partial \bar{x}^r} = 0(1)$$

where $r \leq n$.

This rule is quite useful, but it has several odd points. Condition 1 is very stringent mathematically. Condition 2 is very inexact and also presumes we already know something about the answer. Each of these points can profitably bear a little discussion.

Both conditions are sufficient but not necessary. That is, they are enough to ensure that we can make uniform estimates, if we do so properly, but it may be possible to give uniform estimates in cases that do not meet the conditions. It is easiest to show this by example. We consider two types. It is altogether possible that two derivative terms in a differential equation will be very large but of sign such that they cancel each other at every point. A well-known example of this behavior occurs in potential flow.‡ Consider a two-dimensional potential vortex with velocity components u and v in the x and y directions. The vorticity ζ in such

---

† Called a rule rather than a theorem since it indicates a "trial procedure" for exploration rather than proof of a theorem.

‡ A flow which has a scalar velocity potential φ satisfying Laplace's equation.

a flow is, by definition,

$$\zeta = \frac{\partial u}{\partial y} - \frac{\partial v}{\partial x}$$

In a potential flow the sum of the two terms giving ζ is zero everywhere by definition. In a logarithmic vortex, the flow is potential everywhere except at the origin, as is readily shown from the appropriate expression for the complex potential $F(z)$

$$F(z) = iA \ln z$$

where A is a real constant. Then by definition of $F(z)$

$$u - iv = \frac{dF}{dz} = \frac{iA}{z}$$

Consider now a point arbitrarily near the origin; $\partial u/\partial y$ and $\partial v/\partial x$ become very large. Eq. (4.10b) can provide no estimate of either $\partial u/\partial y$ or $\partial v/\partial x$ which will apply over any domain of the flow field that extends both very close to and very far from the origin. Nevertheless, a uniform estimate for the vorticity ζ can be provided; indeed it is zero everywhere except at the origin, and it can be neglected in a potential flow. Thus we do not always need to have each derivative term small by itself.

A second case often occurs when we are interested, not in local effects, but only in the behavior of some overall quantity. A term can be very large at some point and not satisfy Eq. (4.10b) in that neighborhood without affecting the overall effect appreciably. An example of this type of behavior occurs in the drag on a flat plate. Under the usual assumptions, the equations indicate, fictitiously, an infinite skin friction at the nose, but it is infinite only for a zero distance, and the limit behaves in such a way that the overall drag is not appreciably affected by the infinite value at the nose. That is, even though the equations predict a skin friction at the nose in error by an infinite amount, the overall drag for plates of finite length is given accurately by the same equations.

Even though continuity and differentiability are not always necessary, there is this to say in justification for trying such assumptions in continuum problems. The physics inherent in the problem often suggests (but by no means proves) that we should expect such behavior. This expectation is based on the fact that the nth order derivatives, those of highest order in the differential equation, usually represent differences in forces, energies, and properties; we expect such quantities to be continuous in a continuum theory. Indeed, such principles as the Second Law of Thermodynamics often tell us a good deal about the nature of the functions we must expect at the outset. (At this point the reader might well look back at Sec. 4.6*a*, and ask himself if the Second Law does provide the conditions required by Rule 3 for the cooking problem.) It is emphasized that this type of information is, however, merely suggestive and not conclusive, since we can never be certain that the differential equation we have written is complete. We can expect a given type of physical behavior with a very high degree of certainty, but there must always be residual doubt that the equation we have written will predict this behavior. In the case of the heat conduction equation this doubt is minimal, and the estimates we found are quite useful. In such cases the physical information provides strong motivation for expecting certain types of behavior, hence assumption of such behavior followed by checking is a highly appropriate way to proceed.

This remark by no means implies that the available mathematics should not be used or that additional mathematical theorems should not be sought. It means rather that the researcher cannot allow the absence of formal mathematical proof to deter him from pursuing solutions and that good hints for seeking such solutions can very often be found successfully from the accumulated physical knowledge embodied in what we have called the "completeness of the equations," in the associated physical principles, and in physical data.

This attitude, which we might characterize by the phrase "forge ahead and then check the results," is one we will adopt frequently in the examples below. Its adoption is a characteristic difference between the applied mathematician, who is primarily concerned with solving problems, and the pure mathematician, who is mostly concerned with establishing rigorous relationships within the framework of given conditions and definitions. We need to say a word also on what constitutes a check. It is possible to check against data or against a more complete theory; that is, a more complete equation. The check against data is always the ultimate authority in science, and any check against more complete equations is subject to uncertainty regarding how complete the equations really are, as we have already stressed.

Finally, Rule 3 assumes some crude information about the form of the answer. This is typical of approximation theory procedures, although the point is frequently glossed over. Very often we have the necessary data available, and their use is entirely proper, provided it is consistent with the equations we are using as a mathematical model and it is understood in the context of the remarks about completeness and checking.

Rule 3 gives us one way to establish estimates. It shows, in fact, one reason why it is so often useful to normalize in the way suggested in Sec. 4-1, since if the conditions of Rule 3 are satisfied (and perhaps in other cases), this procedure will make the parameters show the estimate of magnitude of the various terms. As we saw, these estimates, in general, decrease in accuracy as the order of the derivative increases, and all derivatives beyond the first are only estimated to be less than or equal to 1. Hence we may keep terms we do not really need; however, we will not throw away any that should be kept.

There are ways in which the estimates of terms can be improved. One of the commonest is direct use of physical information. This is clearly in keeping with the philosophy we are using; however, such data need to be much more detailed than the information needed for Rule 3. Consequently, we use both procedures, that is, we use data when it is available and we make appropriate assumptions about the gross nature of the solution, subject to later checking, when it is not. In either case we use the estimates to tell us which terms we can drop from the governing equations to obtain simpler correlations or solutions where we cannot handle the complete problem mathematically. With this in mind we turn to the discussion of the relations between the magnitude of terms in differential equations and in integrated results.

To illustrate the ideas simply, we consider first an ordinary differential equation. Take for example

$$T = T(x)$$

and the *DE*

$$T^2 \left(\frac{dT}{dx}\right) + CT = 0 \qquad (4.11a)$$

with boundary conditions

at $x = 0$: $\qquad T = 0$

Again define

$$\bar{T} = \frac{T}{T_a}$$

$$\bar{x} = \frac{x}{L}$$

On substitution we obtain

$$\frac{T_a^3}{L} \bar{T}^2 \frac{d\bar{T}}{d\bar{x}} + T_a C \bar{T} = 0$$

or

$$\bar{T}^2 \frac{d\bar{T}}{d\bar{x}} + \pi_1 \bar{T} = 0$$

where

$$\pi_1 = \frac{LC}{T_a^2}$$

Formal integration on $\bar{x}$ gives

$$\int_o^{\bar{x}} \bar{T}^2 \frac{d\bar{T}}{d\bar{x}} \, d\bar{x} + \pi_1 \int_o^{\bar{x}} \bar{T} \, d\bar{x} = 0 \qquad (4.11b)$$

However, suppose $\bar{T}$ satisfies Rule 3, then

$$\bar{T} \approx U(1)$$
$$\bar{T}^2 = U(1)$$
$$\frac{d\bar{T}}{d\bar{x}} \approx 1$$

We can construct an estimate of the magnitude of the first integral in Eq. (4.11b), as shown by the hatched area A_1 in Fig. 4.5. The estimate of the magnitude of the integral in the second term of Eq. (4.11b) is shown in Fig. 4.6 as A_2.

The solution to Eq. (4.11a) can be written functionally as two terms

$$f_1(\bar{T},\bar{x}) + \pi_1 f_2(\bar{T},\bar{x}) = 0 \qquad (4.12)$$

where the functions f_1 and f_2 are $0(1)$.

Moreover, if the equation involves derivatives of nth order, we can merely repeat the process n times. We will obtain the same result, provided Eq. (4.10b) holds for each order of derivative up to and including n, or some other suitable estimate can be supplied. We can also extend the

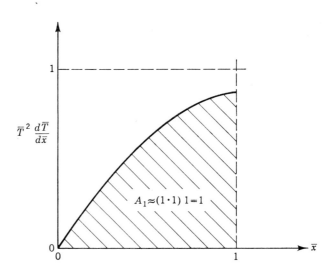

$$A_1 \approx (1 \cdot 1) \, 1 = 1$$

Fɪɢ. 4.5

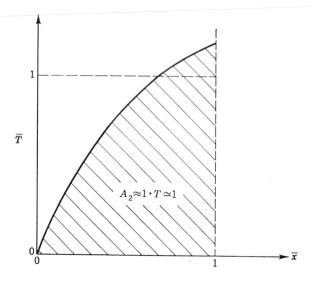

F‌IG. 4.6

procedure to cover terms like

$$T^q x^p \frac{d^n T}{dx^n} \qquad p \text{ and } q \text{ are finite real numbers}$$

and

$$T^q x^p \frac{d^r T}{dx^r} \frac{d^q T}{dx^q} \qquad r < q \le n$$

provided we can supply in advance an estimate of $\partial^r T / \partial x^r$.

Bounded functions, say $g(x)$, can also be included in terms like

$$g(x) T^q x^p \frac{\partial^n T}{\partial x^n}$$

since if the function g has an upper bound, say M_1, we can always define

$$\bar{g} = \frac{g}{M_1} = 0(1)$$

These remarks are sufficient to show that we can handle very general terms. If smooth estimates can be made, or if any other estimates can be provided which are correct over the entire domain of integration, then we can construct the pi's in such a way that they represent the magnitude of the terms in an appropriate integrated relation.

Similar, but slightly different, procedures can be employed for partial differential equations. In partial differential equations, it is necessary to integrate repeatedly over the various independent variables. Consider, for example, the normalized differential equation

$$\bar{T}\frac{d^2\bar{T}}{d\bar{x}^2} + \pi_1\frac{d\bar{T}}{d\bar{y}} = 0 \tag{4.13}$$

Here we must integrate twice on x and once on y to obtain an expression involving only t, x, y, and π_1. Thus

$$\int_{\bar{y}=0}^{\bar{y}} \int_{\bar{x}=0}^{\bar{x}} \int_{\bar{x}=0}^{\bar{x}} \left(\bar{T}\frac{d^2\bar{T}}{d\bar{x}^2} + \pi_1\frac{d\bar{T}}{d\bar{y}} \right) d\bar{x}\, d\bar{x}\, d\bar{y} = 0 \tag{4.14}$$

provided the boundary conditions are suitable. (We will explain this in a moment.) Application of Eq. (4.10) to Eq. (4.14) yields an order of magnitude

$$f_1(\bar{T},\bar{x},\bar{y}) + \pi_1 f_2(\bar{T},\bar{x},\bar{y}) = 0 \tag{4.15}$$

where f_1 and f_2 are $0(1)$.

Note that neither Eq. (4.12) nor (4.15) is a solution of the differential equation; they are merely constructs to show the magnitude relations between derivative terms and integrated effects.

It is now possible to demonstrate another important reason for the normalization procedure suggested in Sec. 4-2. If it is not followed, then in general the order of magnitude of the pi terms found will not be the same in the differential equation and the integrated terms.

In particular, if the range of integration for the independent variables is other than unity, then integration may introduce changes in the value of the multiplicative constants, the pi's, standing in front of each term if the independent variables appear in nonhomogeneous form, as they almost always do. Consider

$$\int_0^{\bar{x}} \bar{x}\, d\bar{x} + \pi_1 \int_0^{\bar{x}} \frac{d\bar{T}}{d\bar{x}}\, d\bar{x} = 0$$

$$\frac{x^2}{2} + \pi_1[\bar{T} - \bar{T}(0)] = 0$$

Thus if we hope to obtain similarity parameters that represent magnitudes not only locally but also for integrated effects, we must, in general, normalize according to the procedure of Sec. 4-2.

Before we try to summarize these ideas, we need to clarify the situation regarding boundary conditions. If we are dealing with an equation higher than first order, we may need to normalize the boundary data relating to intermediate orders of derivatives or account for the fact that we have not done so. This can be observed in the first integration of Eq.

(4.14).   Carrying out this integration symbolically, using the estimate $\bar{T} \approx 1$, we have

$$\int_{\bar{y}=0}^{\bar{y}} \int_{\bar{x}=0}^{\bar{x}} \left[\frac{d\bar{T}}{d\bar{x}} + \pi_1 \left(\frac{d\bar{T}}{d\bar{y}} \right)_{\text{avg}} \right] d\bar{x}\, d\bar{y} + \int_{\bar{y}=0}^{\bar{y}} \int_{\bar{x}=0}^{\bar{x}} [\bar{\varphi}_A(y)$$
$$+ \pi_1 \bar{\varphi}_B(y)]\, d\bar{x}\, d\bar{y}$$

where the functions $\bar{\varphi}_A(y)$ and $\bar{\varphi}_B(y)$ are the values of $d\bar{T}/d\bar{x}$ and $d\bar{T}/d\bar{y}$ along the boundary $\bar{x} = 0$ and $(dT/dy)_{\text{avg}}$ is an average value of $d\bar{T}/d\bar{y}$ integrated over $\bar{x}$.

It is clear that further integrations will involve the magnitudes of $\bar{\varphi}_A$ and $\bar{\varphi}_B$. These terms will influence the relation between the magnitude of the term multiplied by π_1 and the remaining term. Thus the magnitudes of $\bar{\varphi}_A$ and $\bar{\varphi}_B$ in this case must also be made order unity if we are to judge the magnitude of terms in the integrated solution from the magnitude of the nondimensional parameters in the differential equation. This is merely another way of saying that we must normalize sufficient boundary-value data to specify a mathematically appropriate problem.

The gist of Eqs. (4.12) and (4.15) is that we can connect the magnitudes of the terms in the differential equation with those in an integrated solution, provided we can supply from some source the necessary estimates of terms. These equations by no means indicate the way we would actually go about integrating except in very special cases, but they do provide a procedure for demonstrating that we can use the magnitude of the pi's in the differential equations to characterize magnitude of terms under proper conditions. Again these procedures do not constitute a proof but only a path for exploration in specific cases subject to later checking. Moreover, we have so far glossed over the most difficult part of all—the actual provision of estimates in cases which are not smooth; most of Secs. 4-7, 4-8, and 4-9 is devoted to examples of how estimates are constructed in various cases, and these materials give only a very brief introduction. However, once the framework is known, any estimating procedure for a specific case can be fitted into it.

We summarize this situation with another rule.

Rule 4

> If the governing equations can be reformulated in nondimensional coordinates so that each term in the boundary conditions, the variables (and functions of the variables), is unity order, and if the range of integration can also be made approximately unity in terms of the same variables, then the terms in the integrated solution will be of the same order as those in the differential equation and approximation theory can be applied by examining the magnitudes of the parameters in the normalized governing equations.

So far we have suggested three sources for the estimates needed: from Rule 3 in cases of smooth behavior, directly from data, and from appropriate assumptions about the form of the solution. Combinations of these sources can also be used, but finding these estimates correctly is seldom easy. If we know them, we already have at our disposal a great deal of the knowledge about the problem. In many cases the same estimate of terms cannot be used for the entire domain of interest. Whenever an integration over an infinite domain or a singularity of the equation is required, special considerations must be made. We must expect that the estimates will sometimes involve not only the value of the function but also some of the derivatives at the boundaries as we have noted above.

Finally, apparently logical assumptions about magnitude or solution form that turn out to be untrue can easily lead us completely astray in the form of the solution or correlation we are seeking.

In short, approximation theory is in one sense very different from similarity procedures based on the governing equations and conditions. Similarity procedures based on the full differential equations and boundary conditions are rigorous to the same extent as our knowledge of the completeness and appropriateness of the equations and conditions. However, as soon as we go one step further, that is, try to apply the idea of magnitudes as a means for finding simpler solutions and similarity rules, much more difficult problems arise. Despite these difficulties, approximation theory is very important, since it is the only way we can get answers at all in many problems.

We next consider a few very simple examples to illustrate that the difficulties we have been discussing are real. Consider a harmonic oscillator with linear damping; the governing equation is

$$m \frac{d^2x}{dt^2} + c \frac{dx}{dt} + kx = 0 \qquad\qquad (4.16a)$$

(We can consider this to be a simple spring-mass system with viscous damping or a series RLC electric circuit with constant resistance. Since the percepts of the mechanical system are simpler, we use it for discussion.)

Consider first the question of an infinite domain of integration. Let the boundary conditions be

at $t = 0$: $\qquad x = A_0 \qquad \frac{dx}{dt} = 0$

We have purposely chosen an example first where we can find the complete solutions, so that we can compare the actual outcome to that found from approximation theory. Proceding as above, we try to normalize the equation using the variables

$$\bar{x} = \frac{x}{A_0} = U(1) \qquad \bar{t} = \frac{t}{\tau}$$

where τ is the time for one quarter cycle of oscillation. If we consider a quarter cycle, the variables satisfy the magnitudes required for Rule 3. Normalizing, we obtain

$$\frac{d^2\bar{x}}{d\bar{t}^2} + \frac{c\tau}{m}\frac{d\bar{x}}{d\bar{t}} + \frac{k\tau^2}{m}\bar{x} = 0$$

Suppose, further, that $c\tau/m \ll 1$; if we then drop the second term and integrate, we obtain the solution

$$\bar{x} = \cos \beta t \qquad \beta = \sqrt{\frac{k}{m}} \tag{4.16b}$$

This is a steady periodic oscillation. If on the other hand we retain the term $(c\tau/m)d\bar{x}/d\bar{t}$, the final solution is

$$x = e^{-ct/2m}\cos \gamma t \qquad \gamma = \sqrt{\frac{k}{m} - \frac{c^2}{4m^2}} \tag{4.17}$$

When $c/2m \ll 1$, Eq. (4.16b) is a very good approximation of (4.17) for any one cycle, but if we consider many cycles, that is, very large t, the agreement becomes very poor. The difficulty is precisely that while the term $(c\tau/m)d\bar{x}/d\bar{t}$ is small, it acts over an infinite extent in time, hence ultimately it has a very large effect. To misquote an ancient proverb, we might say, "even a single drop of friction can ultimately wear away the largest free vibration."

A problem that behaves in this way is said to be *singular* in its limiting behavior, that is, the behavior of the solution when a parameter is very small is altogether different from when the parameter is identically zero. Singular limiting behavior is not identical with the problem of nonuniform estimates, but it seems to be associated with it in a certain way as we shall see. When singular behavior in the limit occurs, we usually try to resolve the difficulty by expanding in powers of the parameters; some procedures of this type are illustrated in Sec. 4-8.

Next consider the simple harmonic oscillator without friction, that is, with c identically zero. The governing differential equation is

$$m\frac{d^2x}{dt^2} + kx = 0 \tag{4.18}$$

Consider now two sets of boundary conditions:

1. at $t = 0$: $\qquad x = 0 \qquad \dfrac{dx}{dt} = V_o$

2. at $t = 0$: $\qquad x = A_o \qquad \dfrac{dx}{dt} = V_o$

With the first boundary conditions we cannot normalize the displacement

x by initial displacement, since it is zero.   We can use

$$\bar{x} = \frac{x}{V_o/\beta}$$

This normalization shows the importance of boundary-value data for intermediate derivatives even in this very simple case.   The complete solution for the undamped oscillator is, of course,

$$x = c_1 \cos \beta t + c_2 \sin \beta t$$

If we apply the boundary conditions 2, we obtain

$$c_1 = A_o \qquad c_2 = \frac{V_o}{\beta}$$

Here again if we normalize on A_o alone, we still do not get good estimates of x for all possible values of the ratio c_1/c_2.   A better normalization for x is

$$\bar{x} = \frac{x}{c_o} \qquad c_o = \sqrt{c_1^2 + c_2^2} = \sqrt{A_0^2 + \left(\frac{V_o}{\beta}\right)^2}$$

This is not easy to see unless we know a good bit about the complete solution; this emphasizes one of the difficulties in providing good estimates as well as the need to look at all the boundary-value data needed to make an appropriate problem.   That is, we could have found an appropriate normalization formally by demanding that the normalization make all the boundary-value data 0(1).

Normalizing as suggested above for the more general boundary conditions 2 we have

$$\frac{d^2\bar{x}}{d\bar{t}^2} + (\beta\tau)^2\bar{x} = 0 \tag{4.19}$$

with boundary conditions

$$\text{at } \bar{t} = 0: \qquad \bar{x} = \frac{A_o}{c_o}; \qquad \frac{d\bar{x}}{d\bar{t}} = \frac{V_o\tau}{c_o}$$

Suppose we now try approximation theory, that is, we assume fictitiously that $(\beta\tau)^2 \ll 1$.   Approximation theory would then lead to the equation

$$\frac{d^2\bar{x}}{d\bar{t}^2} = 0$$

Integrating directly twice gives

$$\bar{x} = c_3 + c_4\bar{t} = \frac{A_o}{c_o} + \frac{V_o\tau}{c_o}\bar{t} \tag{4.20}$$

But the complete solution of Eq. (4.19) in these coordinates is

$$\bar{x} = \frac{A_o}{c_o} \cos \beta t + \frac{V_o}{\beta c_o} \sin \beta t \tag{4.21}$$

Comparison of Eqs. (4.20) and (4.21) shows that while Eq. (4.20) agrees exactly at $t = 0$, it departs more and more from the complete solution Eq. (4.21) as time increases.

Next consider, again fictitiously, that $(\beta \tau)^2 \gg 1$, and try to drop the term $d^2\bar{x}/d\bar{t}^2$. We obtain only

$$\bar{x} = 0, \qquad x = 0 \tag{4.22}$$

for all t

Using Eq. (4.22) we cannot even match the boundary conditions; we have no solution at all unless the boundary conditions are trivial, that is

$$\text{at } t = 0: \qquad \bar{x} = 0 \qquad \frac{d\bar{x}}{d\bar{t}} = 0$$

This type of difficulty often occurs when we try to drop the most highly differentiated terms; in such cases we can no longer satisfy all the boundary conditions and we can therefore obtain solutions only for certain very limited values of the boundary data. This type of difficulty can sometimes be resolved by various kinds of expansion in powers of the parameters, or by a technique which we call *boundary-layer theory*. These techniques are briefly introduced in Secs. 4-8 and 4-9.

It is emphasized that dropping terms from the equation for the simple harmonic oscillator fails, not because approximation theory is wrong, but because we have supplied erroneous estimates. We have defined $\bar{x}$ and $\bar{t}$ in such a way that the terms $d^2\bar{x}/d\bar{t}^2$ and $\bar{x}$ are approximately unity, but to do so we had to use the free parameter τ. Since we can vary k/m, superficially it would appear that we could make $(k/m)\tau^2$ anything we please; this is not the case. Equation (4.19) is itself a relation between $\bar{t}$, $\bar{x}$, and $(k/m)\tau^2$. If we are to have any oscillatory solution, Eq. (4.19) demands that the two terms $d^2\bar{x}/d\tau^2$ and $(k/m)\tau^2\bar{x}$ must be of the same order. Physically, to maintain an oscillation we must have a dynamic equilibrium between restoring and inertia forces. Since the equation is complete, it shows this behavior also. That is, both physically and mathematically it is not possible to control k/m and τ separately; as k/m becomes large τ becomes small, and conversely. In fact, the relation between k/m and τ^2 is well known, and is seen directly from the complete solution to be

$$\tau \approx \frac{1}{\sqrt{k/m}} \qquad \text{or} \qquad (\beta\tau)^2 \approx 1$$

Thus our assumptions about the magnitude of the parameter are wrong.

We give this almost absurdly simple example to show the type of reasoning that has sometimes been used to give approximation theory a bad name. The trouble is not in the theory, but rather in the adoption of bad estimates.

Two additional comments are pertinent here. First, we have made the difficulty regarding estimates very explicit by choosing to make $\bar{x}$ and $d^2\bar{x}/d\bar{t}^2$ approximately unity so that the magnitudes show in the parameter. In most of the literature this is not done, so that the poor estimate relates not to the parameter but to a term involving derivatives of the dependent variable. If, as is also often done, an attempt is then made to apply approximation theory based on the magnitude of the parameters without regard to the magnitude of the terms in the variables, the procedure hinges on the actual value of the derivatives. In effect one then merely hopes that the terms in the variables are approximately unity in size, and if possible checks this "hope" later on. It would seem preferable to make the need for estimates of the terms in the variables explicit at the beginning, although either procedure will work if one is clear about what is going on.

Second, it is worth mentioning that this same line of argument—that the whole of the two terms must be the same size if the equation is to be satisfied and if solutions are to be of an expected type—can often be used to make estimates of the magnitude of a free parameter such as τ. We shall utilize this procedure later on.

Still another difficulty, beyond those illustrated by use of the simple harmonic oscillator, occurs when the governing equations or boundary conditions are nonhomogeneous. By Theorem 1, the value of the dependent variable plays a role which *cannot* be normalized out. It follows that we may not be able to find a single estimate that will hold for all problems of the class considered; that is, for all possible values of the parameters. (Here we are not talking about nonuniform estimates within a single problem, but rather about nonuniform estimates between one problem and another.) This remark will come as no surprise to anyone familiar with hydromechanics or with problems in electromagnetic theory. The solutions found in such cases are typically *parameter dependent*, that is, gross differences occur in the overall solution between problems with different values of the governing parameters, for example, the Reynolds number. The moral is that when we use data to make estimates for application of Rule 3 or 4, we must be sure that the data apply to the range of values of the parameters of concern when the equations or boundary conditions are nonhomogeneous.

Now that we have given one useful example and also highlighted some of the mathematical deadfalls and booby traps in approximation theory, it is appropriate to summarize what we can do with it, and then turn to the more constructive task of working additional examples.

1. We can attempt to establish the magnitude of all terms in the governing equations and conditions. We can then try to eliminate small terms and thus find approximate governing equations and simpler model laws for various ranges of interest. If we cannot do this, the normalized equations will frequently tell us what measurements are needed in order to carry out such procedures and will thus directly aid in planning efficient experimental work.

2. We can define parameters representing quantities whose value is unknown and seek conditions on that parameter which will make the appropriate term small (or of the same size as the other terms in the governing equations).

3. We can seek similarity conditions in terms of undefined parameters, that is, we can find parameters which must be constant if similarity is to obtain, and then check experimentally whether these conditions are fulfilled.

All these procedures depend directly on the normalization procedures discussed in Secs. 4-2 and 4-3 or their equivalent. In all cases, the treatment of problems with uniform behavior is relatively simple; indeed, such problems often fulfill the conditions of Rule 3. Nonuniform problems are far more difficult, and relatively little rigorous mathematics can be applied to them at the present time. For the most part they must still be treated as special cases. We cannot, however, let these difficulties deter us from using approximation theory when we need it. In line with the philosophy developed, we will proceed with examples and provide checks against complete equations and data. In fact, now that we know where some of the difficulties lie, we are better prepared to treat them.

In Sec. 4-7 additional examples of problems with uniform behavior are discussed. In Secs. 4-8 and 4-9 several methods of treating nonuniform behavior are briefly introduced. In this treatment we will largely ignore the details of problems relating to improper integrals, that is, problems involving infinite domains of integration, singular functions, and unconventional forms of what the mathematician calls "measure." We slight these problems, not because they are unimportant, but because they would carry us well beyond the mathematics assumed available to us.

4-7   SOME PROBLEMS INVOLVING UNIFORM BEHAVIOR

Example 4.3. Consider the problem of the vibration of a simple beam in flexure, discussed previously in Example 2.6. For simplicity take the case of a rectangular cantilever beam of length L, depth h, width

b, mass per unit length ρ.   Assume that the cross section A may vary along the beam.   A sketch of the system is shown in Fig. 4.7a.   Again we seek a model law from which we can determine the frequency of the first natural mode of vibration ω.   The governing differential equation is well known from the theory of elasticity.   For example from Hudson,[18] we find the equation for the governing forces is

$$\frac{\partial}{\partial x^2}\left(EI\,\frac{\partial^2 y}{\partial x^2}\right) + \rho A\,\frac{\partial^2 y}{\partial t^2} = 0 \tag{4.23a}$$

where

$\quad x =$ direction along the beam
$\quad y =$ direction of deflection
$\quad E =$ modulus of elasticity
$\quad I =$ moment of inertia about neutral axis ($bh^3/12$) for rectangular
$\qquad$ beam)
$\quad t =$ time
$\quad \rho =$ mass density of beam
$\quad A =$ cross section area of beam

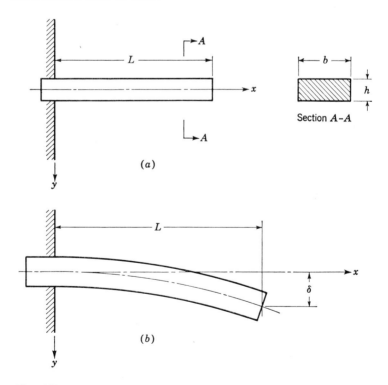

(a)

(b)

Fɪɢ. 4.7

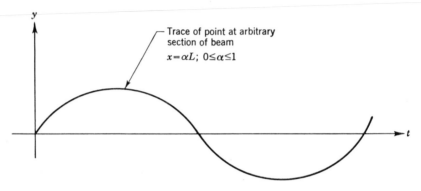

Trace of point at arbitrary section of beam

$x = \alpha L; \ 0 \leq \alpha \leq 1$

Fig. 4.8

For a cantilever beam the boundary and initial conditions for a free vibration can be taken as

at $x = 0$: $y = 0$ $\dfrac{dy}{dx} = 0$

at $x = L$: $\dfrac{d^2y}{dx^2} = 0$ $\dfrac{\partial}{\partial x}\left(EI \dfrac{\partial^2 y}{\partial x^2}\right) = 0$ (4.23b)

at $t = 0$: $y_{x=L} = \delta$† $\left(\dfrac{dy}{dt}\right)_{x=L} = \dot{y}_{x=L} = 0$

Moreover we expect an oscillation with a deflection curve which is smooth. Indeed, we expect a general form like that shown in Fig. 4.8 for the first mode. Note that we do not need the exact equation of the curve, only a very general knowledge of its form. Vast numbers of results also assure us that Eqs. (4.23a) and (4.23b) are complete and appropriate, provided that the material is isotropic and the deflection small. Thus we can expect to find an accurate and complete set of parameters by normalizing these equations. If we consider a quarter cycle of vibration, we can make the various derivative terms $U(1)$ by defining dimensionless variables as follows:

$$\bar{x} = \frac{x}{L}$$

$$\bar{y} = \frac{y}{\delta}$$

$$\bar{t} = \omega t$$

where δ is the maximum deflection at the end of the beam and ω is the reciprocal of the time required for a quarter cycle of vibration. A quarter cycle is used in this case since the beam goes from rest to maximum velocity (or returns) approximately each quarter cycle. Thus the estimate of

† Measured from position of static equilibrium.

acceleration is

$$\frac{\partial^2 y}{\partial t^2} = \frac{(dy/dt)_{t=1/\omega} - (dy/dt)_{t=0}}{1/\omega} = \frac{\delta/(1/\omega) - 0}{1/\omega} = \delta\omega^2$$

The estimate of $\partial^4 y/\partial x^4$ should be given reasonably well by Eq. (4.10b), since the curve of y versus x begins with zero deflection and slope and is expected to be smooth, hence substitution of $\bar{x}$ and $\bar{y}$ as defined should give $\partial^4 \bar{y}/\partial \bar{x}^4 \simeq 1$.

Substituting the nondimensional variables into Eqs. (4.23) yields

$$\frac{\delta}{L^4} \frac{\partial}{\partial \bar{x}^2} \left(EI \frac{\partial^2 \bar{y}}{\partial \bar{x}^2} \right) + \rho A \, \delta\omega^2 \frac{\partial^2 \bar{y}}{\partial \bar{t}^2} = 0$$

Formally differentiating the first term we obtain

$$\frac{\delta}{L^4} \left[EI \frac{\partial^4 \bar{y}}{\partial \bar{x}^4} + 2 \frac{\partial(EI)}{\partial \bar{x}} \frac{\partial^3 \bar{y}}{\partial \bar{x}^3} + \frac{\partial^2(EI)}{\partial \bar{x}^2} \frac{\partial^2 \bar{y}}{\partial \bar{x}^2} \right] + \rho \, \delta\omega^2 A \frac{\partial^2 \bar{y}}{\partial \bar{t}^2} = 0 \quad (4.23c)$$

As a first case, assume EI is a constant along the beam so that

$$\frac{\partial(EI)}{\partial \bar{x}} = \frac{\partial^2(EI)}{\partial \bar{x}^2} = 0$$

On setting this in and dividing by $\delta EI/L^4$, we obtain

$$\frac{\partial^4 \bar{y}}{\partial \bar{x}^4} + \frac{\rho A L^4 \omega^2}{EI} \frac{\partial^2 \bar{y}}{\partial \bar{t}^2} = 0 \qquad (4.24a)$$

In the nondimensional variables the boundary conditions become

$$\text{at } \bar{x} = 0: \qquad \bar{y} = 0 \qquad \frac{\partial \bar{y}}{\partial \bar{x}} = 0$$

$$\text{at } \bar{x} = 1: \qquad \frac{\partial^2 \bar{y}}{\partial \bar{x}^2} = 0 \qquad \frac{\partial^3 \bar{y}}{\partial \bar{x}^3} = 0 \qquad (4.24b)$$

$$\text{at } \bar{t} = 0: \qquad \bar{y}_{\bar{x}=1} = 1 \qquad \left(\frac{\partial \bar{y}}{\partial \bar{t}} \right)_{\bar{x}=1} = 0$$

Since the governing equations are homogeneous in y and the boundary conditions parameter-free, δ cancels from the equations as expected. Equations (4.24) apply to the entire range of deflections where Eq. (4.23) adequately represents the system.

From Eqs. (4.24) it is possible to find two types of results directly. First, it is a simple matter to extract the one governing parameter

$$\pi_1 = \frac{\rho A L^4 \omega^2}{EI} = \left(\frac{L^2 \omega}{Rc} \right)^2 \qquad (4.25)$$

where

$$R = \sqrt{\frac{I}{A}} = \text{radius of gyration of beam section}$$

$$c = \sqrt{\frac{E}{\rho}} = \text{velocity of acoustic waves in material of beam}$$

Equations (4.24) contain only one nondimensional group, and the normalized boundary conditions are parameter-free. Therefore π_1 can at most be a constant. Hence the form of ω is given immediately as

$$\omega = c_1 \frac{Rc}{L^2} \qquad c_1 = \text{constant} \qquad (4.26)$$

Equation (4.26) can be used to give the required model law and similitude rule for vibration in this mode immediately. This is simply that the ratio of acoustic velocity to L^2/R be constant. Thus the researcher can adjust frequency, etc., to meet experimental needs and still obtain accurate predictions. In this sense Eq. (4.26) provides a basis for distorted as well as for normal models for beams of constant cross sectional properties.

If we treat ω as a parameter whose value is unknown but desired, we can extend the solution still further by resort to reasoning based on the meaning of the normalized governing equation. The second term in Eq. (4.24a) is a measure of the inertia forces resulting from acceleration of the mass elements of the beam during vibration; the first term is a measure of the elastic forces arising from the flexural bending of the beam. If a vibration is to persist, these two forces must be of the same magnitude. Since the terms in the variables in Eq. (4.24) have been made approximately unity by construction, the parameter must also be approximately unity if both terms are to be the same magnitude, provided our estimates were correct. For any given beam shape, this allows us to estimate the value of ω. We obtain

$$\omega = \sqrt{\frac{EI}{\rho A L^4}} \qquad \text{rad/sec} \qquad (4.27a)$$

The exact solution to this problem as given, for example, by Jacobsen and Ayre[21] (page 80) for a rectangular cross section, is

$$4\omega = 3.5159 \sqrt{\frac{EI}{\rho bh L^4}} \qquad \text{rad/sec}$$

or

$$\omega = 0.879 \sqrt{\frac{EI}{\rho bh L^4}} \qquad \text{rad/sec} \qquad (4.27b)$$

Hence the very simple estimate of Eq. (4.27a) is entirely correct in form and in error by 12 percent in magnitude.   Considering the crude nature of the estimates employed, the result is surprisingly good.   Moreover, Eq. (4.27a) is not restricted to rectangular cross sections.

Let us consider Eq. (4.23c) further to see if we can determine something about the case where the beam varies smoothly in cross section or modulus with length.   Define the quantity $(EI)_o$ as the largest EI product for any section of the beam.   Take

$$(\bar{E}\bar{I}) = \frac{EI}{(EI)_o}$$

On substituting into Eq. (4.23c) we obtain

$$\frac{2\delta(EI)_o}{L^4}\frac{\partial(\bar{E}\bar{I})}{\partial\bar{x}}\frac{\partial^3\bar{y}}{\partial\bar{x}^3} + \frac{(EI)_o\delta}{L^4}\frac{\partial^2\bar{E}\bar{I}}{\partial\bar{x}^2}\frac{\partial^2\bar{y}}{\partial\bar{x}^2} + \frac{\delta EI}{L^4}\frac{\partial^4\bar{y}}{\partial\bar{x}^4} + \rho A\,\delta\omega^2\frac{\partial^2\bar{y}}{\partial\bar{t}^2} = 0$$

Dividing by $(EI)_o\delta/L^4$ gives

$$\frac{\partial^2(\bar{E}\bar{I})}{\partial\bar{x}^2}\frac{\partial^2\bar{y}}{\partial\bar{x}^2} + 2\frac{\partial(\bar{E}\bar{I})}{\partial\bar{x}}\frac{\partial^3\bar{y}}{\partial\bar{x}^3} + \frac{EI}{(EI)_o}\frac{\partial^4\bar{y}}{\partial\bar{x}^4} + \frac{\rho A\omega^2 L^4}{(EI)_o}\frac{\partial^2\bar{y}}{\partial\bar{t}^2} = 0 \qquad (4.28a)$$

Equation (4.28a) allows us to formulate numerical criteria for when we can use Eq. (4.27b) as an estimate of vibration behavior for beams of non-uniform properties along the length.   Specifically, it is necessary that

$$\frac{\partial(\bar{E}\bar{I})}{\partial\bar{x}} \ll 1$$

$$\frac{\partial^2(\bar{E}\bar{I})}{\partial\bar{x}^2} \ll 1 \qquad (4.28b)$$

$$\frac{EI}{(EI)_o} \simeq 1$$

If the conditions of Eq. (4.28b) are not fulfilled, then an additional modeling condition must be fulfilled for similar behavior, namely,

$$\left[\frac{EI(\bar{x})}{(EI)_o}\right]_m = \left[\frac{EI(\bar{x})}{(EI)_o}\right]_P$$

That is, the distribution of EI as a function of $\bar{x}$ must be the same for model and prototype.   Usually it will be possible to satisfy all three of these conditions simultaneously, hence practical modeling can be achieved in relatively complex cases.   As in the simpler case described by Eq. (4.23), strict geometric similarity is not required to obtain exact modeling of the vibration behavior, and good approximations can be obtained for a very wide range of conditions.

Example 4.4.   Consider a cantilever beam of uniform cross section with a large rigid flange welded to the end as shown in Fig. 4.9.   Assume

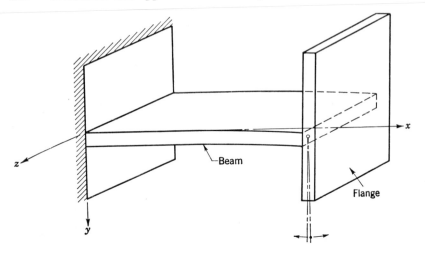

the beam can vibrate up and down.   Assume also that the mass can rotate about the beam center, but that torsional rotation and vibration motion in the z direction are constrained from occurring.

The equation for the beam vibration is again

$$EI \frac{\partial^4 y}{\partial x^4} + \rho A \frac{\partial^2 y}{\partial t^2} = 0 \tag{4.29a}$$

However, the boundary conditions now are

at $x = 0$: $y = 0$ $\dfrac{dy}{dx} = 0$ $\hspace{3cm}$ (4.29b)

at $x = L$: $\dfrac{\partial^2 y}{\partial x^2} = \dfrac{J_F}{EI} \dfrac{\partial^2 \theta_F}{\partial t^2}$ $\dfrac{\partial^3 y}{\partial x^3} = \dfrac{M_F}{EI} \dfrac{\partial^2 y_F}{\partial t^2}$ $\hspace{1cm}$ (4.29c)

at $t = 0$: $y_{x=L} = \delta$ $\left(\dfrac{dy}{dt}\right)_{x=L} = \dot{y}_{x=L} = 0$ $\hspace{1cm}$ (4.29d)

where

y_F = deflection of flange
θ_F = angular displacement of flange
J_F = mass polar moment of inertia of flange
M_F = mass of flange
I = section moment of beam, as in Example 4.3
E = Young's modulus of beam

We note that the boundary conditions at $x = L$ are identically the equations of motion for the vertical and angular displacements of the flange measured from the position of static equilibrium with respect to the beam. To complete the set of equations it is thus only necessary to add the conditions of compatibility at $x = L$

$$y_{x=L} = y_F$$

$$\left(\frac{dy}{dx}\right)_{x=L} = \tan \theta_F$$

It is convenient to employ the same nondimensional variables as in Example 4.3

$$\bar{y} = \frac{y}{\delta}$$

$$\bar{x} = \frac{x}{L}$$

$$\bar{t} = \omega t$$

We also define

$$\bar{\theta} = \frac{d\bar{y}}{d\bar{x}}$$

Then

$$\tan \theta_F = \left(\frac{dy}{dx}\right)_{x=L} \simeq \frac{\delta}{L} \qquad \bar{\theta}_F \simeq 1$$

$$y_F \simeq \delta \qquad \bar{y}_F \simeq 1$$

Upon normalizing, Eq. (4.29a) becomes, as before,

$$\frac{\partial^4 \bar{y}}{\partial \bar{x}^4} + \frac{\rho A L^4 \omega^2}{EI} \frac{\partial^2 \bar{y}}{\partial \bar{t}^2} = 0$$

Equation (4.29b) becomes

at $\bar{x} = 0$: $\qquad \bar{y} = 0 \qquad \frac{d\bar{y}}{d\bar{x}} = 0$

and Eqs. (4.29c) become

at $\bar{x} = 1$: $\qquad \frac{\partial^2 \bar{y}}{\partial \bar{x}^2} = \frac{L J_F \omega^2}{EI} \frac{\partial^2 \bar{\theta}_F}{\partial \bar{t}^2}$

and

$$\frac{\partial^3 \bar{y}}{\partial \bar{x}^3} = L^3 \frac{M_F \omega^2}{EI} \frac{\partial^2 \bar{y}_F}{\partial \bar{t}^2}$$

and Eqs. (4.29d) become

at $\bar{t} = 0$: $\qquad \bar{y}_{\bar{x}=1} = 1 \qquad \left(\frac{d\bar{y}}{d\bar{t}}\right)_{\bar{x}=1} = 0$

Thus the complete equations and boundary conditions contain three parameters

$$\pi_1 = \frac{\rho A L^4 \omega^2}{EI}$$

$$\pi_2 = \frac{L J_F \omega^2}{EI}$$

$$\pi_3 = \frac{L^3 M_F \omega^2}{EI}$$

But all of π_1, π_2, and π_3 contain the parameter ω^2 which we will usually want to be the dependent parameter.   Thus to simplify we form

$$\pi_4 = \frac{\pi_2}{\pi_1} = \frac{J_F L}{\rho A L \cdot L^3} \frac{EI\omega^2}{EI\omega^2}$$

But

$$\rho A L = \text{mass of beam} \triangleq M_B$$

Also

$$J_F = M_F r_F^2$$

where

$$r_F = \text{radius of gyration of flange}$$

Thus we can write

$$\pi_4 = \frac{M_F}{M_B} \frac{r_F^2}{L^2}$$

Similarly we take

$$\pi_5 = \frac{\pi_3}{\pi_1} = \frac{M_F}{M_B}$$

Moreover, π_4 and π_5 are both fixed when M_F/M_B and r_F^2/L^2 are fixed. Thus as the governing parameters we can take the more convenient and simpler groups

$$\pi_1 = \frac{\omega L^2}{Rc}$$

$$\pi_5 = \frac{M_F}{M_B}$$

$$\pi_6 = \frac{r_F^2}{L^2}$$

Since the equations are known to be well posed and to represent the physics very accurately for small deflections, we can expect that these parameters should be an accurate, complete, and quite useful set.

This problem can also be solved with integral equations. The reader who is familiar with the details of beam theory may find it useful to verify the solution in the following way. Using energy methods write a single integral equation governing the behavior of the system. Verify that the transformation of this equation into nondimensional form which satisfies the requirements of Rule 3 will lead to only parameters which are fixed when π_1, π_5, π_6 above are fixed.

4-8 NONUNIFORM BEHAVIOR—BOUNDARY-LAYER METHODS

In treating problems involving nonuniform behavior we employ the concepts utilized in discussing problems of uniform behavior, but it is also necessary to introduce additional ideas. Several concepts have been developed over the years specifically for dealing with problems of nonuniform behavior. The first is the boundary-layer concept due to L. Prandtl. Although Prandtl applied the idea only to fluid mechanics problems, it has much wider applicability. The three examples in this section, including Prandtl's original problem of the fluid boundary layer and one thermal-conduction problem, will give some idea of scope.

The central idea in Prandtl's boundary-layer concept is the use of different estimates in different regions of the system. This same concept forms the basis for more recent formalization which we will call the method of *zonal estimates;* see, for example, Carrier.[8] Prandtl used data on individual terms directly; the method of zonal estimates allows use of minimal information about the general form of the solution as the basis for constructing estimates which can then be checked. Prandtl's method is discussed in Sec. 4-8*a*, zonal estimates in 4-8*b*.

a. Use of Physical Data Alone

Example 4.5. Application of Approximation Theory to the Navier-Stokes Equations for the Flow over an Immersed Object. The problem is to categorize the various regimes of flow and to find appropriate governing nondimensional parameters. The system to be analyzed is shown in Fig. 4.10.

It is assumed that the fluid is Newtonian and that the flow is laminar, steady, incompressible, and two-dimensional. The governing differential equations for this case are well known. They are readily found from the Navier-Stokes equations by dropping the time dependent and the z-com-

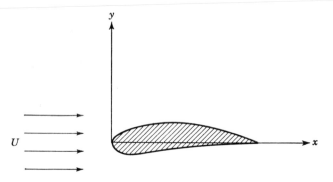

Fɪɢ. 4.10

ponent terms; this yields

$$u \frac{\partial u}{\partial x} + v \frac{\partial u}{\partial y} = - \frac{1}{\rho} \frac{\partial p}{\partial x} + \nu \nabla^2 u$$

and

$$u \frac{\partial v}{\partial x} + v \frac{\partial v}{\partial y} = - \frac{1}{\rho} \frac{\partial p}{\partial y} + \nu \nabla^2 v$$

where

$u = x$ component of velocity
$v = y$ component of velocity
$\nu =$ kinematic viscosity $= \mu/\rho$
$\rho =$ density
$p =$ pressure
$\nabla^2 =$ Laplacian operator

Continuity must also be satisfied. For this case the continuity equation can be written

$$\frac{\partial u}{\partial x} + \frac{\partial v}{\partial y} = 0$$

The boundary conditions usually employed are

at the surface of the object: $\quad u = 0 \qquad v = 0$
at $y = \infty$: $\qquad u = U \qquad v = 0$

If we now attempt to define parameters to satisfy either the condition of Rule 3 or Rule 4, we encounter several difficulties. First, since the flow field is infinite in extent, it is not possible to reduce the limits of the equations to finite intervals. Thus Rule 4 cannot be used directly. If we attempt to use Rule 3, we will find that we cannot define nondimensional variables that will satisfy the conditions required for all values of the parameters. Indeed for some values of the parameters we cannot define variables which give suitable estimates for all regions of the flow. We must therefore proceed in a different way. We seek estimates of the derivative terms which hold only for prespecified ranges of the parameters and in certain zones of the flow. We then attempt to find solutions which apply to each zone for a given range of the parameters and match the solutions at the edge of the two regions.

Even when we distinguish between various regions in the flow, it is not possible to guarantee similar behavior from the equations alone, since we do not have the required existence and uniqueness theorems in the case of the Navier-Stokes equations. However, if we find the necessary estimates from data for typical systems of the class considered with the appropriate values of the parameters, then we can be sure that we will obtain appropriate results, provided only that some single stable solution does appear in nature (which we have at least a philosophical right to expect) and that we stay within the region typified by the measurements, since we do know that the Navier-Stokes equations are a complete mathematical model for incompressible Newtonian fluids. Accordingly, we proceed by attempting to normalize as before, but supply the missing estimates from data.

We define

$$\bar{x} = \frac{x}{L}$$

$$\bar{y} = \frac{y}{\delta}$$

$$\bar{u} = \frac{u}{U}$$

$$\bar{v} = \frac{v}{V}$$

$$\bar{p} = \frac{p}{\Delta p_L}$$

where

L = length of object
δ = undetermined length
U = x component of velocity far upstream
V = undefined velocity
Δp_L = largest pressure difference between two points on the body; p is to be measured from pressure far upstream as datum

By construction $\bar{u}$ and $\bar{p}$ will be unity order and $\bar{x}$ will run from 0 to 1 over the body length. It remains to show that a V and δ can be found such that $\bar{V}$ is unity order and $\bar{y}$ runs 0 to 1 and also to provide estimates of the terms involved; we leave these questions open for the moment.

Substituting the nondimensional variables into the governing equations, one obtains:

x momentum:

$$\frac{U^2}{L}\,\bar{u}\,\frac{\partial \bar{u}}{\partial \bar{x}} + \frac{UV}{\delta}\,\bar{v}\,\frac{\partial \bar{u}}{\partial \bar{y}} = -\frac{\Delta p_L}{\rho L}\,\frac{\partial \bar{p}}{\partial \bar{x}} + \frac{U\nu}{L^2}\left(\frac{\partial^2 \bar{u}}{\partial \bar{x}^2} + \frac{L^2}{\delta^2}\,\frac{\partial^2 \bar{u}}{\partial \bar{y}^2}\right)$$

y momentum:

$$\frac{UV}{L}\,\bar{u}\,\frac{\partial \bar{v}}{\partial \bar{x}} + \frac{V^2}{\delta}\,\bar{v}\,\frac{\partial \bar{v}}{\partial \bar{y}} = -\frac{\Delta p_L}{\rho \delta}\,\frac{\partial \bar{p}}{\partial \bar{y}} + \frac{\nu V}{L^2}\left(\frac{\partial^2 \bar{v}}{\partial \bar{x}^2} + \frac{L^2}{\delta^2}\,\frac{\partial^2 \bar{v}}{\partial \bar{y}^2}\right)$$

continuity:

$$\frac{U}{L}\,\frac{\partial \bar{u}}{\partial \bar{x}} + \frac{V}{\delta}\,\frac{\partial \bar{v}}{\partial \bar{y}} = 0$$

In nondimensional form the continuity equation becomes

$$\frac{\partial \bar{u}}{\partial \bar{x}} + \frac{L}{U}\,\frac{V}{\delta}\,\frac{\partial \bar{v}}{\partial \bar{y}} = 0$$

By construction $\partial \bar{u}/\partial \bar{x}$ is unity order except near the stagnation point, which presents special problems.† We also want $\partial \bar{v}/\partial \bar{y}$ to be unity order and we must satisfy continuity at each and every point; this is possible only if

$$\frac{LV}{U\delta} \approx 1 \qquad\qquad (4.30a)$$

We can guarantee this by defining V as

$$V \triangleq \frac{\delta}{L}\,U \qquad\qquad (4.30b)$$

Since this is only one condition, δ still remains undefined. Equation (4.30b) guarantees that $\partial \bar{v}/\partial \bar{y}$ will be approximately unity by virtue of continuity. With this definition the continuity equation becomes parameter-free, and we need concern ourselves with it no further as far as approximation theory or similarity rules are concerned. We can also use Eq. (4.30b) to eliminate the parameter V from the two momentum equations. If we do this and also make the momentum equations non-dimensional by division of U^2/L, we obtain

x momentum:

$$\bar{u}\,\frac{\partial \bar{u}}{\partial \bar{x}} + \bar{v}\,\frac{\partial \bar{u}}{\partial \bar{y}} = -\frac{\Delta p_L}{\rho U^2}\,\frac{\partial \bar{p}}{\partial \bar{x}} + \frac{\nu}{UL}\left(\frac{\partial^2 \bar{u}}{\partial \bar{x}^2} + \frac{L^2}{\delta^2}\,\frac{\partial^2 \bar{u}}{\partial \bar{y}^2}\right) \qquad (4.31a)$$

---

† This problem has been extensively treated; see, for example, Schlichting,[45] p. 123, or Tsien.[49] We shall not discuss it here.

y momentum:

$$\bar{u}\frac{\partial\bar{v}}{\partial\bar{y}} + \bar{v}\frac{\partial\bar{v}}{\partial\bar{y}} = -\frac{\Delta p_L}{\rho U^2}\left(\frac{L}{\delta}\right)^2\frac{\partial\bar{p}}{\partial\bar{y}} + \frac{\nu}{UL}\left(\frac{\partial^2\bar{v}}{\partial\bar{x}^2} + \frac{L^2}{\delta^2}\frac{\partial^2\bar{v}}{\partial\bar{y}^2}\right) \qquad (4.31b)$$

With the boundary conditions

at surface of object:

$$\bar{u} = 0 \qquad \bar{v} = 0$$

at $\bar{y} = \infty$: $\qquad\qquad\qquad\qquad\qquad\qquad\qquad\qquad\qquad$ (4.31c)

$$\bar{u} = 1 \qquad \bar{v} = 0$$

The set of normalized governing equations and boundary conditions thus contains three pi's

$$\pi_1 = \left(\frac{L}{\delta}\right)^2$$

$$\pi_2 = \frac{UL}{\nu} = \text{Reynolds number} \triangleq Re_L$$

$$\pi_3 = \frac{\Delta p_L}{\rho U^2} = \text{Euler number} \triangleq Eu$$

Since Eqs. (4.31) are nonhomogeneous in the dependent variables u and v, they contain a parameter U representing the dependent variable. They would also contain one representing v except that we eliminated it in favor of U by demanding that the continuity equation be satisfied everywhere in the flow. We must discuss in more detail the implication of the dependent parameter.

Equations (4.31) and the continuity equation represent three independent equations for the three dependent variables u, v, and p. Together they constitute a relationship among these variables and the independent variables and parameters. But since they are nonhomogeneous in u, we cannot specify a correlation independent of the value of U. That is, U appears explicitly in the normalized equations and is thus related to the independent parameters. To put this differently, if we specify values of the independent variables and two of the three parameters π_1, π_2, and π_3, then the third parameter is fixed by Eqs. (4.31); this is unlike the case of homogeneous equations which we have treated up to this point. That is, if we specify the value of Reynolds number and Euler number, then a certain value of the dependent parameter is fixed by the equations or can be measured in the laboratory; it is no longer free. Thus in the case of nonhomogeneous equations we must always note that they contain the dependent as well as the independent parameters.

Thus we see again that we must expect solutions that are parameter-dependent. That is, we should anticipate the possibility of finding different solutions, possibly even entirely different types of solution, for different values of the independent nondimensional governing parameters. This possibility indeed occurs, as is well verified experimentally in the case of the flows governed by Eqs. (4.31) for a large variety of cases.

In this instance also we normally invert the variables. That is, the mathematical form shows δ as independent and U as dependent. However, this would be exceedingly awkward experimentally, and we normally prefer to treat U as independent and δ as dependent.

In this particular problem we are still seeking a choice of parameters such that the terms in the variables of Eqs. (4.31) will be made unity order; but since we are treating δ as dependent, we may not be able to select a single value that will achieve this for all possible values of Reynolds and Euler numbers. This is in fact the case. Hence we examine the nature of possible solutions and approximations when Re_L is small compared to 1 when it is approximately one, and when it is large compared to 1. Take first the case where the Reynolds number is small compared to 1.

If Re_L is small compared to unity, then Eqs. (4.31) show that regardless of the size of $(L/\delta)^2$ one of the two viscous terms multiplied by $1/Re_L$ must be large compared to unity.

The order of magnitude of the terms near the body is as indicated below each term in the following equation

$$\bar{u}\frac{\partial \bar{u}}{\partial \bar{x}} + \bar{v}\frac{\partial \bar{u}}{\partial \bar{y}} = Eu_x\frac{\partial \bar{p}}{\partial \bar{x}} + \frac{1}{Re_L}\left[\frac{\partial^2 \bar{u}}{\partial \bar{x}^2} + \left(\frac{L}{\delta}\right)^2\frac{\partial^2 \bar{u}}{\partial \bar{y}^2}\right]$$

$$\begin{array}{ccccccc} 1 & \quad 1 & \quad \underbrace{\gg 1} & \quad \gg 1 & \quad 1 & \quad ? & \quad 1 \end{array}$$

Thus if the flow field is confined (or near the body) it is possible to drop the inertia terms, and the governing x momentum equation becomes

$$0 = Eu\frac{\partial \bar{p}}{\partial \bar{x}} + \frac{1}{Re_L}\left[\frac{\partial^2 \bar{u}}{\partial \bar{x}^2} + \left(\frac{L}{\delta}\right)^2\frac{\partial^2 \bar{u}}{\partial \bar{y}^2}\right] \qquad (4.32a)$$

If the flow field is infinite, we cannot guarantee that Eq. (4.32a) will hold, for the reasons discussed in Sec. 4-6b. Indeed, it frequently does not give correct results for the flow at infinity.

Similarly for confined flows or near the body, the y momentum equation can be simplified for low Re_L. It is also useful to multiply by Re_L; this yields for the two momentum equations

$$\frac{L\,\Delta p_L}{\mu U}\frac{\partial \bar{p}}{\partial \bar{x}} + \frac{\partial^2 \bar{u}}{\partial \bar{x}^2} + \frac{L^2}{\delta}\frac{\partial^2 \bar{u}}{\partial \bar{y}^2} = 0$$

$$\frac{L\,\Delta p_L}{\mu U}\frac{L^2}{\delta^2}\frac{\partial \bar{p}}{\partial \bar{y}} + \frac{\partial^2 \bar{v}}{\partial \bar{x}^2} + \frac{L^2}{\delta^2}\frac{\partial^2 \bar{v}}{\partial \bar{y}^2} = 0 \qquad (4.32b)$$

The first parameter $L\,\Delta p_L/\mu U$ is recognizable as a Stokes number, which was shown to be the most appropriate parameter in one problem of this kind in Example 3.4.

In the middle range of Reynolds number, that is, neither small nor large compared to 1, we cannot drop any of the terms. Since we are unable, in most cases, to solve the complete Eqs. (4.31) analytically, virtually no solutions are known for this region in closed form.

The final region, and that of most technical interest, is that described by Re_L large compared to unity. To study this case we rearrange the x momentum equation (4.31a) by factoring $(L/\delta)^2$. It then reads

$$\bar{u}\frac{\partial\bar{u}}{\partial\bar{x}} + \bar{v}\frac{\partial\bar{u}}{\partial\bar{y}} = -\,Eu\,\frac{\partial\bar{p}}{\partial\bar{x}} + \frac{(L/\delta)^2}{Re_L}\left[\frac{\partial^2\bar{u}}{\partial\bar{y}^2} + \left(\frac{\delta}{L}\right)^2\frac{\partial^2\bar{u}}{\partial\bar{x}^2}\right]\qquad(4.31d)$$

As already noted, the equations are nonhomogeneous and we cannot specify the magnitude of δ independent of the other parameters, since the equation itself is a relation between the value of the parameters representing dependent variables and those representing the independent parameters, and we have let δ be the dependent parameter. Since we have specified the value of Re_L, we have only two sources for finding δ: (1) the complete analytical solution and (2) typical data. Since the complete analytical solution has remained unobtainable, we must employ data to proceed further with derivation of approximate equations or governing parameters.

In much of the nineteenth-century literature of fluid mechanics, it was argued that since $1/Re_L$ is small, we should drop all terms multiplied by this parameter, that is, all the viscous terms for flow with large Re_L. This leads to the well-known Euler equations for a fluid with identically zero viscosity. The Euler equations are often soluble, but they lead to predictions of zero drag for all bodies of this type and to many other predictions in order-of-magnitude disagreement with experiment on technically important problems.

In the context of the present discussion it is clear that the difficulty is simply that we cannot drop these terms unless we can also show that the set of terms in the nondimensional variables associated with the parameter $1/Re_L$ have been made unity order. This clearly depends on the value of δ and, up until now, this has been unknown. Indeed, Prandtl's key contribution was to observe from the data that δ decreased as Re_L increased, so that for large Re_L the viscous effects are largely confined to a narrow region near the body. Prandtl called this region the *boundary layer*. He then defined δ to be the thickness of this layer as measured by the distance from the body where viscous effects are small, say 1 percent of the velocity which would be found by solving the Euler equations of inviscid flow. We shall here adopt the same definition. As shown by Fig. 4.11,

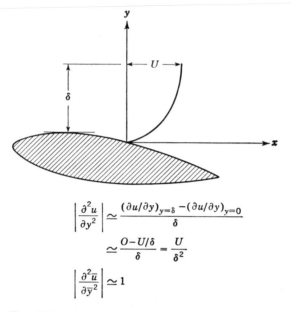

$$\left|\frac{\partial^2 u}{\partial y^2}\right| \simeq \frac{(\partial u/\partial y)_{y=\delta} - (\partial u/\partial y)_{y=0}}{\delta}$$

$$\simeq \frac{0 - U/\delta}{\delta} = \frac{U}{\delta^2}$$

$$\left|\frac{\partial^2 \bar{u}}{\partial \bar{y}^2}\right| \simeq 1$$

Fig. 4.11

this definition of δ does provide an estimate for $\partial^2 \bar{u}/\partial \bar{y}^2$ that is unity order inside the boundary layer.

We must add that this normalization leads to approximate, rather than exact, boundary conditions, since we replace

$$\bar{u} = 1 \qquad \text{at} \qquad \bar{y} = \infty \qquad \text{by} \qquad \bar{u} = 1 \qquad \text{at} \qquad \bar{y} = 1$$

This still does not settle the actual numerical value of δ. However, we observe from Eq. (4.31d) that if $\delta/L = 1$, then we would still drop all the viscous terms and again be led back to the discrepancies of the Euler equations. Some writers have accordingly argued that we must therefore take

$$\frac{(\delta/L)^2}{Re_L} \approx 1$$

or

$$\frac{\delta}{L} \approx \sqrt{\frac{1}{Re_L}} \tag{4.33}$$

We can do this on a trial basis; however, since δ is dependent, the only real proof of Eq. (4.33) is from data. Examination of a great deal of typical data shows that Eq. (4.33) is satisfied for bodies where $Re_L \gg 1$ in the case of attached flows.

With this knowledge of the value of δ, it is possible to estimate the magnitude of all the terms in both equations of momentum. Outside the boundary layer we discover that the viscous terms are small, hence we try dropping them entirely in this region. Inside the boundary layer the magnitudes of the terms are as shown below the equation which follows

$$\bar{u}\frac{\partial \bar{u}}{\partial \bar{x}} + \bar{v}\frac{\partial \bar{u}}{\partial \bar{y}} = -Eu\frac{\partial \bar{p}}{\partial \bar{x}} + \frac{(L/\delta)^2}{Re_L}\left[\frac{\partial^2 \bar{u}}{\partial \bar{y}^2} + \left(\frac{\delta}{L}\right)^2\frac{\partial^2 \bar{u}}{\partial \bar{x}^2}\right]$$

$$\approx (1) \qquad \approx (1) \qquad\quad 0(1) \qquad\quad \approx 1 \qquad \approx (1) \quad \ll 1 \ \approx(1)$$

Thus we try dropping the term $\partial^2 \bar{u}/\partial \bar{x}^2$ from the x momentum equation. The y momentum equation has magnitudes as indicated

$$\bar{u}\frac{\partial \bar{v}}{\partial \bar{x}} + \bar{v}\frac{\partial \bar{v}}{\partial \bar{y}} = -Eu\frac{\partial \bar{p}}{\partial \bar{y}}\left(\frac{L}{\delta}\right)^2 + \frac{1}{Re_L}\frac{\partial^2 \bar{v}}{\partial \bar{x}^2} + \left(\frac{L}{\delta}\right)^2\frac{\partial^2 \bar{v}}{\partial \bar{y}^2}$$

$$(1) \qquad (1) \qquad\quad 0(1) \ ? \ \gg 1 \qquad \ll 1 \quad 1 \qquad\qquad 1$$

We are particularly interested in the pressure term, but so far we have only that $Eu = 0(1)$. Euler number could be $\approx$ unity or very small, and the difference might be significant. To make this estimate more accurate, we define the pressure difference across the boundary layer as Δp_δ and also define

$$p^* = \frac{p}{\Delta p_\delta}$$

where, again, the datum for p is free stream pressure.† Then by construction

$$\frac{\partial p^*}{\partial \bar{y}} \approx 1$$

The total term involving the pressure in the y momentum equation can then be written

$$+Eu\frac{\partial \bar{p}}{\partial \bar{y}}\left(\frac{L}{\delta}\right)^2 = \frac{\Delta p_L}{\rho U^2}\frac{\Delta p_\delta}{\Delta p_L}\frac{\partial p^*}{\partial \bar{y}}\left(\frac{L}{\delta}\right)^2$$

$$\approx 1 \ \gg 1$$

Thus for the normalized equation to be valid, we must have

$$\frac{\Delta p_\delta}{\rho U^2} \ll 1$$

at least to the same order as

$$\left(\frac{\delta}{L}\right)^2 \ll 1$$

† The reader should note that the crux of this derivation lies in the distinction between magnitudes in the x direction $(L, \Delta p_I)$ and y direction $(\delta, \Delta p_\delta)$. See remarks on Huntley's addition in Chap. 2.

This follows from the fact that there is no other term in the equation greater than unity, and there would be no way to create an equality, unless Δp_δ is at least this small. (Δp_δ could be smaller than this, but not larger.) Consequently, to the accuracy of the boundary-layer approximation we can take

$$\Delta p_\delta = 0$$

This yields the well-known Prandtl boundary-layer equations; in dimensional form the equations are

$$u\frac{\partial u}{\partial x} + v\frac{\partial u}{\partial y} = -\frac{1}{\rho}\frac{\partial p}{\partial x} + \mu\frac{\partial^2 u}{\partial y^2} \qquad (4.34a)$$

$$\Delta p_\delta \approx 0 \qquad (4.34b)$$

It is now possible to proceed with solutions for the entire flow field in the way suggested by Prandtl. We first solve the inviscid equations, and assume that this solution is correct outside the boundary layer. Since $\Delta p_\delta = 0$ across the boundary layer, it is possible as a first approximation to use the pressure distribution found from the inviscid equations to supply values of $\partial p/\partial x$. This pressure distribution is then used to solve the x momentum equation of the boundary-layer equation (4.34a). Thus the y momentum equation is used simply to provide the match between the two regions. The fundamental approximation is that the flow can be treated as two regions: a boundary layer in which the Eqs. (4.34) apply, and a region outside the boundary layer where the inviscid flow equations are adequate.

This method has been widely used and is well verified as a first approximation. See, for example, Schlichting,[45] where many solutions are presented and checked against data. However, there are two instances in which this method does not work. The first is well known, it is the region around the nose of the body. As already noted, the estimates above do not apply in that region; $\partial \bar{u}/\partial \bar{x}$ is not unity order and Re_L is not large compared to 1. The method thus cannot be expected to work. The second case is when the flow separates from the body. Under these conditions, the data show that $(\delta/L)^2$ does not satisfy Eq (4.33) and measurements show that $\Delta p_\delta \neq 0$ near the separation point. Nor can agreement be expected, since the derivation of the equations relies on the value of δ given by data, and the magnitude employed no longer holds.

If we look back now at the idea of smooth estimates as shown in Fig. 4.2, we can see more clearly what is happening in this boundary-layer problem. Outside the boundary layer, things change only slowly and we can supply a smooth estimate of magnitudes. However, we cannot carry these estimates all the way to the boundary unless the boundary values happen to be those very particular ones we would get from the solution based on smooth estimates. The situation is like that found in the case of the simple harmonic oscillator; we cannot match the boundary conditions at all if we drop the derivatives of highest order. Here the particular boundary conditions that would agree with smooth estimates are those of the inviscid solution. Since this is not the case, a rapid change occurs near the boundary, creating the boundary layer. This particular kind of behavior frequently occurs when we try to drop terms involving the highest order of derivatives in a given variable. It thus often pays to *assume* the solution has the general form of Fig. 4.3 in such cases even when data are lacking and then to check the result against the more general equation. This idea is quite powerful, as we shall see in discussing the method of zonal estimates in Sec. 4-8*b*. The basic concept, as we have already stated, hinges on dividing the problem into a series of regions in each of which we can supply uniform estimates. These regions need not actually be at the boundary; for example, we often treat a shock wave in the body of a fluid by similar approximations. Also we may need more than two distinct regions.

A comparison of the procedure given above with the derivation of the boundary-layer equations found in most texts will also show the advantages of making terms in the variables $\approx$ unity. In particular, the great improvement in knowledge embodied in the parameter $(L/\delta)^2/Re_L$ compared to Re_L alone will be immediately evident to anyone familiar with the solutions and correlations of boundary-layer theory. In connection with the earlier remarks on force ratios (Sec. 4-5*c*) the particular Reynolds number which gives the ratio of inertia to viscous forces for this type of boundary layer is $(L/\delta)^2/Re_L$; it is therefore not surprising that it is a peculiarly useful form.

In fluid mechanics, nonuniform behavior is very common indeed. Since presently available mathematical methods are usually inadequate to obtain solutions to the complete equations, use of data on overall flow patterns for typical cases is extremely important. In this sense data are even more crucial in fluid mechanics than in many other fields. As is well illustrated by the discussion of Prandtl's boundary-layer equations, these data need not be very detailed, but they must characterize the typical overall flow pattern which actually occurs. Most of the really important analytical errors in the history of fluid mechanics have arisen from an implicit assumption of an overall flow pattern that does not actually occur in nature for the values of the governing nondimensional parameters of concern.

Example 4.6. Kármán Similarity Criteria for Turbulent Shear Layers. As a next example we consider Kármán's derivation of the similarity conditions for turbulent boundary layers. For the present purpose the derivation provides one of the few available examples of the use of intermediate derivatives and of the search for criteria in terms of a priori undefined parameters. Despite the historical importance of the result as a basis for construction of analytical forms of the mean velocity profiles, the derivation has several shortcomings. However, these also turn out to be instructive.

Define a stream function for two-dimensional, incompressible flow as

$$\Psi_1 = \Psi_m + \Psi$$

where

Ψ_1 = total stream function
Ψ_m = stream function of mean flow
Ψ = stream function of perturbation

Using these definitions, the Navier-Stokes equations for a two-dimensional flow can be written as[†]

$$\frac{\partial \nabla^2 \Psi_1}{\partial t} + \frac{\partial \Psi_1}{\partial y}\frac{\partial \nabla^2 \Psi_1}{\partial x} - \frac{\partial \Psi_1}{\partial x}\frac{\partial \nabla^2 \Psi_1}{\partial y} = \nu \nabla^4 \Psi_1$$

Now, orient the axes such that

$$u = u_m(y) \qquad v_m = 0$$

Then

$$u = u_m + \frac{\partial \Psi}{\partial y}$$

$$v = 0 - \frac{\partial \Psi}{\partial x}$$

u = component of velocity in x direction
$(\ )_m$ = time mean
v = component of velocity in y direction

An equation for perturbation (fluctuating motion) only is then obtained by expanding the original equation and substituting the conditions above. This yields

$$\frac{\partial(\nabla^2 \Psi)}{\partial t} + \left(u_m + \frac{\partial \Psi}{\partial y}\right)\frac{\partial \nabla^2 \Psi}{\partial x} - \left(\frac{\partial^2 u_m}{\partial y^2} + \frac{\partial \nabla^2 \Psi}{\partial y}\right)\frac{\partial \Psi}{\partial x} = \nu\left(\nabla^4 \Psi + \frac{\partial^3 u_m}{\partial y^3}\right)$$

We next try to define nondimensional parameters which satisfy the conditions of Rule 3 for the region which is not immediately adjacent to the wall but slightly farther out, called the turbulent core or logarithmic

[†] See, for example, Schlichting,[45] p. 58ff.

region. Kármán used definitions equivalent to

$$\bar{x} = \frac{x}{l}$$

$$\bar{y} = \frac{y}{l}$$

$$\bar{\Psi} = \frac{\psi}{Bl}$$

$$\bar{t} = \omega t$$

$$\bar{u} = \frac{u_m}{B}$$

where

l = largest characteristic length of the perturbation in velocity due to turbulent fluctuations, assumed same in x and y directions.

B = undefined velocity such that $\Psi \approx 1$

ω = undefined characteristic frequency

Setting the differential equation into nondimensional form yields

$$\frac{\omega Bl}{l^2}\frac{\partial \nabla^2 \bar{\Psi}}{\partial \bar{t}} + B\left(\bar{u} + \frac{\partial \bar{\Psi}}{\partial \bar{y}}\right)\frac{B}{l^2}\frac{\partial \nabla^2 \bar{\Psi}}{\partial \bar{x}} - B\frac{\partial \bar{\Psi}}{\partial x}\frac{B}{l^2}\left(\frac{\partial^2 \bar{u}}{\partial \bar{y}^2} + \frac{\partial \nabla^2 \bar{\Psi}}{\partial \bar{y}}\right)$$
$$= \frac{\nu B}{l^3}\left(\nabla^4 \bar{\Psi} + \frac{\partial^3 \bar{u}}{\partial \bar{y}^3}\right)$$

Dividing by B^2/l^2 gives

$$\frac{\omega l}{B}\frac{\partial \nabla^2 \bar{\Psi}}{\partial \bar{t}} + \left(\bar{u} + \frac{\partial \bar{\Psi}}{\partial \bar{y}}\right)\frac{\partial \nabla^2 \bar{\Psi}}{\partial \bar{x}} - \frac{\partial \bar{\Psi}}{\partial \bar{x}}\left(\frac{\partial^2 \bar{u}}{\partial \bar{y}^2} + \frac{\partial \nabla^2 \bar{\Psi}}{\partial \bar{y}}\right)$$
$$= \frac{\nu}{Bl}\left(\nabla^4 \bar{\Psi} + \frac{\partial^3 \bar{u}}{\partial \bar{y}^3}\right) \quad (4.35)$$

In the original derivation Kármán dropped the time-dependent and viscous effects, the first and last terms of Eq. (4.35). For this to be correct it is necessary that at least

$$\frac{\omega l}{B} \ll 1 \qquad (4.36a)$$

and

$$\frac{Bl}{\nu} \gg 1 \qquad (4.36b)$$

Kármán noted the physical meaning of these assumptions: in a strong velocity gradient the shear forces due to lateral fluctuations are large compared to those generated by temporal fluctuations and by viscosity. Two further comments are also in order.

We are trying to drop the terms of highest order. It is thus to be expected that the solution obtained cannot hold for the entire flow. And, indeed, physical evidence shows that $l \to 0$ at the wall. Thus some region very near the wall does exist where the condition of Eq. (4.36b) cannot be satisfied.

Second, Eq. (4.36a) can hold only when ω is small. It thus requires that the turbulent shear is dominated by the low-frequency motion. In the original derivation, conditions (4.36a) and (4.36b) were not made explicit; to the author's knowledge condition (4.36a), in particular, has never been examined explicitly in this sense.

In order to finish the derivation along the lines followed by Kármán, let us assume that the conditions of Eqs. (4.36) are satisfied. We then use a Taylor series expansion about an arbitrary point denoted ( )$_o$ to approximate u as follows

$$u_m = u_{m_o} + \left(\frac{du_m}{dy}\right)_o (y - y_o) + \frac{1}{2}\left(\frac{d^2 u_m}{dy^2}\right)_o (y - y_o)^2 + \cdots$$

Taking point ( )$_o$ as reference and working only with the motion of the perturbation, we then have the following equation as a *linear* approximation in the perturbation:

$$(y - y_o)\left(\frac{du_m}{dy}\right)_o \frac{\partial \nabla^2 \Psi}{\partial x} - \left(\frac{\partial^2 u_m}{\partial y^2}\right)_o \frac{d\Psi}{dx} + \frac{d\Psi}{dy}\frac{\varphi \nabla^2 \Psi}{\partial x} - \frac{\partial \Psi}{\partial x}\frac{\partial \nabla^2 \Psi}{\partial y} = 0$$

We now shift the coordinate system so that we use the point ( )$_o$ as reference for $\bar{x}$ and $\bar{y}$. Thus

$$\bar{x} = \frac{x - x_o}{l}$$

$$\bar{y} = \frac{y - y_o}{l}$$

and as before

$$\bar{\Psi} = \frac{\Psi}{Bl}$$

The differential equation in this coordinate system becomes

$$\frac{y - y_o}{l}\frac{\partial u_m}{\partial y}\frac{B}{l}\frac{\partial \nabla^2 \bar{\Psi}}{\partial \bar{x}} - \left(\frac{\partial^2 u_m}{\partial y^2}\right)_o \frac{Bl}{l}\frac{\partial \bar{\Psi}}{\partial \bar{x}} + \frac{Bl}{l}\frac{\partial \bar{\Psi}}{\partial \bar{y}}\frac{Bl}{l^3}\frac{\partial \nabla^2 \bar{\Psi}}{\partial \bar{x}}$$

$$- \frac{Bl}{l}\frac{\partial \bar{\Psi}}{\partial \bar{x}}\frac{Bl}{l^2 l}\frac{\partial \nabla^2 \bar{\Psi}}{\partial \bar{y}} = 0$$

We choose to normalize by division of $(B/l)(\partial u_m/\partial y)_o$. [Note that

$(\partial u_m/\partial y)_o$ and $(\partial^2 u_m/\partial y^2)_o$ are constant parameters dependent on the mean velocity profile, not variable in size, in this treatment.]

$$\bar{y}\,\frac{\partial \nabla^2 \bar{\Psi}}{\partial \bar{x}} - \frac{l(\partial^2 u_m/\partial y^2)_o}{(\partial u_m/\partial y)_o}\,\frac{\partial \bar{\Psi}}{\partial \bar{x}} + \frac{B}{l(\partial u_m/\partial y)_o}\,\frac{\partial \nabla^2 \bar{\Psi}}{\partial \bar{x}}\,\frac{\partial \bar{\Psi}}{\partial \bar{y}}$$
$$- \frac{B}{l(\partial u_m/\partial y)_o}\,\frac{\partial \bar{\Psi}}{\partial x}\,\frac{\partial \nabla^2 \bar{\Psi}}{\partial y} = 0$$

This equation requires that similarity between two different situations can exist only if the two dimensionless parameters

$$\frac{l(\partial^2 u_m/\partial y^2)_o}{(\partial u_m/\partial y)_o} = \pi_1 \qquad \text{and} \qquad \frac{B}{l(\partial u_m/\partial y)_o} = \pi_2$$

are the same in the two cases. If we are looking for a general sort of similarity law, that is, one which holds for all problems of this class, then it must follow that such a law can exist only if both of these parameters are constant in all flows of this type. If we have normalized the equations properly, this must be so, since if either π_1 or π_2 could vary, then some cases would exist in which similarity would not occur. Thus to the order of the approximation made, necessary conditions for a possible similarity law can be stated as follows:

$$\pi_1 = \frac{l(\partial^2 u_m/\partial y^2)_o}{(\partial u_m/\partial y)_o} = C_1 = \varkappa \qquad\qquad (4.37a)$$

and

$$\pi_2 = \frac{B}{l(\partial u_m/\partial y)_o} = C_2 \qquad\qquad (4.37b)$$

However, since B represents the dependent variable, only one of these equations is independent. We conclude that only one of Eqs. (4.37a) and (4.37b) is necessary. If we adopt Eq. (4.37a), we have precisely Kármán's *similarity law.*

The second condition can be used to evaluate the still undetermined velocity B, using Reynolds' expression for the shear stress, as follows:

$$\tau = \rho\,\frac{\partial \Psi}{\partial x}\,\frac{\partial \Psi}{\partial y} = \rho l^2\,\frac{B^2}{l^2}\,\frac{\partial \bar{\Psi}}{\partial \bar{x}}\,\frac{\partial \bar{\Psi}}{\partial \bar{y}}$$

We want B such that $\partial \bar{\Psi}/\partial \bar{x} = 0(1)$ and $\partial \bar{\Psi}/\partial \bar{y} = 0(1)$ for all cases. We therefore set B^2 such that $\tau/\rho = B^2 0(1)$. Thus we can define B^2 as:

$$B^2 = \frac{\tau_w}{\rho} \qquad B = v^* = \sqrt{\frac{\tau_w}{\rho}}$$

Thus we see that a definition for B that will satisfy the conditions for Rule 4 is the familiar "friction velocity" of hydraulics. Adopting this definition, Eq. (4.36*b*) becomes

$$\tau = \rho B^2 = \rho C_2 l^2 \left(\frac{\partial u_m}{\partial y}\right)_o^2$$

This result shows that to be entirely consistent with Prandtl's older mixing length theory we need only define l such that

$$C_2 = 1$$

Since the mixing length l is a finite quantity, we can utilize the available data (see, for example, Schlichting,[45] Chap. 10) to assure ourselves that an l exists which satisfies the conditions of Rule 3.

At first glance this derivation appears to be free from any physical assumption or ad hoc hypothesis regarding the nature of the solution.   If this were so, one would hope that it would give general conditions for similarity among flows of this type and that similarity, or lack of it, could then be tested directly by checking whether the required conditions are fulfilled from data, as just noted.   In a certain sense this turns out to be true, that is, the data show that some form of similarity does hold for pipe flow, for flow over a flat plate, and probably also for flows which F. H. Clauser[9] has called "equilibrium flows," although this last point has not been entirely demonstrated.   However, closer examination of the Kármán derivation shows that it does, in effect, assume that the fluctuations at a given point in the flow depend on local conditions at that point; this is implied in the use of a Taylor series expansion for the velocity fluctuations in terms of the mean flow.   Moreover, recent studies of the energetics and dynamics of the turbulent shear layer (Kline and Runstadler,[25] and others) show that this is not the case.   These studies show quite clearly that the bulk of the turbulence, particularly the large eddy structure which controls the shear, is produced in a narrow zone relatively near the wall.   The details of this model are still under study by a number of workers.   The parameters which control this production are such that they give simple overall similarity, in a certain sense, for the cases just mentioned.   But certain dynamic similarities of a more complex nature appear to exist even in the other cases.   Moreover, the dynamics observed make the assumption of equal length scales in the various directions and the lack of time dependence appear highly questionable.

For all these reasons, the good results achieved by Kármán are probably largely fortuitous and depend on the fact that almost any reasonable assumption leads to good estimates of the mean velocity profile.   Such fortuitous outcomes are, of course, typical of early results obtained by really first-rate analysts on difficult problems.   However, the example illustrates that provision of proper estimates is by no means simple. Indeed, in the turbulence problem it is still not altogether clear what the correct estimates are, although some of the length scales that must be used are now known. We must know a good deal about the physics of a problem before it is certain which normalizations lead to good estimates.

Example 4.7. A Thermal-conduction Boundary Layer. As already noted, the boundary-layer concept can be applied to many other physical situations in addition to the fluid mechanical boundary layer for which Prandtl first conceived it. Here we apply the idea to the thermal system we have thus far called the cooking problem. This example brings out particularly clearly the large effects which can arise from alteration in boundary conditions alone.

Assume that the analysis of Sec. 4-6a is known and that the Biot number is large compared to unity; we need then consider only conduction heat transfer. Consider regulation of oven temperature so that the atmosphere around the body varies periodically in time. For simplicity, assume this temperature variation is a harmonic wave of one pure frequency given by the equation

$$T_{\text{oven}} = T_o \sin \frac{t}{\tau} + T_a \tag{4.38}$$

From Sec. 4-6a, the governing equation for conduction in normalized form is

$$\frac{\partial^2 \bar{T}}{\partial \bar{x}^2} + \frac{L^2}{M^2} \frac{\partial^2 \bar{T}}{\partial \bar{y}^2} + \frac{L^2}{N^2} \frac{\partial^2 \bar{T}}{\partial \bar{z}^2} = \frac{L^2}{t_c \alpha} \frac{\partial \bar{T}}{\partial \bar{t}} \tag{4.39}$$

where

$$\bar{t} \triangleq \frac{t}{t_c}$$

$$\bar{x} = \frac{x}{L}$$

$$\bar{y} = \frac{y}{M}$$

$$\bar{z} = \frac{z}{N}$$

$$\bar{T} = \frac{T}{T_s}$$

and

$$t_c = \text{time constant of body}$$
$$L, M, N = \text{characterizing lengths in } x, y, z \text{ directions, respectively}$$
$$l = \text{smallest of } L, M, N$$
$$T_s = \text{temperature at surface of body}$$

Since this equation is linear, we can superpose solutions. It is therefore possible to treat the steady-state and transient portions of the problem separately. Initially, the average temperature may be different from T_a. However, the analysis of Sec. 4-6a shows that the average (steady-state) temperature of the body will approximate T_a as soon as the time exceeds a value given by

$$\bar{t} = \frac{t}{t_c} > 1 \tag{4.40a}$$

Also from Sec. 4-6a, $t_c \simeq l^2/\alpha$. Inserting this into Eq. (4.40a) gives

$$t \gg \frac{l^2}{\alpha} \tag{4.40b}$$

Since we are not now interested in the early transient period, we assume Eq. (4.40b) is satisfied and examine only the periodic steady-state behavior.

Since the Biot number is large, the boundary conditions for this portion of the problem are

$$T_s = T_{\text{surface}} = T_o \sin \frac{t}{\tau}$$

where all T's are measured from T_a as datum. For simplicity, let us also assume the body is roughly spherical, so that $L \simeq M \simeq N \simeq l$; this simplifies, but does not restrict, the analysis in this case. Equation (4.39) thus becomes

$$\frac{\partial^2 \bar{T}}{\partial \bar{x}^2} + \frac{\partial^2 \bar{T}}{\partial \bar{y}^2} + \frac{\partial^2 \bar{T}}{\partial \bar{z}^2} = \frac{l^2}{t_c \alpha} \frac{\partial \bar{T}}{\partial \bar{t}}$$

with boundary conditions

$$\bar{T}_s = \frac{T_s}{T_o} = \sin\left(\frac{t_c}{\tau} \bar{t}\right)$$

Thus, as before, we obtain a Fourier number $l^2/t_c\alpha$, but we also find the added nondimensional parameter t_c/τ from the boundary conditions.

We now consider the effect of variations in the parameter t_c/τ. Suppose first that

$$\frac{t_c}{\tau} \ll 1$$

The solution of Sec. 4-6a shows that the entire body will reach a temperature within 1 percent of any newly applied surface temperature in a time of approximately $3t_c$. It follows that for $t_c/\tau \ll 1$, the temperature in the body will essentially "follow" the applied wave. On the other hand, suppose that

$$\frac{t_c}{\tau} \gg 1$$

Then we observe that the fluctuations are too rapid for the body as a whole to follow. The typical depth of penetration of the temperature effect, which we will call δ, can be estimated directly from Eq. (4.40b) by reasoning as follows. The transient effect is important only where the Fourier number $l^2/t\alpha$ is ≥ 1. Hence, if we want to find the depth to which the temperature change is roughly 1 percent of that applied (T_s), then we must find the section where $l^2/t\alpha \simeq 3$;† the value of l at this point gives us δ. Since we know the time involved (time for one-quarter cycle $= \frac{\pi}{2}\tau$), we can solve for the length δ

$$\delta = \sqrt{3t\alpha} = \sqrt{\frac{3\pi}{2}\alpha\tau} \tag{4.40c}$$

As we decrease τ (raise frequency) further and further, the depth of penetration δ becomes smaller and smaller and a larger and larger portion of the center of the body remains approximately constant at temperature T_a.

Alternatively, we can consider a temperature oscillation at the surface of fixed frequency and let the body thickness l increase. For large enough l we must then always obtain a *thermal boundary layer* confined to a region near the surface of depth given by Eq. (4.40c); this equation estimates the thickness of a *99-percent boundary layer*, that is, the section where the fluctuation is reduced to 1 percent of T_o (actually, any desired level can be estimated). Thus whenever $t_c/\tau \gg 1$, we find a boundary layer near the surface which includes nearly all the temperature change. We must then provide separate estimates for this boundary layer and for the rest of the body if we want to satisfy the conditions of Rule 3 or 4.

Since thermal time constants are relatively large, this kind of thermal boundary layer is very frequently important in natural events and in engineering devices. Familiar examples are the daily fluctuations from the radiant heat of the sun on the earth, and the quarter-cycle high-temperature wave due to combustion in the cylinders of internal combustion engines. In this latter case the fact that δ is very small com-

---

† The use of $3t_c$ gives an estimate, based on exponential behavior, that is appropriate for linear equations.

pared with the cylinder wall thickness allows operation with gas temperatures far higher than those which can be utilized in systems where steady high temperatures are necessary, such as gas turbine engines.

This example shows clearly that (1) a change in boundary conditions alone can entirely alter the important parameters and (2) a boundary-layer problem can occur even in linear, homogeneous equations. However, we still have the advantage of homogeneity, in that the system response can be correlated independent of the magnitude of T_o when measured in $\bar{T}$ coordinates. We can also still employ the linear property of the governing equation to argue as follows. Superposition allows consideration of the temperature wave $T_o \cos (t/\tau)$ as one component of a Fourier analysis of a more complex wave shape. Both the simple and more complex waves can be considered as departures from an average or *backbone* curve which gives the steady-state solution. This wave is a function solely of the mean inputs of heat, that is, temperature distribution, applied to the surface over a long time. In this way, a very clear picture of virtually all of the important features of heat conduction can be found from the differential equation and the boundary conditions without need for solution. Moreover, such results are readily formulated for bodies of very complex shapes; time-consuming and costly detailed calculations can in this way often be avoided.

b. *Zonal Estimates*

A very useful systematization of the boundary-layer idea has recently been discussed by several workers; a good summary is given by Carrier.[8] This method provides a procedure for seeking estimates applicable to each region in a problem with nonuniform behavior using only minimal information about the expected solution form. As we have already seen, when the small parameter in a differential equation modifies the most highly differentiated term in a given variable, then a boundary-layer problem may occur; whether it will or not, in general, depends on the value of the boundary conditions applied. There is no proof of this rule, but it seems to hold. When such a situation occurs, we must then necessarily be prepared to deal with nonuniform estimates for various regions. We can then proceed in the following way.

1. Make an estimate of the gross nature of the solution; this can be found from known results or assumed, based on experience with similar systems or equations. We need only to know where to expect boundary-layer behavior.
2. Drop the most highly differentiated term and seek a solution of the simpler resulting equation. If we can find one, we assume for the

moment that it applies in the region where the curve is smooth, that is, outside the boundary layer.

3. In the boundary-layer region perform a change of scale; provide in the transformation a degree of arbitrariness by inserting an undefined exponent. Use the complete differential equation to determine what value of the exponent will simultaneously make all terms of the same order through the boundary layer that we think we need and provide for a region of overlap between the boundary-layer region and the smooth zone.

4. We then try to solve the new equation for the boundary layer, but we assume it holds only through the boundary-layer region and the zone of overlap.

Since no theorems covering this procedure are known, each problem presents something of a special case. The solutions found should be checked against data if possible, since they depend not only on the equations but also on an initial assumption about overall form, and usually no statements about uniqueness of solutions are available when we resort to methods of this type. The method of zonal estimates nevertheless has appeared to be extremely powerful and very effective in the problems to which it has been applied thus far. We now give a simple introductory example.†

Consider the differential equation

$$\epsilon \frac{d^2\bar{u}}{d\bar{x}^2} + (1 - \bar{x}^2)\bar{u} + \bar{u}^2 = 0 \qquad 0 \le \bar{x} \le 1$$

with boundary conditions

at $\bar{x} = -1$: $\bar{u} = 0$
at $\bar{x} = +1$; $\bar{u} = 0$

Suppose that the variables $\bar{u}$ and $\bar{x}$ have already been normalized. Suppose further that we are interested in a particular problem where we know that $0 < \epsilon \ll 1$. Under these conditions boundary-layer behavior is a possibility. On a trial basis we can assume that the solution is smooth except near $\bar{x} = +1$ and $\bar{x} = -1$, where we may have a boundary layer. We look first for a solution applicable in the interior (away from the boundaries) which is assumed to be smooth. Dropping the $\epsilon \, d^2\bar{u}/d\bar{x}^2$ term we have

$$(1 - \bar{x}^2)\bar{u} + \bar{u}^2 = 0$$

† From unpublished notes by G. F. Carrier.

This is a quadratic algebraic equation for $\bar{u}$ as a function of $\bar{x}$. Solving by the usual rule and calling the result $\bar{u}_o$, we get

$$2\bar{u}_o = (1 - \bar{x}^2) = \sqrt{(1 - \bar{x}^2)^2 + 4}$$

$\bar{u}_o$ is symmetric about $\bar{x} = 0$; it has two branches as shown.

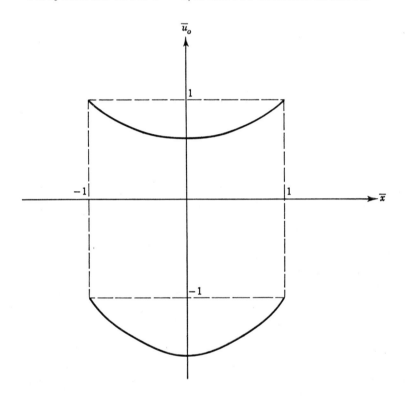

Note that neither branch satisfies the boundary conditions; at $x = \pm 1$ we get $+1$ for the upper branch and -1 for the lower one.

Now we define a new variable $\bar{\eta}$ as follows

$$\bar{\eta} = (\bar{x} + 1)\epsilon^\beta$$

ϵ is the parameter from the original differential equation; β is to be found. We put in the $+1$ since we want the solution to match the smooth solution near the point $\bar{x} = -1$, that is, we are now looking for the boundary layer behavior near $\bar{x} = -1$.   Eliminating $\bar{x}$ in favor of $\bar{\eta}$ in the complete differential equations gives

$$\epsilon^{1+2\beta} \frac{\partial^2 \bar{u}}{\partial \bar{\eta}^2} + \epsilon^{-\beta}\bar{\eta}(2 - \epsilon^{-\beta}\bar{\eta})\bar{u} + \bar{u}^2 = 1$$

We want to keep $\partial^2 \bar{u}/\partial \bar{\eta}^2$ in the boundary layer and at the corner, since we anticipate that the second derivative must be large near the corner (see discussion relating to Figs. 4.2 to 4.4 on pages 102 to 105). Accordingly we set $\beta = -\frac{1}{2}$; this gives

$$\frac{\partial^2 \bar{u}}{\partial \bar{y}^2} + \epsilon^{\frac{1}{2}}\bar{\eta}(2 - \epsilon^{\frac{1}{2}}\bar{\eta})\bar{u} + \bar{u}^2 = 1$$

This equation is not easy to work with. For convenience we look for a solution $\bar{u}$ which blends directly into u_o. We define a new function $\bar{\omega}(\bar{\eta})$ as

$$\bar{u} = \bar{u}_o(\bar{x}) + \bar{\omega}(\bar{\eta})$$

Substituting this into the differential equation, we obtain

$$\epsilon^{1+2\beta}\frac{\partial^2 \bar{\omega}}{\partial \bar{\eta}^2} + \epsilon^{-\beta}\bar{\eta}(2 - \epsilon^{-\beta}\bar{\eta})\bar{\omega} + 2\bar{u}_o\bar{\omega} + \bar{\omega}^2$$
$$+ [\epsilon^{-\beta}\bar{\eta}(2 - \epsilon^{-\beta}\bar{\eta})\bar{u}_o + \bar{u}_o^2 - 1] = 0$$

But by construction of $\bar{u}_o$ the three terms set off inside the brackets at the end are zero. Also we want to retain $\partial^2 \bar{\omega}/\partial \bar{\eta}^2$ for the reasons already stated; so again we take $\beta = -\frac{1}{2}$. This gives

$$\frac{\partial^2 \bar{\omega}}{\partial \bar{\eta}^2} + 2\bar{u}_o\bar{\omega} + \bar{\omega}^2 + 2\epsilon^{\frac{1}{2}}\bar{\eta}\bar{\omega} - \epsilon\bar{\eta}^2\bar{\omega} = 0$$

Since $\epsilon \ll 1$, we drop the last two terms. The resulting equation integrates once immediately on multiplication by $\partial\bar{\omega}/\partial\bar{\eta}$. This gives

$$\frac{1}{2}\left(\frac{\partial\bar{\omega}}{\partial\bar{\eta}}\right)^2 + 2\bar{u}_o\bar{\omega}^2 + \frac{\bar{\omega}^3}{3} = C_1$$

Since for large $\bar{\eta}$ we want to match smoothly to $\bar{u}_o$, we require that both $\bar{\omega}$ and $\partial\bar{\omega}/\partial\bar{\eta}$ approach zero. If this is to hold, we can have a solution for large $\bar{\eta}$ only if $C_1 = 0$. This application of an extra boundary condition ($\partial\bar{\omega}/\partial\bar{\eta} = 0$ for a large $\bar{\eta}$) is typical of the matching required at the edges of zones in boundary-layer methods. Moreover, we only need a solution for $\bar{\omega}$ near $\bar{x} = 1$. In this region $\bar{u} = 1 + H$ where H involves terms of order $\epsilon^{\frac{1}{2}}$ and higher. We can show this by inserting the definition of $\bar{\eta}$ into the solution for $\bar{u}_o$.

$$\bar{\eta} = (1 + \bar{x})\epsilon^{-\frac{1}{2}}$$
$$\bar{x} = \bar{\eta}\epsilon^{\frac{1}{2}} - 1$$
$$\bar{x}^2 = \bar{\eta}^2\epsilon - 2\bar{\eta}\epsilon^{\frac{1}{2}} + 1$$
$$2\bar{u}_o = \pm\sqrt{4 + (1 - \bar{x}^2)^2} - (1 - \bar{x}^2)$$
$$= \pm\sqrt{4 + (2\bar{\eta}\epsilon^{\frac{1}{2}} - \bar{\eta}^2\epsilon)} - (2\bar{\eta}\epsilon^{\frac{1}{2}} - \bar{\eta}^2\epsilon)$$

The last term has only terms in ϵ^1 and higher; the lowest power of ϵ from the term with the radical is $\epsilon^{\frac{1}{3}}$. Since we have neglected terms of this size in finding $\bar{u}_o$, it is consistent to use

$$2\bar{u}_o = \pm \sqrt{4} \qquad \bar{u}_o = \pm 1$$

in the equation for $\bar{\omega}$. Moreover $(\partial^2\bar{\omega}/\partial\bar{\eta}^2)^2$ is necessarily >0, and if $\bar{u}_o = +1$, then for $\bar{\eta} = 0$, $\omega = -1$. But then the equation for $\bar{\omega}$ becomes

$$\tfrac{1}{2}(+\text{value}) + 2(-1)^2 - \tfrac{1}{3} \neq 0$$

That is, there is no way to satisfy the differential equation for $\bar{\omega}$ and also the boundary condition at $\bar{\eta} = 0$ simultaneously if $\bar{u}_o = +1$. Accordingly we set $\bar{u}_o = -1$. The boundary conditions for $\bar{\omega}$ then are

at $\bar{\eta} = 0$: $\qquad \bar{\omega} = +1 \qquad \bar{u} = 0$
at $\bar{\eta} \to \infty$: $\qquad \bar{\omega} \to 0 \qquad \bar{u} \to \bar{u}_o$

The solution to this equation and boundary conditions is

$$\bar{\omega} = 3\left[1 - \tanh^2\left(\frac{\bar{\eta}}{\sqrt{2}} + A\right)\right]$$

where

$$A = \operatorname{arctanh}\sqrt{\frac{2}{3}}$$

This gives the boundary layer near $x = -1$. Since the solution is symmetric, we can write the boundary-layer expression near $x = +1$ by inspection as

$$\bar{\nu} = 3\left[1 - \tanh^2\left(\frac{\zeta}{\sqrt{2}} + A\right)\right]$$

where

$$\zeta = (\bar{x} - 1)\epsilon^{\frac{1}{3}}$$

And a solution for u is given in three pieces as

near $-1 \leq x \leq -1 + \zeta$:

$$\bar{u} = -1 + \bar{\omega}$$

for $-1 + \zeta \leq x \leq 1 - \zeta$:

$$\bar{u} = -\bar{u}_o$$

$1 - \zeta \leq x \leq 1$:

$$\bar{u} = -1 + \bar{\nu}$$

For this solution to be meaningful we must show that there is a $\delta \ll 1$ for which $\omega \simeq 1$, that is, $\bar{\eta} \gg 1$. If we can do this, the mathematics will display boundary-layer behavior and we will have constructed a good solution for the values of ϵ which give us the properties of δ and $\bar{\eta}$ just stated.   Since the example is contrived, there is no problem of physical completeness to concern us; the mathematical check suffices.

Near $x = -1$ we can write $\bar{u}_o$ from before as

$$\bar{u}_o = -\sqrt{4 + \bar{\eta}\epsilon(2 - \bar{\eta}\epsilon^{\frac{1}{2}})} - \bar{\eta}\epsilon^{\frac{1}{2}}(2 - \bar{\eta}\epsilon^{\frac{1}{2}})$$

So for $x - 1$, but $\bar{\eta}$ large, $\bar{u}_o$ behaves like

$$\bar{u}_o - 1 + a_1\bar{\eta}\epsilon^{\frac{1}{2}} + a_2\bar{\eta}^2\epsilon + \cdots$$

and

$$\frac{\bar{\omega}}{3} = 1 - \left[\tanh\left(\frac{\bar{\eta}}{2} + A\right)\right]^2$$

Moreover

$$(\tanh y)^2 = \left(\frac{e^y - e^{-y}}{e^y + e^{+y}}\right)^2 = \left(\frac{e^{2y}-1}{e^{2y}+1}\right)^2$$

so that $(\tanh y)^2 \to 1$ as soon as $e^{2y} \gg 1$.   Thus we need to show there are values of $x \leq \delta$ where both $\eta\epsilon^{\frac{1}{2}} \ll 1$ and $\epsilon\sqrt{2\eta+2A} \gg 1$.   This is easily done provided $\epsilon^{\frac{1}{2}} \ll 1$.   To show this explicitly, consider the location where $u/u_o = 0.99$, that is, $\bar{\omega}/u_o = 0.01$, $\bar{\omega} \simeq 0.001$.   Solving for the distance from the boundary $1 + x$ we find then the boundary thickness is

$$\delta_{0.99} = 1 + x = 2.55\sqrt{2}\,\epsilon^{\frac{1}{2}}$$

Thus the interior solution $\bar{u}_o$ is accurate to 1 percent at a distance of one-tenth of a unit from the walls if $\epsilon = \frac{1}{1,300}$ and to one-hundredth percent if $\epsilon = \frac{1}{13} \times 10^{-4}$.

Boundary layers are much commoner in nature than might be surmised from intuition.   The method of zonal estimates, although lacking a rigorous foundation, appears to be very useful and powerful not only for providing estimates in nonuniform problems but indeed for finding good approximate solutions in problems too difficult to be solved completely. The reader interested in further study of this method should see the article by Carrier[8] where four actual, but more complicated, problems are analyzed concisely.   The discussion above may prove of some value in providing motivation and insight into the procedures given.

4-9   NONUNIFORM BEHAVIOR — EXPANSION METHODS AND UNIFORMIZATION

In Sec. 4-8 methods for treating nonuniform behavior based on the boundary-layer concept were presented.   In the boundary-layer method one treats the problem by breaking the domain of interest into distinct regions, in each of which uniform estimates can be supplied. Complete solutions are obtained by patching together the solutions for the various regions by use of suitable compatibility conditions at the boundaries.

In this section, we consider very briefly several closely related procedures for treating nonuniform behavior usually attributed, respectively, to H. Poincaré;[39] M. J. Lighthill;[31] and Wentzel, Kramers, Brillouin, and Jeffreys (WKBJ). These three procedures are all attempts to improve the approximation made either locally or over the entire domain. They are all based on some sort of expansion in a series of powers of the parameters. It is emphasized that the discussion here is only introductory; it is not comprehensive nor does it cover the underlying theory. The purpose of this discussion is to introduce the ideas involved as simply as possible, to indicate when such methods may be useful. References to more complete discussions are given.

Poincaré's method consists of seeking a solution in terms of a series expansion of unknown functions multiplied by powers of the parameter. Such an expansion only makes sense if the parameter has a small value since we attempt to drop terms in higher powers of the parameter. In such a procedure, the boundary-layer approximation is sometimes the solution found when terms up to order 1 in the parameter are retained and all terms containing higher orders of the parameter are dropped. In this sense one can take the approximation-theory result, that is, the result found by dropping all terms modified by small parameters as the zeroth-order approximation and boundary-layer theory as the first-order calculation. It then becomes possible to compute second-order approximations which include terms neglected in boundary-layer theory. In this way one can estimate the relative importance of various effects which have been omitted in lower order approximations if the series converges.†
Such a calculation has been made in considerable detail recently by M. Van Dyke[51] for the hydrodynamic boundary layer. Van Dyke clearly exhibits the terms which become important at various orders of approximation.

Lighthill's technique can be viewed as a method for treating artificial singularities which sometimes arise in the Poincaré expansion; such singularities normally cannot be removed merely by considering terms of higher order in the Poincaré expansion. Lighthill's method proceeds by expanding both the dependent variable and the independent variable in a series of arbitrary functions and powers of the parameter of concern. This is equivalent to combining the Poincaré expansion with a transformation to new variables. One then seeks a choice of the arbitrary functions representing the independent variable which eliminates the

---

† We will not here discuss the question of convergence since this would involve us in the theory of asymptotic expansions (see Jeffreys and Jeffreys,[22] Chap. 17).

undesired singularity by construction.   This function can then be viewed
as a new "stretched" independent coordinate, and it may provide
uniformly valid estimates in the new coordinates.   In a few instances,
Lighthill's method is strikingly successful and even produces exact
solutions for a boundary-layer region and an outer region simultaneously.
In other problems, it does not succeed, and there seems to be no way at
present to anticipate success or failure;† each problem must be treated
essentially as a special case.   A summary of Lighthill's method has been
given by Tsien.[49]

The WKBJ method is a transformation of variables which forms a
basis for useful expansions in certain problems where the parameter
becomes very large instead of approaching zero.   (See Jeffreys and
Jeffreys,[22] R. E. Langer,[27] and references therein; also Morse and Feshbach;[36] Sellars, Tribus, and Klein.[47])

All three of these methods, like the boundary-layer procedures, are
attempts to improve solutions found from approximate equations.   Such
approximate equations are logically based on the processes of approximation theory.   The topics thus provide a link between fractional
analysis and complete solutions.   Moreover, these methods constitute a
quite large, but still rapidly developing, body of knowledge.   This
knowledge at present can best be presented in terms of examples, since
adequate underlying mathematical theory is largely unknown.

a.   Poincaré's Expansion

Example 4.8.   We now consider again the very simple illustration
of the free vibration of a spring-mass system with one degree of freedom
to bring out the ideas with a minimum of detail.   The governing equation
is

$$m \frac{d^2x}{dt^2} + kx = 0 \tag{4.41a}$$

We take boundary conditions

$$\text{at } t = 0: \qquad x = 0 \qquad \frac{dx}{dt} = v_o \tag{4.41b}$$

Define nondimensional variables, as before,

$$\bar{x} = \frac{x}{v_o \tau}$$

$$\bar{t} = \frac{t}{\tau}$$

---

† Accumulating experience begins to suggest that the method is somehow appropriate to hyperbolic differential equations, but this is by no means yet certain!

where τ = time for one-quarter cycle of oscillation. The normalized equation is

$$\frac{d^2\bar{x}}{d\bar{l}^2} + \frac{k\tau^2}{m}\,\bar{x} = 0 \tag{4.41c}$$

with initial conditions:

at $\bar{l} = 0$: $\bar{x} = 0$ $\dfrac{d\bar{x}}{d\bar{l}} = 1$

As in Sec. 4.6c, we seek an approximate solution under the fictitious assumption that $k\tau^2/m \rightarrow 0$. As before we find on integrating $d^2\bar{x}/d\bar{l}^2$ twice

$$\bar{x} = c_1 + c_2\bar{l}$$

Employing the initial conditions gives

$$c_1 = 0 \qquad \text{and} \qquad c_2 = 1$$

Thus

$$\bar{x} = \bar{l} \tag{4.41d}$$

Thus $\bar{x}$ increases indefinitely in time, but we are seeking an oscillatory solution. So the solution (4.41d) is unsatisfactory, as we found in Sec. 4-6c. Now let us see what can be done about it. We try to find a better solution using Poincaré's expansion. Assume a solution of the form

$$\bar{x} = \bar{x}^{\circledcirc} + \epsilon\bar{x}^{\circled{1}} + \epsilon^2\bar{x}^{\circled{2}} + \epsilon^3\bar{x}^{\circled{3}} + \cdots \tag{4.42a}$$

where $\epsilon = \dfrac{k\tau^2}{m}$ and the circled superscripts refer to order of approximation; each of $\bar{x}^{\circledcirc}$, $\bar{x}^{\circled{1}}$, $\bar{x}^{\circled{2}}$, etc., is considered to be an unknown function. Formally we write $d\bar{x}/d\bar{l}$ and $d^2\bar{x}/d\bar{l}^2$ as

$$\frac{d\bar{x}}{d\bar{l}} = \frac{d\bar{x}^{\circledcirc}}{d\bar{l}} + \epsilon\frac{d\bar{x}^{\circled{1}}}{d\bar{l}} + \epsilon^2\frac{d\bar{x}^{\circled{2}}}{d\bar{l}} + \epsilon^3\frac{d\bar{x}^{\circled{3}}}{d\bar{l}} + \cdots \tag{4.42b}$$

and

$$\frac{d^2\bar{x}}{d\bar{l}^2} = \frac{d^2\bar{x}^{\circledcirc}}{d\bar{l}^2} + \epsilon\frac{d^2\bar{x}^{\circled{1}}}{d\bar{l}^2} + \epsilon^2\frac{d^2\bar{x}^{\circled{2}}}{d\bar{l}^2} + \epsilon^3\frac{d^2\bar{x}^{\circled{3}}}{d\bar{l}^2} + \cdots \tag{4.42c}$$

Substituting into the differential equation gives

$$\frac{d^2\bar{x}^{\circledcirc}}{d\bar{l}^2} + \epsilon\frac{d^2\bar{x}^{\circled{1}}}{d\bar{l}^2} + \epsilon^2\frac{d^2\bar{x}^{\circled{2}}}{d\bar{l}^2} + \epsilon^3\frac{d^2\bar{x}^{\circled{3}}}{d\bar{l}^2}$$
$$+ \epsilon(x^{\circledcirc} + \epsilon x^{\circled{1}} + \epsilon^2 x^{\circled{2}} + \epsilon^3 x^{\circled{3}} + \cdots) = 0$$

The zeroth-order approximation is found by equating to zero all terms in

ϵ to zeroth power, that is, without ϵ. This gives

$$\frac{d^2 \bar{x}^\circledcirc}{d\bar{t}^2} = 0$$

which gives, as before,

$$\bar{x}^\circledcirc = \bar{t} \tag{4.43}$$

Thus the zeroth-order solution gives the same result as dropping the $\bar{x}$ term entirely in the original equation. Forming the first-order equation by equating to zero all terms with coefficients ϵ to the first power, we have

$$\frac{d^2 \bar{x}^\circledone}{d\bar{t}^2} = \bar{x}^\circledcirc = 0 \tag{4.44}$$

Equation (4.44) is a differential equation for $x^\circledone$. However, from Eq. (4.43), $\bar{x}^\circledcirc = \bar{t}$. Inserting Eq. (4.43) into (4.44) and integrating twice, we obtain

$$\bar{x}^\circledone = -\frac{\bar{t}^3}{3!} + c_3 \bar{t} + c_4 \tag{4.45}$$

We must now formulate the boundary conditions for the unknown function $x^\circledone$. By construction

$$\bar{x} = \bar{x}^\circledcirc + \epsilon \bar{x}^\circledone + \epsilon^2 \bar{x}^\circledtwo + \epsilon^3 \bar{x}^\circledthree + \cdots \tag{4.42a}$$

and

$$\frac{d\bar{x}}{d\bar{t}} = \frac{d\bar{x}^\circledcirc}{d\bar{t}} + \epsilon \frac{d\bar{x}^\circledone}{d\bar{t}} + \epsilon^2 \frac{d\bar{x}^\circledtwo}{d\bar{t}} + \epsilon^3 \frac{d\bar{x}^\circledthree}{d\bar{t}} + \cdots \tag{4.42b}$$

But we have already satisfied the initial condition for $\bar{x}^\circledcirc$ and $(d\bar{x}/d\bar{t})_{x=0}$ by construction of $x^\circledcirc$. Thus we must take

$$\bar{x}^\circledone(0) = 0 \qquad \bar{x}^\circledtwo(0) = 0 \qquad \text{etc.} \tag{4.46a}$$

$$\left(\frac{d\bar{x}^\circledone}{d\bar{t}} \right)_{x=0} = 0 \qquad \left(\frac{d\bar{x}^\circledtwo}{d\bar{t}} \right)_{x=0} = 0 \qquad \text{etc.} \tag{4.46b}$$

Addition of the conditions (4.46a) and (4.46b) will then satisfy the original conditions (4.41b). On setting Eqs. (4.46) into Eq. (4.45), we obtain $c_4 = c_3 = 0$. Hence

$$\bar{x}^\circledone = -\frac{\bar{t}^3}{3!}$$

By continuation of the same processes, we find

$$\bar{x}^\circledtwo = +\frac{\bar{t}^5}{5!}$$

$$\bar{x}^\circledthree = -\frac{\bar{t}^7}{7!}$$

and by induction the general term in this Poincaré series is

$$\bar{x}^{\circledn} = (-1)^n \frac{\bar{t}^{2n+1}}{(2n+1)!}$$

Thus Eq. (4.42a) becomes

$$\bar{x} = \frac{1}{\sqrt{\epsilon}}\left[\sqrt{\epsilon}\,\bar{t} + \frac{(\sqrt{\epsilon}\,\bar{t})^3}{3!} + \frac{(\sqrt{\epsilon}\,\bar{t})^5}{5!} + \cdots \frac{(-1)^n(\sqrt{\epsilon}\,\bar{t})^{2n+1}}{(2n+1)!}\right]$$

$$(4.47)$$

Formal construction of a Taylor series for the sine function or consultation with a table of functions will show that the limit $n \to \infty$ for the series in brackets in Eq. (4.47) is $\sin\sqrt{\epsilon}\,\bar{t}$. Thus the Poincaré method yields as a limit the exact solution to this problem. Equation (4.47) also shows that the zeroth-order approximation gives the proper slope and value of $\bar{x}$ at $\bar{t} = 0$, but that it deviates increasingly as $\bar{t}$ increases in value. Each approximation in the Poincaré series will hold for a longer and longer time, and ultimately, if we take an infinite number of terms, the series converges to the exact solution.

Suppose now we try the same type of procedure under our other fictitious assumption of Sec. 4-6c that the parameter $\dfrac{k\tau^2}{m} \gg 1$. For convenience call $\nu = 1/\epsilon = m/k\tau^2$. Then the equation is

$$\nu\frac{d^2\bar{x}}{d\bar{t}^2} + \bar{x} = 0$$

Again take boundary conditions

at $t = 0$: $\bar{x} = 0$ $\dfrac{d\bar{x}}{d\bar{t}} = 1$

If we let $\nu \to 0$ and try the zeroth-order approximation, we obtain

$$\bar{x} = 0$$

then

$$\frac{d\bar{x}}{d\bar{t}} = 0$$

And we cannot satisfy the boundary conditions. If we attempt a Poincaré-type expansion, we set

$$\bar{x} = x^{\circled0} + \nu x^{\circled1} + \nu^2 x^{\circled2} + \cdots$$
$$\frac{d\bar{x}}{dt} = \frac{d\bar{x}^{\circled0}}{dt} + \nu\frac{d\bar{x}^{\circled1}}{dt} + \nu^2\frac{d\bar{x}^{\circled2}}{dt} + \cdots$$
$$\frac{d^2\bar{x}}{d\bar{t}^2} = \frac{d^2\bar{x}^{\circled0}}{d\bar{t}^2} + \nu\frac{d^2\bar{x}^{\circled1}}{d\bar{t}^2} + \nu^2\frac{d^2\bar{x}^{\circled2}}{d\bar{t}^2} + \cdots$$

The terms in ν^0 give, as before,

$$\bar{x}^{\circledcirc} = 0$$
$$\frac{d\bar{x}^{\circledcirc}}{d\bar{t}} = 0$$
$$\frac{d^2\bar{x}^{\circledcirc}}{d\bar{t}^2} = 0$$

The terms in ν then give

$$\frac{d^2\bar{x}^{\circledcirc}}{d\bar{t}^2} + \bar{x}^{\circledS} = 0$$

but

$$\frac{d^2\bar{x}^{\circledcirc}}{d\bar{t}^2} = 0$$

so

$$\bar{x}^{\circledS} = 0$$
$$\frac{d\bar{x}^{\circledS}}{d\bar{t}} = 0$$
$$\frac{d^2\bar{x}^{\circledS}}{d\bar{t}^2} = 0$$

Repeating the procedure for higher orders, we find only

$$\bar{x}^{\circledcirc} = \bar{x}^{\circledS} = \bar{x}^{\circledS} \cdots = \bar{x}^{\circledR} = 0$$
$$\frac{d\bar{x}^{\circledcirc}}{d\bar{t}} = \frac{d\bar{x}^{\circledS}}{d\bar{t}} = \cdots \frac{d\bar{x}^{\circledR}}{d\bar{t}} = 0$$

Thus we cannot satisfy the boundary conditions; we obtain no solution at all.

We now examine the implications of this example. First, recall that our estimate was fictitious. Conventionally, one does not proceed quite as we have done here, but instead notes that a parameter, say k/m, is small, and then tries to drop the term(s) associated with it. As we have stressed, however, it is not the size of the parameter but the size of the total term that counts. In this case what happens is that as k/m becomes small, x becomes big, that is, the estimate is not really proper. Here we have made this fact explicit in terms of the parameters by appropriate normalization. In the conventional procedure, the poor estimate remains implicit in the terms involving the variables.

In the case where we dropped x, we found that the zeroth-order approximation, that is, the result found from approximation theory, held only in a very small region near where we applied the boundary conditions.

However, each successive term in the Poincaré expansion gave a result that held for a longer and longer time. Thus, in this sense, we can view the Poincaré expansion as a method for seeking to "repair" our bad initial estimate. Since the method is iterative, this allows us to guess about the initial estimate and then proceed formally to improve our guess.

We also observe that if we supply a bad estimate (or guess) initially, then the solution we find is not a good one whether we drop the most highly differentiated term or only other terms. However, when we drop only the less differentiated terms, we obtain a solution that does satisfy the boundary conditions initially and holds for very small $\sqrt{\epsilon}\,\bar{t}$.

We can see this in the following way. If we expand the exact solution by expressing the sine as a power series in ascending powers of $\sqrt{\epsilon}\,\bar{t}$, then we see that for small $\sqrt{\epsilon}\,\bar{t}$ we can approximate the series by its first term, which is just what we found from approximation theory. Such a solution we say is asymptotically valid for small values of $\sqrt{\epsilon}\,\bar{t}$. We can improve this solution iteratively by a Poincaré expansion.

On the other hand, when we try to drop the most highly differentiated term, we do not get even an asymptotically valid solution; we cannot satisfy the boundary conditions at all, and we cannot improve the situation by iteration of a series in powers of the parameters. Such a solution, in which the behavior of the solution for small values of the parameter is totally different from that for the parameter identically zero, we call a singular perturbation problem. Such singular perturbation problems we find by experience are usually associated with attempts to drop the most highly differentiated term. Since we have already seen that this is also associated with the likelihood of boundary-layer behavior, we would expect that one of the boundary-layer methods of the previous section would be more appropriate in such instances. This is generally the case. Again we stress that all these remarks have no proofs; they are merely what we have come to expect based on experience.

When the Poincaré expansion worked, in this example, it proved valid over the entire domain of interest. Unfortunately this is not always the case. In some instances the approximate equation may contain a singularity not found in the complete equation (or conversely); in the neighborhood of such a singularity the approximation found must be bad. The Lighthill extension of the Poincaré method will sometimes remove this kind of difficulty. We illustrate this in Example 4.9b.

b.   Lighthill's Expansion

Example 4.9.   The essence of this method is the combination of Poincaré's expansion with a change to a new variable. We strive to make *uniform* estimates by proper definition of the new variable. Consider the equation

$$(\bar{t} + \epsilon\bar{x})\frac{d\bar{x}}{d\bar{t}} + \bar{x} = 0 \tag{4.48a}$$

and the boundary condition

$$\text{at } \bar{t} = 1: \qquad \bar{x} = 1 \tag{4.48b}$$

Suppose ϵ is a parameter, and we are seeking a solution as $\epsilon \to 0$. The exact solution to this equation is

$$\bar{x} = -\frac{\bar{t}}{\epsilon} + \sqrt{\left(\frac{\bar{t}}{\epsilon}\right)^2 + \frac{2}{\epsilon} + 1} \tag{4.49}$$

The solution is readily verified by substituting Eq. (4.49) into Eqs. (4.48). As $\epsilon \to 0$, the exact solution shows $x \to \infty$. If we try to drop the term $\epsilon\bar{x}$ from Eq. (4.48a) altogether, we obtain

$$\bar{t}\frac{d\bar{x}}{d\bar{t}} + \bar{x} = 0 \qquad \text{or} \qquad \frac{d(\bar{x}\bar{t})}{d\bar{t}} = 0$$

The solution so obtained is

$$\bar{x}\bar{t} = c_1 = 1 \tag{4.50}$$

where 1 is found from Eq. (4.48b). Equation (4.50) does not exhibit the proper behavior as $\epsilon \to 0$. Hence we try the Poincaré expansion. Again let

$$x = x^{(0)} + \epsilon x^{(1)} + \epsilon^2 x^{(2)} + \cdots$$

then

$$\frac{d\bar{x}}{d\bar{t}} = \frac{d\bar{x}^{(0)}}{d\bar{t}} + \epsilon\frac{d\bar{x}^{(1)}}{d\bar{t}} + \epsilon^2\frac{d\bar{x}^{(2)}}{d\bar{t}} + \cdots$$

Substituting into Eq. (4.48a) gives

$$(\bar{t} + \epsilon\bar{x}^{(0)} + \epsilon^2\bar{x}^{(1)} + \epsilon^3\bar{x}^{(2)} + \cdots)\left(\frac{d\bar{x}^{(0)}}{d\bar{t}} + \epsilon\frac{d\bar{x}^{(1)}}{d\bar{t}} + \epsilon^2\frac{d\bar{x}^{(2)}}{d\bar{t}}\right)$$
$$+ \bar{x}^{(0)} + \epsilon\bar{x}^{(1)} + \epsilon^2\bar{x}^{(2)} + \cdots = 0$$

with boundary conditions

$$\text{at } t = 1: \qquad \bar{x}^{(0)} = 1 \qquad \bar{x}^{(1)} = 0 \qquad \bar{x}^{(2)} = 0 \qquad \text{etc.}$$

Solution for $\bar{x}^{(0)}$ from the terms without ϵ gives

$$\bar{t}\frac{d\bar{x}^{(0)}}{d\bar{t}} + \bar{x}^{(0)} = 0$$

or, as before,

$$\bar{x}^{\circledcirc}\bar{l} = 1$$
$$\bar{x}^{\circledcirc} = \frac{1}{\bar{l}}$$

But this solution not only has the wrong values for small ϵ it also has an undesired singularity at $\bar{l} = 0$. So we try the solution for $\bar{x}^{\circledcirc}$. We obtain on equating to zero terms in ϵ to the first power

$$\bar{x}^{\circledcirc}\frac{d\bar{x}^{\circledcirc}}{d\bar{l}} + \bar{x}\frac{d\bar{x}^{\circledcirc}}{d\bar{l}} + \bar{x}^{\circledcirc} = 0$$

Solving by inserting the solution for $\bar{x}^{\circledcirc}$ and $\dfrac{d\bar{x}^{\circledcirc}}{d\bar{l}}$ and by evaluating constants from the boundary conditions gives

$$\bar{x}^{\circledcirc} = -\frac{1}{2\bar{l}}\left(1 - \frac{1}{\bar{l}^2}\right)$$

Thus $\bar{x}^{\circledcirc}$ has an even worse singularity at $\bar{l} = 0$. Computation of higher order terms only makes matters still worse, as the reader can verify for himself.

When artificial and undesirable singularities of this sort appear, we try next the expansion method of Lighthill. The essence of the method is to expand not only the dependent variable but also the independent variable in powers of the small parameter. To do this we define a new variable $\bar{\tau}$ which replaces $\bar{l}$; we then seek a form for $\bar{\tau}$ which will eliminate the singularity and hence make the problem uniformly valid in $\bar{\tau}$. We proceed as follows. Let

$$\bar{x} = x^{\circledcirc}(\bar{\tau}) + \epsilon x^{\circledcirc}(\bar{\tau}) + \epsilon x^{\circledcirc}(\bar{\tau}) + \cdots$$

and

$$\bar{l} = \bar{\tau} + \epsilon\bar{l}^{\circledcirc}(\bar{\tau}) + \epsilon^2\bar{l}^{\circledcirc}(\bar{\tau}) + \cdots$$

Substituting these expansions into Eq. (4.48a), we obtain

$$(\bar{l} + \epsilon\bar{x})\frac{d\bar{x}}{d\bar{\tau}}\frac{d\bar{\tau}}{d\bar{l}} + \bar{x} = 0$$

or

$$(\bar{l} + \epsilon\bar{x})\frac{d\bar{x}}{d\bar{\tau}} + \bar{x}\frac{d\bar{\tau}}{d\bar{l}} = 0$$

and writing terms only to first order, we have

$$[\bar{\tau} + \epsilon\bar{l}^{\circledcirc}(\bar{\tau}) + \cdots + \epsilon\bar{x}^{\circledcirc}(\bar{\tau}) + \epsilon^2\bar{x}^{\circledcirc}(\bar{\tau}) + \cdots]$$
$$\left[\frac{d\bar{x}^{\circledcirc}}{d\bar{\tau}} + \epsilon\frac{d\bar{x}^{\circledcirc}}{d\bar{\tau}} + \cdots\right] + [\bar{x}^{\circledcirc} + \epsilon\bar{x}^{\circledcirc} + \cdots]$$
$$\left[1 + \epsilon\frac{d\bar{l}^{\circledcirc}}{d\bar{\tau}} + \cdots\right] = 0$$

Equating to zero terms in ϵ to the zeroth power gives

$$\bar{\tau}\frac{d\bar{x}^{\textcircled{0}}}{d\bar{\tau}} + \bar{x}^{\textcircled{0}} = 0$$

Thus, as before, the zeroth-order solution is

$$\bar{x}^{\textcircled{0}}(\tau) = \frac{1}{\bar{\tau}} \tag{4.51}$$

But the variable is now $\bar{\tau}$, not $\bar{t}$, and $\bar{\tau}$ is still subject to choice, that is, we have not yet determined its form. Equating to zero terms in ϵ to first power gives

$$\bar{\tau}\frac{d\bar{x}^{\textcircled{1}}}{d\bar{\tau}} + \bar{x}^{\textcircled{1}} = -(\bar{t}^{\textcircled{0}} + \bar{x}^{\textcircled{0}})\frac{d\bar{x}^{\textcircled{0}}}{d\bar{\tau}} - \bar{x}^{\textcircled{0}}\frac{d\bar{t}^{\textcircled{1}}}{d\bar{\tau}}$$

Substituting in Eq. (4.51) and solving gives

$$\frac{d(\bar{x}^{\textcircled{0}}\bar{\tau})}{d\bar{\tau}} = \frac{\bar{t}^{\textcircled{0}}}{\bar{\tau}^2} + \frac{1}{\bar{\tau}^3} - \frac{1}{\bar{\tau}}\frac{d\bar{t}^{\textcircled{1}}}{d\bar{\tau}}$$

Now the function $\bar{t}^{\textcircled{0}}$ is still undefined; we are free to choose it to be such that

$$\frac{1}{\bar{\tau}}\frac{d\bar{t}^{\textcircled{1}}}{d\bar{\tau}} - \frac{\bar{t}^{\textcircled{0}}}{\bar{\tau}^2} = \frac{1}{\bar{\tau}^3} \tag{4.52}$$

Equation (4.52) is a differential equation for $\bar{t}^{\textcircled{0}}(\bar{\tau})$. Solving it as

$$\frac{d}{d\tau}\left(\frac{\bar{t}^{\textcircled{1}}}{\tau}\right) = \frac{1}{\bar{\tau}^3}$$

and inserting boundary conditions yields

$$\bar{t}^{\textcircled{1}} = \frac{\bar{\tau}}{2}\left(1 - \frac{1}{\bar{\tau}^2}\right)$$

Then at this order of approximation

$$\bar{x} = \frac{1}{\bar{\tau}} \tag{4.53a}$$

and

$$\bar{t} = \bar{\tau} + \epsilon\frac{\bar{\tau}}{2}\left(1 - \frac{1}{\bar{\tau}^2}\right) \tag{4.53b}$$

Elimination of $\bar{\tau}$ between Eqs. (4.53a) and (4.53b) gives

$$x = \frac{\bar{t}}{\epsilon} \pm \sqrt{\left(\frac{\bar{t}}{\epsilon}\right)^2 + \frac{2}{\epsilon} + 1} \tag{4.53c}$$

This is the exact solution.

This example is, of course, contrived to show the power of the method. Lighthill's expansion does not always work so neatly, nor indeed does it always work at all. Both the Poincaré and the Lighthill expansions can also be used with partial differential equations by employing expansions formed with appropriate partial derivatives. As can be seen, the method becomes complicated in detail, however, and the reader who has use for such applications should see Tsien[49] and the references therein.

c.   *WKBJ Expansion*

The initials WKBJ stand for Wentzel, Kramers, Brillouin, and Jeffreys, all of whom are usually associated with the discovery of this method.

The WKBJ method is a transformation which allows treatment of certain problems when the value of the parameter is large. It was developed first to handle certain problems in quantum mechanics and appears primarily in the physics literature (see, for example, Jeffreys and Jeffreys,[22] R. E. Langer,[27] or Morse and Feshbach[36]). Relatively recently Sellars, Tribus, and Klein[47] have employed the method to extend a heat-transfer solution due to Graetz; we illustrate this solution to stay with continuum problems here.

In the Graetz problem one finds an equation of the form†

$$\bar{x}\frac{d^2\bar{R}_n}{d\bar{x}^2} + \frac{d\bar{R}_n}{d\bar{x}} + \lambda_n^2\bar{x}(1 - \bar{x}^2)R_n = 0$$

where λ_n is a large parameter. One can attempt to find the eigenvalues of λ_n needed to solve the problem by an expansion of the form

$$R = \lambda_o f_o(\bar{x}) + f_1(\bar{r}) + \frac{1}{\lambda}f_2(\bar{r}) + \cdots$$

However, this does not lead to converging series. If instead one transforms the equation by setting

$$\bar{R} = e^{g(x)}$$

then the λ can be evaluated using a series of the form

$$g(\bar{x}) = \lambda g_0(\bar{x}) + g_1(\bar{x}) + \frac{1}{\lambda}g_2(\bar{x}) + \cdots$$

This technique is useful in many problems where large values of param-

† From notes due to Prof. W. C. Reynolds, Thermosciences Division, Department of Mechanical Engineering, Stanford University, Calif.

eters are encountered. For details, the reader should see the references above.

d. Inner and Outer Expansions

In the past decade a group of workers primarily at California Institute of Technology have investigated the bases of systematic procedures for developing higher approximations in boundary-layer problems. The calculation proceeds in stages calculating alternately the inner (boundary layer) and outer (smooth) part of the domain; the conditions are matched between the zones at each stage. No simple example of this method has been found by the author to date. Accordingly, no example is given herein; the reader interested in these methods should see particularly Lagerstrom and Cole,† the references therein, and Van Dyke.[51]

4-10 PROCESSES INVOLVING TRANSFORMATIONS OF VARIABLES

In discussing the meaning of normalized coordinates in Sec. 4-2b, we noted that the solution to a normalized equation can be expressed in functional form in terms of the nondimensional variables and parameters. For example, if we are concerned with a dependent variable $\bar{T}$, and if the complete normalized governing equations and boundary conditions contain the parameters π_1, π_2, π_3 and the independent variables $\bar{x}$, $\bar{y}$, $\bar{z}$, and $\bar{t}$, then we can write the solution for all problems of this class in functional form as

$$\bar{T} = \bar{T}(\pi_1, \pi_2, \pi_3; \bar{x}, \bar{y}, \bar{z}, \bar{t}) \tag{4.54}$$

A change in the value of one of the pi's implies changing from one system to another in the class of interest, and a change in one of the variables implies a change of location inside a given system of the class. Thus far we have dealt only with similitude and model laws which require constancy of the pi's. This provides relations between two problems in a single class for any specified point in both, as given by fixed values of the nondimensional variables. It is, however, entirely possible to seek other kinds of similarity by manipulations based solely on the governing equations and conditions without any requirement for constructing a solution. Such procedures rest on transformation of the variables. In particular, we seek new coordinates in which the number of parameters, the number of variables, or both, are reduced in the normalized governing

† P. A. Lagerstrom and J. D. Cole, Examples Illustrating Expansion Procedures for the Navier-Stokes Equations, *J. of Rational Mech. Anal.*, **4** (6): (1955).

equations and conditions. If such coordinates can be found, then Eq. (4.54) indicates that a simpler correlation can be achieved. A reduction in the number of parameters has a different physical meaning from a reduction in the number of variables. For this reason we will treat each separately, even though examples are given when one transformation could be used to simultaneously reduce both the number of variables and the number of parameters.

a. *Absorption of Parameters and Natural Coordinates*

In the process, which is here called *absorption of parameters*, we attempt to define new variables so that normalized equations *and boundary conditions* in these new variables will be free of all parameters. However, variables which result from absorption of parameters are almost always extremely useful for creating improved correlations, and the transformations by which these variables are constructed usually contain important physical implications. For the present purposes, the most important points are the following. If it is possible to find new coordinates in which the normalized governing equations and conditions are parameter-free, and if these equations and conditions are complete and appropriate in the sense of Sec. 4-3, then it must follow that:

1. There is only one solution possible for the dependent variable for all problems of the class considered in the new coordinates.
2. This solution must hold for all values of both the variables and the parameters of the original equation.

The utility of these remarks is illustrated by some examples which follow.

Example 4.10a.   Consider once again the simple spring-mass system in free vibration without friction initially released from a nonrest position with zero velocity. The governing differential equation and boundary conditions are

$$m \frac{d^2x}{dt^2} + kx = 0$$

$$\text{at } t = 0: \qquad x = \delta \qquad \frac{dx}{dt} = 0$$

We normalize this equation by use of the variables found previously

$$\bar{x} = \frac{x}{\delta}$$

$$\bar{t} = \frac{t}{\tau}$$

where τ = time for one-quarter cycle.   As before

$$\frac{d^2\bar{x}}{d\bar{t}^2} + \frac{k\tau^2}{m}\bar{x} = 0 \tag{4.55a}$$

at $\bar{t} = 0:$ $\bar{x} = 1$ $\dfrac{d\bar{x}}{d\bar{t}} = 0$ (4.55b)

The equation and boundary conditions have only one parameter.   Since the equation is homogeneous in $\bar{x}$ and the boundary conditions parameter-free, we expect a uniform behavior for all values of δ.   It follows that we can find a solution which has appreciable effects of both terms in the normalized equation only if the parameter is constant.   Thus

$$\frac{k\tau^2}{m} = \text{constant} = C_1$$

$$\frac{1}{\tau} = C_1\sqrt{\frac{k}{m}}$$

We now ask, "Can we find a set of coordinates in which the number of parameters can be reduced?"   (We cannot here hope to reduce the number of independent variables, since there is only one.)   It is clear on inspection of the equation that we need only make the transformation

$$(t^+)^2 = \frac{\bar{t}^2 k\tau^2}{m} = \frac{t^2 k}{m}$$

$$t^+ = \frac{t}{\sqrt{m/k}}$$

on inserting the new coordinate t^+, Eqs. (4.55) become

$$\frac{d^2\bar{x}}{dt^{+2}} + \bar{x} = 0 \tag{4.56a}$$

at $t^+ = 0:$ $\bar{x} = 1$ $\dfrac{d\bar{x}}{dt^+} = 0$ (4.56b)

Equations (4.56) are parameter-free; we have succeeded in reducing the number of parameters from 1 to 0.   The implications of this reduction are considerable.   The solution to Eqs. (4.56) can be written in functional form as

$$\bar{x} = \bar{x}(t^+) \tag{4.57}$$

This implies that we can express the entire solution to all problems of this class in terms of one coordinate t^+.   Since Eqs. (4.55) are known to be complete and appropriate for problems of this type, it follows that for a given value of t^+, all problems of this class will have the same $\bar{x}$.   Thus we have achieved a generalization and simplification.

At this point it is desirable to verify formally that all problems in this class do indeed reduce to Eqs. (4.56). This is readily achieved by considering two arbitrary systems, denoted by, say, subscripts 1 and 2, with different values of k and m, say, k_1 and k_2, m_1 and m_2. Substitution of these values into the differential equation and boundary conditions (4.56) leads to identical equations and boundary conditions in $\bar{x}_1$, t_1^+ and $\bar{x}_2$, t_2^+. Verification is left to the reader. Thus the generalizations obtained depend on an invariance to the value of the parameters not possessed by the equation in the original coordinates.

A good insight into the meaning of transformations to parameter-free equations and conditions can be achieved by viewing them as the adoption of new units for measurement of the coordinate(s) concerned. In this case we can view use of t^+ as abandonment of a unit of time based on the mean solar day and adoption of a unit time given by $\sqrt{m/k}$. The time unit $\sqrt{m/k}$ is based on the properties of the spring-mass system itself, and is natural to it. We accordingly call coordinates measured in such units *natural coordinates* and denote them by a superscript $(\ )^+$.

Once we have found the natural coordinates for a given problem, it is usually a simple matter to derive similarity rules. In the spring-mass system, we reason as follows. Since the value of $\bar{x}$ is uniquely determined by t^+, if we quadruple the mass and keep k constant, we must take a unit of time twice as large to achieve similar results between the two systems. This type of similarity is different from that discussed previously. Here we allow the value of the parameter k/m to vary and compensate by a change in time (which is a variable) to maintain similarity.† This idea, when employed in connection with space instead of time variables, leads to a rigorous basis for distorted models, as we shall see in the more complicated illustration of Examples 4.11 and 4.12, where supersonic and transonic similarity rules are discussed.

Moreover, we can employ Eq. (4.56) to provide an estimate of the parameter representing an eigenvalue (in this case, the reciprocal of frequency τ). We reason, as in Examples 4.4 and 4.7, that if we are to have appreciable effects of both terms in the equation, they must be of equal order of magnitude. Here, however, we have made the equation parameter-free and also made $\bar{x}$ unity order by definition. As already noted, if a free oscillation is to occur at all, we must have an effect of both spring force and inertia; the equation then demands equal magnitude of terms, that is

$$\frac{d^2\bar{x}}{d\bar{t}^2} = U(1)$$

---

† Note t^+ also contains the previous type of similarity, since for fixed time behavior we require k and m or k/m = constant.

Considering any simple oscillation in $\bar{t}^+,\bar{x}$ coordinates we observe that the estimate of $d^2\bar{x}/dt^{+2}$ is

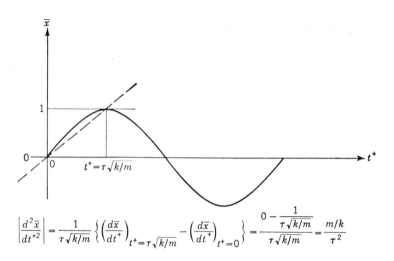

$$\left|\frac{d^2\bar{x}}{dt^{+2}}\right| = \frac{1}{\tau\sqrt{k/m}}\left\{\left(\frac{d\bar{x}}{dt^+}\right)_{t^+=\tau\sqrt{k/m}} - \left(\frac{d\bar{x}}{dt^+}\right)_{t^+=0}\right\} = \frac{0-\dfrac{1}{\tau\sqrt{k/m}}}{\tau\sqrt{k/m}} = \frac{m/k}{\tau^2}$$

If a harmonic oscillation is to occur, $d^2\bar{x}/dt^{+2}$ must be $U(1)$; hence $\tau \simeq \sqrt{m/k}$, and the period $4\tau = 4\sqrt{m/k}$. The true period is, of course, $2\pi\sqrt{m/k}$; the estimate is 36 percent low, but it is of the proper form and in error by a constant amount.

We now extend the illustration to further exhibit the power of natural coordinates for correlation purposes. Consider the spring-mass system in Fig. 4.12, with the addition of a force on the mass given by $F_o = P_o \cos \beta t$, where β is a parameter. Let the initial conditions be the

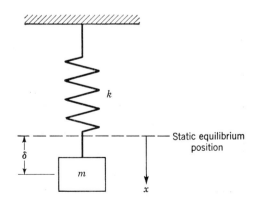

Fig. 4.12

same as before.   The equations are then

$$m \frac{d^2x}{dt^2} + kx = P_o \cos \beta t$$

at $t = 0$: $x = \delta_A$† $\frac{dx}{dt} = 0$

Now if we want to determine properties of the steady-state solution, rather than initial displacement, we should normalize x on the steady-state amplitude, which we denote as δ_A.   We define

$$\bar{x} = \frac{x}{\delta_A}$$

and employ as before

$$t^+ = \frac{t}{\sqrt{m/k}}$$

We obtain

$$\frac{d^2\bar{x}}{dt^{+2}} + \bar{x} = \frac{P_o}{\delta_A k} \cos \left(\frac{\beta}{\sqrt{k/m}} \right) t^+$$

$$\text{at } t^+ = 0: \qquad \bar{x} = 1 \qquad \frac{d\bar{x}}{dt^+} = 0$$

(4.58)

Equation (4.58) contains the two parameters $\beta/\sqrt{k/m}$ and $P_o/\delta_A k$. Moreover, the second of these can be written as the system response $\delta_{\text{static}}/\delta_A$, since $P_o/k = \delta_{\text{static}}$ by definition.   Since the equations are known to be complete and appropriate, they can have but one solution, and we should expect to find a single curve representing $\delta_A/\delta_{\text{static}}$ in the form

$$\frac{\delta_A}{\delta_{\text{static}}} = f \left(\frac{\beta}{\sqrt{k/m}} \right)$$

This result is, of course, correct and very well known (see, for example, Jacobsen and Ayre[21] or Den Hartog,[12] where this result is plotted in terms of closed-form solutions).

The point here is not the originality of the solution, but rather that it has been obtained without any need to solve the differential equation. The processes tell us explicitly that these natural coordinates will give a simpler correlation than coordinates based on any other unit of time. They also tell us that if we wish to avoid considering the transient period,

† We take the initial displacement $x = \delta_A$ to eliminate the need for considering the transient period and damping effects, in order to keep the illustration simple in detail.

we must start with a condition which makes the initial conditions parameter-free. This is, of course, true for entirely undamped systems, although it is unnecessary for real systems at $t^+ \gg 1$, since any finite damping results in a steady-state condition independent of the initial conditions after a long time. In this case, if we had taken $x = \delta \neq \delta_A$ at $t = 0$, then the initial conditions would have read

$$\text{at } t^+ = 0: \qquad \bar{x} = \frac{\delta}{\delta_A} \qquad \frac{d\bar{x}}{dt^+} = 0$$

Under these conditions, the undamped oscillation depends on three parameters, namely,

$$\frac{\delta_{\text{static}}}{\delta_A} \qquad \frac{\beta}{\sqrt{k/m}} \qquad \frac{\delta}{\delta_A}$$

Such forms are not usually plotted, since all real systems have damping.

It is interesting to note again in this example the effect of Theorem 1. The homogeneous equation (4.56) for the free vibration in natural coordinates is entirely parameter-free so the solution does not depend on the value of the parameters. The solution to the nonhomogeneous equation (4.58) for the forced vibration does depend on the value of the parameters; however, both cases are linear.

Example 4.10b. Natural Coordinates for Transverse Beam Oscillations. The equations for transverse oscillation of a beam discussed in Example 4.3 can also easily be put into natural coordinates. Consider again Eqs. (4.24)

$$\frac{\partial^4 \bar{y}}{\partial \bar{x}^4} + \frac{\rho A L^4 \omega^2}{EI} \frac{\partial^2 \bar{y}}{\partial \bar{t}^2} = 0 \tag{4.24a}$$

where

$$\bar{y} = \frac{y}{\delta_{\text{init}}} \qquad \bar{t} = t\omega \qquad \bar{x} = \frac{x}{L}$$

$$\left. \begin{array}{lll}
\text{at } \bar{x} = 0: & \bar{y} = 0 & \dfrac{\partial \bar{y}}{\partial \bar{x}} = 0 \\[2ex]
\text{at } \bar{x} = 1: & \dfrac{\partial^2 \bar{y}}{\partial \bar{x}^2} = 0 & \dfrac{\partial^3 \bar{y}}{\partial \bar{x}^3} = 0 \\[2ex]
\text{at } \bar{t} = 0: & \bar{y}_{\bar{x}=1} = 1 & \left(\dfrac{\partial \bar{y}}{\partial \bar{t}}\right)_{\bar{x}=1} = 0
\end{array} \right\} \tag{4.24b}$$

The boundary conditions contain no parameters and

$$\frac{\rho A L^4 \omega^2}{EI} = \frac{L^2 \omega^2}{rc}$$

where

L = beam length
ω = reciprocal of time for one-quarter cycle
r = radius of gyration of beam section
c = acoustic velocity in beam

An appropriate t^+ is then

$$t^+ = \frac{\bar{t}rc}{L^2\omega} = \frac{t\omega rc}{L^2\omega} = \frac{t}{L^2/rc} \tag{4.59}$$

Thus the natural unit of time for the free oscillation of the beam in the first mode of transverse vibration is L^2/rc.

A sketch of the curve expected for the second mode will show that the appropriate time is $(L/2)^2/rc$; thus the pattern of eigenvalues (transverse free-vibration frequencies for various modes) also can be estimated crudely.

In Eq. (4.24a) it is also possible to obtain a parameter-free equation by defining a variable

$$\bar{x}^+ = \sqrt{\frac{L^2\omega}{rc}}\,\bar{x} = \sqrt{\frac{\omega}{rc}}\frac{Lx}{L} = \frac{x}{\sqrt{rc/\omega}} \tag{4.60}$$

Hence we observe the natural unit of length for free transverse vibrations as $\sqrt{rc/\omega}$. However, this produces a parameter in the boundary condition at $\bar{x} = 1$, since x^+ then equals $L^2\omega/rc$. Moreover, ω is in general unknown initially, so the coordinates of Eq. (4.59) would appear to be a better choice than those of Eq. (4.60). Inserting Eq. (4.59) into (4.28a), we have

$$\frac{\partial^4 \bar{y}}{\partial \bar{x}^4} + \frac{\partial^2 \bar{y}}{\partial t^{+2}} = 0 \tag{4.61}$$

and the boundary conditions (4.24b) are unaltered. From Eq. (4.61) all the results of Example 4.3 are easily achieved by reasoning as follows. For a free vibration to occur, the terms in Eq. (4.24a) must be of the same order. For smooth vibration curves, which are expected on physical grounds, $\partial^4\bar{y}/\partial\bar{x}^4 = U(1)$ and $\bar{y} = U(1)$; it follows that $\bar{t}$ must run $0 \to 1$ over a one-quarter cycle. This leads directly to the estimate found previously as Eq. (4.27a), namely,

$$\omega = \sqrt{\frac{EI}{\rho A L^4}} = \sqrt{\frac{rc}{L^2}} \qquad \text{rad/sec} \tag{4.27a}$$

Equation (4.61) also provides directly all the information needed to specify similar vibration behavior for *any* value of the parameters. Equation (4.24a) shows that two beams will have similar behavior for the same values of $\bar{x}$, $\bar{t}$, and $L^2\omega/rc$. But Eq. (4.61) shows the same result can be achieved by requiring constant values of $\bar{x}$ and t^+. Hence we need not require constant $L^2\omega/rc$ if we adopt L^2/rc as the unit for time measurement. This, in turn, suggests correlation of beam vibrations with a time coordinate t^+. This correlation is more powerful than necessary for the free vibration alone. However, it is useful for forced vibrations. Consider a uniformly distributed forcing function on a cantilever beam of F lb per unit length. The governing equation is then

$$EI \frac{\partial^4 y}{\partial x^4} + \rho A \frac{\partial^2 y}{\partial t^2} = F_o \cos \beta t \tag{4.62}$$

with boundary conditions given by Eq. (4.24b). Normalizing in the same way on x and t, but employing the y variable $\bar{y}/\delta_A$ for the same reasons as in Example 4.9, the governing equations and boundary conditions become

$$\frac{\partial^4 \bar{y}}{\partial \bar{x}^4} + \frac{\partial^2 \bar{y}}{\partial t^{+2}} = \frac{F_o L^4}{EI \delta_A} \cos \left(\frac{\beta L^2}{rc} \right) t^+ \tag{4.63a}$$

at $\bar{x} = 0$: $\qquad \bar{y} = 0 \qquad \frac{\partial \bar{y}}{\partial \bar{x}} = 0$

at $\bar{x} = 1$: $\qquad \frac{\partial^2 \bar{y}}{\partial \bar{x}^2} = 0 \qquad \frac{\partial^3 \bar{y}}{\partial \bar{x}^3} = 0 \tag{4.63b}$

at $\bar{t} = 0$: $\qquad \bar{y}_{\bar{x}=1} = 1 \qquad \frac{\partial \bar{y}}{\partial \bar{t}} = 0$

And

$$\frac{\beta L^2}{rc} = \frac{\beta}{\omega} = \frac{\text{forcing frequency}}{\text{natural frequency}}$$

$$\frac{F_o L^4}{EI} \triangleq \text{length}$$

We thus can employ it as a measure of deflection δ_n and

$$\frac{F_o L^4}{EI \delta_A} = \frac{\delta_n}{\delta_A}$$

which is the reciprocal system response measured in units of δ_n.

Hence Eqs. (4.63) suggest correlation of problems of this type in the form δ_A/δ_n versus β/ω. This correlation is analogous to the correlation of $\delta/\delta_{\text{static}}$ versus $\beta/\sqrt{k/m}$ for the simple harmonic oscillator of Example 4.9, but it does not seem to have been as widely used. It should give a clear picture of system response in terms of a single response curve for each mode of oscillation under specified loading and end conditions.

As emphasized in this example and in the previous one, the achievement of natural coordinates is a one-step generalization beyond simple normalization and contains the results embodied in the normalization. As an exercise, the reader may find it instructive to verify that (1) natural coordinates for the heat-conduction equation can be found by proper choice of time units when $L \simeq M \simeq N$ and (2) use of this result with approximation theory and the definition of l in Sec. 4-6a leads, with the result of (1), to all the results on heat conduction in Sec. 4-6a and in Example 4.7 and, in addition, provides a basis for use of distorted models.

b. Supersonic and Transonic Similarity Rules

We now examine two problems where natural coordinates must be used to achieve usable similarity rules and feasible testing procedures based upon them. Again, it will be seen that similarity based on natural coordinates is equivalent to an invariance property of the equations and boundary conditions. It is stressed that the similarity obtained is not one which requires the same value of parameters in all cases, but instead allows for compensation of altered values of the parameters by changes in the magnitude of the variables. This technique is the key to the success of aeronautical engineers in achieving feasible test methods for airships at Mach numbers in excess of approximately 0.2. Without this procedure, the number of tests required to correlate performance would be extremely burdensome, if not impossible, and the advance of high-speed aircraft would have been considerably delayed. In Example 4.11, the equations are linear and homogeneous and solutions can be found. In Example 4.12 the equations are essentially nonhomogeneous and the similarity properties derivable from natural coordinates become particularly important.

Example 4.11. Similarity and Natural Coordinates in Linearized Compressible Flow. The equations for compressible flow about objects have been thoroughly studied and well verified. For two-dimensional flow about an object (Fig. 4.13), which causes only small disturbances, and for Mach numbers not near unity, the equations can be written

$$\frac{\partial^2 \varphi}{\partial x^2} + \frac{1}{1 - M^2} \frac{\partial^2 \varphi}{\partial y^2} = 0 \qquad (4.64a)$$

where φ is the perturbation velocity potential defined so that $\nabla \varphi$ gives the deviation of the velocity from the mean speed far upstream, x and y are the coordinates shown in Fig. 4.13, and M is the Mach number far

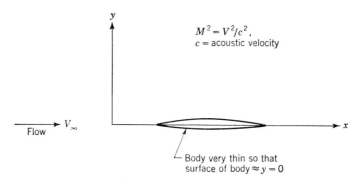

FIG. 4.13

upstream. For the linearized two-dimensional flow, the boundary conditions can be taken as

$$\left(\frac{\partial \varphi}{\partial y}\right)_{y=0} = U_1 \left(\frac{dy}{dx}\right)_{\text{body}} \tag{4.64b}$$

and at ∞: $\qquad \dfrac{\partial \varphi}{\partial x} = \dfrac{\partial \varphi}{\partial y} = 0 \tag{4.64c}$

Since normalization or absorption of parameters will not affect Eq. (4.64c), we need only work with Eqs. (4.64a) and (4.64b). In aerodynamic testing the principal quantity of concern is pressure coefficient c_p given by

$$c_p = \frac{p - p_\infty}{\frac{1}{2}\rho_\infty U_\infty^2}$$

where the subscript ∞ denotes free-stream properties, U is the total velocity, U_1 is the potential flow velocity at the body, p is the local static pressure. We are primarily concerned with pressure distribution on the body. For linearized flow this can be shown to be

$$(c_p)_{\text{body}} = -\frac{2}{U_1}\left(\frac{\partial \varphi}{\partial x}\right)_{y=0} \tag{4.65}$$

In particular, we want to find coordinates in which $(c_p)_{\text{body}}$ is preserved for different values of the free-stream Mach number M.

Note that approximation theory has already been applied to the complete inviscid equations of motion to obtain Eq. (4.64a). We need not concern ourselves with magnitude to find the desired condition. Hence, for convenience, we normalize as follows:

Let

$$\bar{\varphi} = \frac{\varphi}{U_1 L}$$

$$\bar{x} = \frac{x}{L}$$

$$\bar{y} = \frac{y}{L}$$

where

L = body length

Then Eq. (4.64a) becomes

$$\frac{\partial^2 \bar{\varphi}}{\partial \bar{x}^2} + \frac{1}{1 - M^2} \frac{\partial^2 \bar{\varphi}}{\partial \bar{y}^2} = 0 \qquad (4.66a)$$

and boundary conditions (4.64b) become

$$\left(\frac{\partial \bar{\varphi}}{\partial \bar{y}} \right)_{y=0} = \frac{L}{U_1 L} \left(\frac{\partial \varphi}{\partial y} \right)_{y=0} = \left(\frac{dy}{dx} \right)_{\text{body}} \qquad (4.66b)$$

Equation (4.65) becomes

$$(c_p)_{\text{body}} = -\frac{2UL}{UL} \left(\frac{\partial \bar{\varphi}}{\partial \bar{x}} \right)_{\bar{y}=0} = -2 \left(\frac{\partial \bar{\varphi}}{\partial \bar{x}} \right)_{\bar{y}=0} \qquad (4.67)$$

Inspection of Eq. (4.66a) shows it is possible to obtain a parameter-free equation by absorption of the parameter $1 - M^2$ into either $\bar{x}$ or $\bar{y}$ (but not φ). However, we wish to preserve $(c_p)_{\text{body}}$ which involves $\bar{\varphi}$ and $\bar{x}$; we therefore seek to absorb $1 - M^2$ into y. Defining

$$y^+ = \sqrt{1 - M^2} \, \bar{y} \qquad (4.68)$$

Eq. (4.66) becomes

$$\frac{\partial^2 \bar{\varphi}}{\partial \bar{x}^2} + \frac{\partial^2 \bar{\varphi}}{\partial y^{+2}} = 0 \qquad (4.69)$$

But Eq. (4.66b) becomes

$$\left(\frac{\partial \bar{\varphi}}{\partial y^+} \right)_{y^+=0} = \frac{1}{\sqrt{1 - M^2}} \left(\frac{\partial \bar{\varphi}}{\partial \bar{y}} \right)_{\bar{y}=0} = \frac{1}{\sqrt{1 - M^2}} \left(\frac{d\bar{y}}{d\bar{x}} \right)_{\text{body}} \qquad (4.70)$$

Thus absorption of parameters in the differential equation results in the appearance of a parameter in the boundary conditions. This difficulty can be overcome by purposeful use of a distorted similarity rule for the body. For convenience let the body shape be described as

$$\bar{y}_{\text{body}} = \frac{y_{\text{body}}}{L} = t \cdot f \left(\frac{x}{L} \right) = t \cdot f(\bar{x}) \qquad (4.71)$$

We consider $f(\bar{x})$ as a shape of the body *family* and t as a *thickness factor*. Then

$$\left(\frac{d\bar{y}}{d\bar{x}}\right)_{\text{body}} = tf'(\bar{x}) \tag{4.72}$$

Then Eq. (4.70) can be written

$$\left(\frac{\partial\bar{\varphi}}{\partial y^+}\right)_{y^+=0} = \frac{1}{\sqrt{1-M^2}} tf'(\bar{x}) \tag{4.73}$$

We further define

$$t^+ = \frac{t}{\sqrt{1-M^2}}$$

Then Eq. (4.73) becomes

$$\left(\frac{\partial\bar{\varphi}}{\partial y^+}\right)_{y^+=0} = t^+f'(\bar{x}) \tag{4.74a}$$

Thus two bodies, say a and b, will have the same governing equation and boundary conditions in $\bar{\varphi}$, $\bar{x}$, y^+ coordinates *if we adjust their thickness factors to give the same t^+*. That is, the required rule for constancy of $(c_p)_{\text{body}}$ is

$$t^+ = \text{constant} = \frac{t_a}{\sqrt{1-M_a^2}} = \frac{t_b}{\sqrt{1-M_b^2}} \tag{4.74b}$$

where M_a and M_b are the free-stream Mach numbers of bodies a and b. Thus to obtain constant $(c_p)_{\text{body}}$ in $\bar{\varphi}$, $\bar{x}$ coordinates, we must adjust the thickness of the body according to Eq. (4.74b), but retain the same family or shape, that is, the same $f(\bar{x})$.

Several points are of interest here. We observe that a different normalization of $\bar{\varphi}$ would not affect Eq. (4.69), since it is homogeneous in $\bar{\varphi}$; it might, however, affect the expression for c_p. For example, if one defines

$$\varphi^* = B\frac{\varphi}{U_1L} = B\bar{\varphi}$$

where B is an arbitrary nondimensional constant, Eq. (4.69) is unaltered and the boundary condition (4.70) becomes

$$\left(\frac{\partial\bar{\varphi}^*}{\partial y^+}\right)_{y^+=0} = B\left(\frac{\partial\bar{\varphi}}{\partial y^+}\right)_{y^+=0} = Bt^+f(\bar{x}) \tag{4.75}$$

Since we are here concerned only with constancy of the boundary conditions for varying values of M, Eq. (4.75) meets the requirement. However, the expression for pressure coefficient Eq. (4.67) becomes

$$(c_p)_{\text{body}} = -2 \left(\frac{\partial \bar{\varphi}}{\partial \bar{x}} \right)_{y^+=0} = -\frac{2}{B} \left(\frac{\partial \varphi^*}{\partial \bar{x}} \right)_{y^+=0} \tag{4.76}$$

The constant B is thus a free parameter, that is, we can give it any convenient value. Thus we have not used up all the choices available to us. By proper selection of B it is possible to derive all the usual similarity rules for compressible flow under these conditions. These rules are called the Prandtl-Glauert rules and Göthert's rule. These relations are summarized in recent texts on aerodynamics along with examples of application; a particularly good discussion is given by Liepmann and Roshko.[30]

The equation as given above would result in imaginary values of t^+ for supersonic flow ($M^2 > 1$). However, restudy of the equations shows that it is only necessary to insert $\sqrt{|1 - M^2|}$ for $\sqrt{1 - M^2}$ in order to make the rules correct for both subsonic and supersonic flow.[†] These rules do not hold for $M \simeq 1$, however, since the Eq. (4.64a) is not complete for such cases. Transonic flow is discussed in the next example.

Liepmann and Roshko[30] develop results identical to those above by using two sets of coordinates, one represents a body a and the other body b. They then demonstrate that the equations for body a will yield those of body b, provided the coordinates are selected to satisfy the equations for y^+ and t^+, that is, Eqs. (4.68) and 4.74b). The reader may want to verify that either procedure is equivalent to stating an invariance property of the equations and boundary conditions in $\bar{\varphi}$, $\bar{x}$, y^+ coordinates with boundary conditions stated in terms of t^+.

It is noted that the rule for similarity in the flow is not the same as that for the boundary conditions. Similar points in the flow field are given by constant values of y^+, that is, by

$$y^+ = \sqrt{1 - M^2}\, y = \text{constant} \tag{4.68}$$

Similar boundary conditions are maintained by constant values of t^+, that is, by

$$t^+ = \frac{t}{\sqrt{1 - M^2}} = \text{constant} \tag{4.74b}$$

Thus, for example, as M increases from zero in subsonic flow, we retain similarity by using a "narrower" body according to Eq. (4.74b), but the effect on the flow field becomes "wider" according to Eq. (4.68).

Finally, it is again emphasized that similarity rules can be found directly upon establishment of natural coordinates for the equations and

[†] Note, however, one does not compare a subsonic body with a supersonic one or conversely.

boundary conditions. This example is particularly instructive because it shows that the method can be applied even where it is essential, and not merely convenient, to develop a distorted model law.

Example 4.12. Two-dimensional Transonic Similarity Rule. Tests of pressure distribution on thin airfoils show the rule derived in Example 4.11 to be accurate until the Mach number approaches unity somewhere on the body, then serious deviations are observed. The trouble lies not in the deviation of the rule but rather in the completeness of the differential equation (4.64a) in the transonic regime. Test data together with approximation theory show that an adequate approximate equation for modeling transonic behavior of thin bodies is

$$\frac{\partial^2\varphi}{\partial x^2} + \frac{1}{1-M^2}\frac{\partial^2\varphi}{\partial y^2} = \frac{(\gamma+1)M^2}{1-M^2}\frac{1}{U}\frac{\partial\varphi}{\partial x}\frac{\partial^2\varphi}{\partial x^2} \tag{4.77}$$

where all symbols are as in Example 4.11 and γ = ratio of specific heats. The boundary conditions can also be taken as those of Example 4.11.

Again, we seek a rule which preserves $(c_p)_{body}$. Since Eq. (4.77) is not homogeneous in φ, we must expect to lose the free parameter B of Example 4.11; indeed to find a similarity rule we must take a definite value for B. Accordingly, we normalize using the variables

$$\varphi^* = \frac{B\varphi}{UL}$$

$$\bar{x} = \frac{x}{L}$$

$$\bar{y} = \frac{y}{L}$$

Equation (4.77) becomes

$$\frac{UL}{BL^2}\frac{\partial^2\varphi^*}{\partial\bar{x}^2} + \frac{1}{1-M^2}\frac{UL}{BL^2}\frac{\partial^2\varphi^*}{\partial\bar{y}^2} = \frac{(\gamma+1)M^2}{1-M^2}\frac{U^2L^2}{UL^3B^2}\frac{\partial\varphi^*}{\partial\bar{x}}\frac{\partial^2\varphi^*}{\partial\bar{x}^2}$$

Dividing by U/BL yields

$$\frac{\partial^2\varphi^*}{\partial\bar{x}^2} + \frac{1}{1-M^2}\frac{\partial^2\varphi^*}{\partial\bar{y}^2} = \frac{(\gamma+1)M^2}{1-M^2}\frac{1}{B}\frac{\partial\varphi^*}{\partial\bar{x}}\frac{\partial^2\varphi^*}{\partial\bar{x}^2} \tag{4.78}$$

We can obtain a parameter-free equation if we set

$$B = \frac{(\gamma+1)M^2}{1-M^2} \tag{4.79}$$

and again take

$$y^+ = \sqrt{1-M^2}\,\bar{y} \tag{4.80}$$

then

$$\varphi^* = \frac{(\gamma + 1)M^2}{1 - M^2} \frac{\varphi}{UL}$$

The boundary conditions at infinity are again unaltered by the transformation of variables. The boundary condition

$$\left(\frac{\partial \varphi}{\partial y}\right)_{y=0} = U\left(\frac{dy}{dx}\right)_{\text{body}}$$

becomes

$$\left(\frac{\partial \varphi^*}{\partial y^+}\right)_{y^+=0} = \frac{1}{\sqrt{1 - M^2}} \left(\frac{\partial \varphi^*}{\partial \bar{y}}\right)_{\bar{y}=0} = \frac{1}{\sqrt{1 - M^2}} \frac{BL}{UL} \left(\frac{\partial \varphi}{\partial y}\right)_{y=0}$$

or

$$\left(\frac{\partial \varphi^*}{\partial y^+}\right)_{y^+=0} = \frac{B}{\sqrt{1 - M^2}} \left(\frac{d\bar{y}}{d\bar{x}}\right)_{\text{body}} = \frac{(\gamma + 1)M^2}{(1 - M^2)^{\frac{3}{2}}} \left(\frac{d\bar{y}}{d\bar{x}}\right)_{\text{body}}$$

We again express $(d\bar{y}/d\bar{x})_{\text{body}}$ as

$$\left(\frac{d\bar{y}}{d\bar{x}}\right)_{\text{body}} = t \cdot f'(\bar{x}) \tag{4.81}$$

Then

$$\left(\frac{\partial \varphi^*}{\partial y^+}\right)_{y^+=0} = \frac{(\gamma + 1)M^2}{(1 - M^2)^{\frac{3}{2}}} t \cdot f'(\bar{x})$$

We can achieve a similarity rule by requiring

$$t^+ = \frac{(\gamma + 1)M^2 t}{(1 - M^2)^{\frac{3}{2}}} = \text{constant} \tag{4.82a}$$

so that

$$\left(\frac{\partial \varphi^*}{\partial y^+}\right)_{y^+=0} = t^+ f(\bar{x}) \tag{4.82b}$$

However, the pressure coefficient c_p now is

$$c_p = \frac{-2}{U}\left(\frac{\partial \varphi}{\partial x}\right)_{y=0} = \frac{-2}{U} \frac{UL}{BL} \left(\frac{\partial \varphi^*}{\partial \bar{x}}\right)_{y^+=0}$$

$$= \frac{-2(1 - M^2)}{(\gamma + 1)M^2} \left(\frac{\partial \varphi^*}{\partial \bar{x}}\right)_{y^+=0} \tag{4.83}$$

Thus we do not achieve a constant c_p in φ^*, y^+, $\bar{x}$ coordinates as in Example 4.11, but one which must be scaled according to the rule (4.83). We employ the rule by observing that in φ^*, y^+, $\bar{x}$ coordinates we must get a constant value of $(\partial \varphi^*/\partial \bar{x})$. This can be achieved for any body with the same curve of $f(x)$ by describing its shape and thickness in terms of

$$t^+ = \frac{(\gamma + 1)M^2}{(1 - M^2)^{\frac{3}{2}}}, \qquad t = \text{constant}$$

It follows that for any one point that is any given $\bar{x}$

$$\frac{c_p(\gamma + 1)M^2}{1 - M^2} = \text{constant} \qquad\qquad (4.84)$$

The rule (4.84) allows computation of the pressure coefficient of a body at one Mach number from tests on a body of different thickness at a different Mach number, although the values will not be the same.

c. Reduction in Number of Independent Variables— Separation and Similarity Coordinates

In Secs. 4-10a and 4-10b several cases of increasing complexity were treated to show that generalization of similarity can be achieved by seeking natural coordinates in which parameter-free equations and boundary conditions can be found. In this section, it will be shown that a different generalization of similarity can be found by seeking new coordinates which reduce the number of independent variables in the governing equations. Such coordinates have usually been called *similarity variables*. It is also possible to seek natural coordinates which are fewer in number than the coordinates of the original equation and thus to generalize in two ways at once. These two processes are often carried out in one step; here we keep them distinct to clarify the meaning of procedures.

Once again a correspondence will be found between the search for similarity properties, invariance under coordinate transformation, and a form of constancy of the equations in the similarity variables. We shall also find a close relation with *separation of the variables* in the sense of partial differential equations. The transformation properties have been extensively discussed by Morgan[35] and Michal.[33] The invariance idea has been employed by Birkhoff.[4,5] Hansen[17] has employed the method of separation of variables. We will emphasize the last method here, since it is simplest mathematically, achieves equal results, and brings out more clearly the symmetry properties we are seeking. We will also make a few remarks about the utility and meaning of the results achieved by Morgan.[35]

Similarity variables arise from two distinct kinds of what can be called *internal symmetry*. The first kind is the familiar physical symmetry of the physical system. An example is a problem which inherently possesses spherical symmetry, such as a blast wave emanating from a point in space in an unconfined gas. Most physical workers tend to adopt coordinates expressing symmetries of this type naturally. That is, most analysts would choose to express the behavior of the blast wave in spherical coordinates instead of rectangular coordinates and would assume that the solution depends only on the radius, not on angular position in the spherical coordinates. This assumption carries with it inherently a kind of internal similarity and modeling behavior. It implies that the properties of the solution at a given radius are the same for any angular position and hence that we can model one angular position by any other at the same radius. The model relation is then internal in the sense that *it relates two different points inside the system rather than two similar points in different systems.* Internal similitude thus refers to variables rather than to parameters in the sense of this discussion. Of course, such assumed symmetries do not always occur in nature for symmetric boundary conditions and the assumption must be checked. This point has been emphasized by Birkhoff[5] regarding the behavior of viscous fluids. Birkhoff discusses the whole question from the viewpoint of invariance under coordinate transformation and group theory; he gives a number of examples of symmetry of this kind. Here we shall concern ourselves only with internal symmetry of the second kind, which is less obvious.

The second type of internal symmetry arises from the structure of the governing equations, thus it is a procedure which falls within the general scope of the present discussion. It reflects internal similarity, since it also concerns the variables, not the parameters. Although the process at first appears to offer rather general results, the exact solutions found thus far have been restricted to problems which are *lacking a characteristic length in one of the original coordinates.* The mathematical aspects of such solutions are not well understood, and there seems to be no proof that the solutions must be so restricted. However, the list of such solutions compiled recently by K. T. Yang† and slightly extended and published by Abbott and Kline[1] shows no exceptions to the rule. Moreover, validity of this rule is suggested by study of the boundary conditions. In any event the lack of a characteristic length for one coordinate can often be taken as a hint to seek a solution and correlations in terms of a similarity variable.

Again the discussion is limited to methods, and only a few examples have been given. The reader interested in more examples covering cases with more than two independent variables, greater discussion of the details of various techniques, and more direct methods for constructing similarity variables, should see Morgan,[35] and Abbott and Kline.[1] Since the nature of the similarity variables is to some degree complex and is

† Thanks are due to Prof. Yang for generously supplying the author with this list.

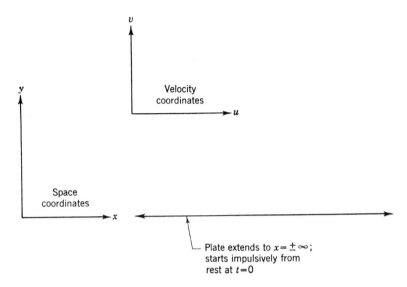

FIG. 4.14

best made clear by example, we defer further general remarks to the end
of this section.

Example 4.13.   The Suddenly Accelerating Flat Plate.   Consider a thin plate of infinite length initially at rest in the coordinates shown
by Fig. 4.14.   The plate is immersed in an incompressible, viscous fluid of
infinite extent, which is also at rest.   At time $t = 0$ the plate is accelerated
to velocity U.   The motion of the fluid layers for times greater than
$t = 0$ is sought.   For this case all but two of the terms in the governing
momentum equation are zero, so the governing equation reduces to

$$\frac{\partial u}{\partial t} = \nu \frac{\partial^2 u}{\partial y^2} \qquad\qquad (4.85a)$$

where ν = the kinematic viscosity coefficient.   The details of this reduction can be found in Schlichting,[45] Chap. 11.   Appropriate boundary
conditions are

$$\begin{aligned}
&\text{at } t = 0 (y \geq 0): &\quad u = 0 \\
&\text{at } y = 0 (t > 0): &\quad u = U \\
&\text{at } y = \infty \text{ (all } t): &\quad u = 0
\end{aligned} \qquad (4.85b)$$

Since we want to show the connection to the conventional method of
separation of variables, we attempt a solution in the usual form, that is,
we assume a solution can be found in the form

$$u = T(t) Y(y)$$

Then

$$T'Y = \nu TY''$$

where primed quantities denote differentiation of the function with respect to its argument. Upon division by TY we obtain

$$\frac{T'}{T} = \nu \frac{Y''}{Y} = \text{constant} = -\lambda$$

where λ is a pure constant by the usual argument. The separated ordinary differential equations are then

$$T' + \lambda T = 0 \qquad \text{and} \qquad Y'' + \frac{\lambda}{\nu} Y = 0$$

The general solutions for these equations are

$$T = c_1 e^{-\lambda t}$$

$$Y = c_2 \cos\left(\frac{\lambda}{\nu} y\right) + c_3 \sin\left(\frac{\lambda}{\nu} y\right)$$

Thus the expression for the velocity is

$$u = e^{-\lambda t}\left[c_4 \cos\left(\frac{\lambda}{\nu} y\right) + c_5 \sin\left(\frac{\lambda}{\nu} y\right)\right] \qquad (4.86)$$

The boundary condition at $y = 0$ requires

$$\text{at } y = 0 (t > 0): \qquad u = \text{constant} = u_0 = c_4 e^{-\lambda t}$$

Therefore we obtain the result that λ must be zero,[†] Eq. (4.86) gives $u = c_4 = \text{constant}$, but this is a trivial solution. Hence, *direct* application of the classic method of separation of variables will not solve the problem. For linear equations there are techniques available which can be used to obtain a solution (for example, by application of the Fourier integral). However, here the problem is solved by shifting to coordinates in which the classic separation-of-variables method will work, since this brings out the relation to similarity solutions which we are seeking, and is useful for nonlinear equations.

In particular we ask, "Does a transformation of variables exist which reduces the number of independent variables in Eq. (4.85a) from two to one?" The dependent variable u would then transform to a function of a new independent variable η alone, that is,

$$u(y,t) \rightarrow u(\eta)$$

[†] The same result is readily obtained for λ negative or complex.

where

$$\eta = \eta(y,t)$$

The resulting equation would be second-order in the new independent variable η; it would thus require two boundary conditions on η, unlike the original equation where three boundary conditions in y and t are required.

This reduction in number of boundary conditions requires that two of the original boundary conditions be related in a specific way if we are to obtain an exact solution of the transformed equation. In particular it requires

$$u[\eta(\alpha,y)] = u[\eta(t,\beta)] \tag{4.87}$$

Condition (4.87) follows from the fact that, if it were not true, it would then be impossible to satisfy all three of the original boundary conditions in terms of only two boundary conditions on η.

Thus two of the boundary conditions of the problem as originally set can be written as

$$
\begin{aligned}
\text{at } t = \alpha: \qquad & u = u[\eta(\alpha,y)] \\
\text{at } y = \beta: \qquad & u = u[\eta(t,\beta)]
\end{aligned}
\tag{4.88}
$$

where

$$u[\eta(\alpha,y)] = u[\eta(t,\beta)]$$

The particular, boundary conditions that are so reduced are found by comparison of the right side of Eq. (4.88) and the original boundary conditions (4.85b). If such a condition cannot be found, in general, we do not expect to find a similarity solution in terms of the variable η. This condition at least lends plausibility to our earlier remarks concerning lack of a characteristic length in one or more directions, since then a constant boundary condition at zero and infinity can be related in terms of a negative power in a coordinate. However, it would seem possible to satisfy Eq. (4.88) in other ways, even though examples are not known.

For the specific problem at hand, we observe from Eq. (4.85b) that $u(0,y) = u(t,\infty)$, and therefore η can be made to satisfy Eq. (4.87) if we take $\alpha = 0$, $\beta = \infty$, and $\eta(0,y) = \eta(t,\infty)$. One transformation which is consistent with this condition is

$$\eta = a\frac{y^n}{t^m} = a\left(\frac{y}{t^{m/n}}\right)^n$$

where a is a constant and n and m are real numbers which may either be greater or less than zero; their exact values are to be determined.

In order to keep our new variables distinct from the old set, we choose a second new variable ζ to be equal to t, the old independent variable appearing in the denominator† of η.   Next we require the resulting equation, after the transformation of variables $t, y \rightarrow \zeta, \eta$, to be separable into a function of ζ alone and a function of η alone.

By the chain rule of calculus we can write $\partial u / \partial y$ in terms of the new coordinates ζ, η as follows

$$\frac{\partial u}{\partial y} = \frac{\partial u}{\partial \zeta} \frac{\partial \zeta}{\partial y} + \frac{\partial u}{\partial \eta} \frac{\partial \eta}{\partial y} = 0 + an \frac{y^{n-1}}{t^m} \frac{\partial u}{\partial \eta} = an \frac{y^{n-1}}{\zeta^m} \frac{\partial u}{\partial \eta}$$

The value of n can be chosen arbitrarily, because if there is a solution in the form $u = u(\eta)$, there must be a solution in the form $u = u(\eta^n)$. The resulting functional form of the solution is, in general, dependent on the value of n.   The best value of n is that value which yields the most easily solved form of the resulting ordinary differential equation; this is a problem which always faces the worker who is trying to solve a given equation.   The point here is that there is no loss of generality in assuming a particular value of n.   It can be seen from the above expression for $\partial u / \partial y$ that a simplification results for $n = 1$, and therefore this value of n will be used.

Inserting $n = 1$, $\partial u / \partial y$ becomes

$$\frac{\partial u}{\partial y} = \frac{a}{\zeta^m} \frac{\partial u}{\partial \eta}$$

Differentiating again by the chain rule, we obtain

$$\frac{\partial^2 u}{\partial y^2} = \frac{a}{\zeta^{2m}} \frac{\partial^2 u}{\partial \eta^2}$$

Similarly, $\partial u / \partial t$ becomes

$$\frac{\partial u}{\partial t} = \frac{\partial u}{\partial \zeta} \frac{\partial \zeta}{\partial t} + \frac{\partial u}{\partial \eta} \frac{\partial \eta}{\partial t} = \frac{\partial u}{\partial \zeta} - am \frac{y}{t^{m+1}} \frac{\partial u}{\partial \eta} = \frac{\partial u}{\partial \zeta} - m \frac{\eta}{\zeta} \frac{\partial u}{\partial \eta}$$

Putting these expressions into Eq. (4.85a), we obtain the transformed differential equation

$$\frac{\partial u}{\partial \zeta} - m \frac{\eta}{\zeta} \frac{\partial u}{\partial \eta} = \nu \frac{a^2}{\zeta^{2m}} \frac{\partial^2 u}{\partial \eta^2} \tag{4.89}$$

† This is the simplest choice for ζ from the standpoint of the mathematics involved in the transformation (because the highest order derivative of u with respect to t is less than that of u with respect to y).   Whether this choice for ζ works or not must be found by carrying through the analysis; if it does not work, the only conclusion obtained is that the assumed transformation does not yield a similarity solution.

We now formally try the classic method of separation of variables on Eq. (4.89) with $u = b \cdot g(\zeta) \cdot f(\eta)$, where b is a constant. Division by $b \cdot g \cdot f$ and rearranging results in

$$\frac{g'}{g} \zeta^{2m} = m \frac{\eta}{\zeta^{1-2m}} \frac{f'}{f} + \nu a^2 \frac{f''}{f} \tag{4.90}$$

Examination of Eq. (4.90) now shows that it will separate into a function of ζ alone on one side and function of η alone on the other if $\zeta^{1-2m} = $ constant,[†] that is, $2m - 1 = 0$ or $m = \frac{1}{2}$. Thus we find the required separation variable is $\eta = 2y/\sqrt{t}$. Again defining λ as the separation constant, Eq. (4.90) becomes, on insertion of $m = \frac{1}{2}$.

$$\frac{g'}{g} \zeta = \frac{\eta}{2} \frac{f'}{f} + \nu a^2 \frac{f''}{f} = \lambda \tag{4.91}$$

The ordinary differential equation $g' \cdot \zeta/g = \lambda$ can immediately be solved to give $g = c_1 \zeta^\lambda$. The solution for g must be compatible with the boundary conditions. Thus applying the boundary condition at $\eta = 0(y = 0)$, we have

$$u = \text{constant} = u_0 = bc_1 \zeta^\lambda f(0)$$

Since b, c_1, and $f(0)$ are all constants, we have the condition that $\lambda = 0$. The function g is then determined; $g = \text{constant} = c_1$. Equation (4.91) can then be written as

$$2\nu a^2 f'' + \eta f' = 0 \tag{4.92}$$

Thus we have achieved the objective of reducing the number of independent variables from two to one. We can also express η as a natural coordinate by proper choice of the constant a. We take $a^2 = \frac{1}{4}\nu$; η then becomes

$$\eta = \frac{y}{2\sqrt{\nu t}}$$

and Eq. (4.92) becomes

$$f'' + 2\eta f' = 0 \tag{4.93a}$$

with boundary conditions

$$\begin{array}{ll} \text{at } \eta = 0: & f = 1 \\ \text{at } \eta = \infty: & f = 0 \end{array} \tag{4.93b}$$

[†] This requirement that the coefficients containing t (or ζ) have zero exponent is the general condition required to fix m. See, for example, Yang[56] and Hansen.[17]

The solution of Eq. (4.93) is

$$f = 1 - erf\eta$$

where *erf* is an abbreviation for the tabulated function

$$erf \frac{x}{\sqrt{2}} = \frac{1}{\sqrt{2\pi}} \int_{-x}^{x} e^{-t^2/2}\, dt$$

In this case, the investigation of similarity properties has led us all the way to a complete solution of the problem. Equation (4.85a) can also be solved in similarity variables in somewhat more general form without any assumption of initial condition. One can then seek the initial conditions for which the solution can be shown to hold (details are given by Abbott and Kline[1]). One employs the more general transformation of variables

$$\eta = \frac{ay}{\gamma(t)}$$

where γ is an unknown function. We will not give the details here, but instead present two other examples and then turn to a discussion of the meaning of such solutions, their similarity properties, and some general remarks about solutions of this type.

Example 4.14.   Steady Laminar Boundary Layer on a Flat Plate.   A somewhat more complicated example of a similarity solution is the Blasius solution for the laminar incompressible boundary layer on a flat plate. We give a solution somewhat different from the original here. Since the pressure distribution for potential flow past a flat plate is constant, Prandtl's boundary-layer equations in the coordinates of Fig. 4.14 then reduce to

$$u \frac{\partial u}{\partial x} + v \frac{\partial u}{\partial y} = \nu \frac{\partial^2 u}{\partial y^2} \tag{4.94}$$

Equation (4.94) is solved in conjunction with the continuity equation

$$\frac{\partial u}{\partial x} + \frac{\partial v}{\partial y} = 0 \tag{4.95}$$

The boundary conditions are

$$\begin{array}{lll} \text{at } y = 0: & u = 0 & v = 0 \\ \text{at } \quad \infty: & u = U & \end{array}$$

It is convenient to introduce the stream function Ψ defined by†

$$\frac{\partial \Psi}{\partial x} = -v \qquad \frac{\partial \Psi}{\partial y} = u$$

The two equations (4.94) and (4.95) then reduce to one equation in Ψ

$$\frac{\partial \Psi}{\partial y}\frac{\partial^2 \Psi}{\partial x \partial y} - \frac{\partial \Psi}{\partial x}\frac{\partial^2 \Psi}{\partial y^2} = \nu \frac{\partial^3 \Psi}{\partial y^3} \qquad (4.96)$$

with boundary conditions

at $y = 0 \ (x \geq 0)$: $\qquad \dfrac{\partial \Psi}{\partial y} = 0 \qquad \dfrac{\partial \Psi}{\partial x} = 0$

at $y = \infty \ (x \geq 0)$: $\qquad \dfrac{\partial \Psi}{\partial y} = U$

We make no statement about an initial condition at $x = 0$ and employ the "trial" transformation

$$\eta = \frac{ay}{\gamma(x)}$$

Formally differentiating gives

$$\frac{\partial \Psi}{\partial x} = \frac{\partial \Psi}{\partial \zeta} - \frac{\gamma'}{\gamma}\eta\frac{\partial \Psi}{\partial \eta}$$

$$\frac{\partial^2 \Psi}{\partial x \partial y} = \frac{a}{\gamma}\frac{\partial^2 \Psi}{\partial \zeta \partial \eta} - a\frac{\gamma'}{\gamma^2}\frac{\partial \Psi}{\partial \eta} - a\frac{\gamma'}{\gamma^2}\eta\frac{\partial^2 \Psi}{\partial \eta^2}$$

$$\frac{\partial \Psi}{\partial y} = \frac{a}{\gamma}\frac{\partial \Psi}{\partial \eta}$$

$$\frac{\partial^2 \Psi}{\partial y^2} = \frac{a^2}{\gamma^2}\frac{\partial^2 \Psi}{\partial \eta^2}$$

$$\frac{\partial^3 \Psi}{\partial y^3} = \frac{a^3}{\gamma^3}\frac{\partial^3 \Psi}{\partial \eta^3}$$

Substituting this transformation into Eq. (4.96) yields

$$\gamma\frac{\partial \Psi}{\partial \eta}\frac{\partial^2 \Psi}{\partial \eta \partial \zeta} - \gamma'\left(\frac{\partial \Psi}{\partial \eta}\right)^2 - \gamma\frac{\partial \Psi}{\partial \zeta}\frac{\partial^2 \Psi}{\partial \eta^2} = \nu a\frac{\partial^3 \Psi}{\partial \eta^3} \qquad (4.97)$$

Applying the method of separation of variables to Eq. (4.97), we try $\Psi = b \cdot g(\zeta) \cdot f(\eta)$; on substituting into Eq. (4.97), we obtain

$$(\gamma g' - \gamma'g)f'^2 - \gamma g'ff'' = \frac{\nu a}{b}f''' \qquad (4.98)$$

---

† It is worth noting that the variable Ψ reduces two independent variables to one; it is another type of "natural coordinate" that provides generalized correlations in some problems.

and dividing by f'^2 yields

$$\gamma g' - \gamma' g = \gamma g' \frac{f f''}{f'^2} + \frac{\nu a}{b} \frac{f'''}{f'^2} \tag{4.99}$$

Equation (4.99) will be separated if $\gamma g' = \text{constant} = c_1$. This is one condition on two unknowns γ and g, so that another relation between γ and g must be found.† The required relation can be found for this particular problem by considering the boundary conditions. There are problems which arise, however, where the boundary conditions do not supply the necessary equation; such cases are discussed below.

To find a second relation between γ and g, consider the boundary condition

at $\eta = \infty$: $\dfrac{\partial \Psi(x, \infty)}{\partial y} = \dfrac{a}{\gamma} \dfrac{\partial \Psi(x, \infty)}{\partial \eta} = ab \dfrac{g}{\gamma} f'(\infty) = u_o$

Since a, b, $f'(\infty)$, and u_o are all constants, the necessary relation is $g/\gamma = \text{constant} = c_2$. Solving the two relations $\gamma g' = c_1$ and $g/\gamma = c_2$ simultaneously gives

$$g = \sqrt{2 c_1 c_2 (\zeta + \zeta_o)} \qquad \text{and} \qquad \gamma = \sqrt{2 (c_1 c_2)(\zeta + \zeta_o)}$$

Evaluation of the term $\gamma g' - \gamma' g$ shows it is identically zero. Hence the separation constant λ is zero, and Eq. (4.99) becomes

$$f''' + \frac{c_1 b}{\nu a} f f'' = 0 \tag{4.100}$$

Again the arbitrary constants are chosen to make η a natural coordinate. This requires $c_1 = u_o$, $a \cdot b = \frac{1}{2}$, $c_1 b / \nu a = \frac{1}{2}$, and $c_2 = 2 c_1$; it follows that $a^2 = u_o / \nu$ and $f'(\infty) = 1$, as before. Thus we obtain the differential equation due to Blasius

$$f f'' + 2 f''' = 0 \tag{4.101}$$

The boundary conditions are

at $\eta = 0$: $f(0) = 0$
at $\eta = 0$: $f'(0) = 0$ (4.102)
at $\eta = \infty$: $f'(\infty) = 1$

† The other term involving γ and g in Eq. (4.99) is not independent of the first relation $\gamma g' = c_1$. This can be seen as follows. Set $\gamma g' - \gamma' g = c_2$ and $\gamma g' = c_1$. Then $\gamma' g = \text{constant} = c_3$. Combining these last two equations gives

$$\gamma \gamma'' = (c_1 / c_3) \gamma'^2 = 0$$

which has the solution $\gamma = ax + b^{1/(1 + c_1/c_3)}$ for $c_1 \neq -c_3$, and $\gamma = a e^{bx}$ for $c_1 = -c_3$. This provides a "general" separation variable η for the boundary-layer equations. However, we cannot determine the similarity variable of a particular problem without

Equations (4.101) and (4.102) give the similarity variable

$$\eta = y \sqrt{\frac{U}{\nu(x + x_0)}} \tag{4.103}$$

There is no way to evaluate the constant of integration x_o from the information given in the problem statement. If the conventional initial condition that $\partial\Psi/\partial y = U$ at $x = 0 (y \neq 0)$ is used, then one finds that $x_o = 0$. This yields the conventional Blasius variable $\eta_B = y \sqrt{U/\nu x}$.

The additive constant x_o is not trivial, as will be seen in the next example. A closed form solution for Eq. (4.101) is not known, but the equation has been evaluated numerically by Blasius. The results are tabulated in standard texts on boundary-layer theory (see, for example, Schlichting,[45] page 121). Excellent agreement with drag and measured profiles is obtained.

Moreover, the variable η in Eq. (4.103) satisfies the equation and boundary condition of Blasius; thus the Blasius solution is correct in this variable. This indicates that the Blasius solution can be a limiting solution for large values of x, regardless of the initial conditions, since, as x becomes large, the effect of the starting conditions embodied in x_o become small. The more general similarity variable of Eq. (4.103) thus aids in alleviating to some extent the difficulties arising from the fact that Prandtl's boundary-layer equations are not correct near $x = 0$.

It is tempting at this point to conclude that the similarity variables which allow reduction in the number of independent variables can all be found merely by examining the orders of derivatives in the governing equations. If this were true, then the similarity variables would always be indicated by the form of the parameters when the equations were normalized by the method of Sec. 4-2. They could also be found merely by inspection of the equations; this would be equivalent to applying Huntley's extension (see Sec. 2-6) to counting the terms in the equation. Sedov[46] has indeed shown that many similarity variables can be found in this way. However, this procedure does not give all possible similarity variables, as is shown by the next example.

Example 4.15. Laminar, Two-Dimensional Jet. The equations of motion for the steady two-dimensional incompressible laminar flow of a fluid into an infinite region of the same fluid are (see Pai[38])

$$u \frac{\partial u}{\partial x} + v \frac{\partial u}{\partial y} = \nu \frac{\partial^2 u}{\partial y^2} \tag{4.104}$$

$$\frac{\partial u}{\partial x} + \frac{\partial v}{\partial y} = 0 \tag{4.105}$$

knowing c_1 and c_3. The conclusion, as stated above, remains the same: another relation between γ and g is required.

and the boundary conditions are

$$\text{at } y = 0: \qquad v = 0 \qquad \frac{\partial u}{\partial y} = 0 \tag{4.106}$$
$$\text{at } y = \infty: \qquad u = 0$$

The system is shown in Fig. 4.15.

Since the pressure is constant and the motion is steady, the total momentum flux across a section of the jet at any given value of x must be constant. That is

$$2\rho \int_0^\infty u^2 \, dy = \text{constant} \tag{4.107}$$

Again, we employ a stream function Ψ defined by

$$\frac{\partial \Psi}{\partial x} = -v \qquad \frac{\partial \Psi}{\partial y} = u$$

Equations (4.104) and (4.105) reduce to

$$\frac{\partial \Psi}{\partial y} \frac{\partial^2 \Psi}{\partial x \, \partial y} - \frac{\partial \Psi}{\partial x} \frac{\partial^2 \Psi}{\partial y^2} = \nu \frac{\partial^3 \Psi}{\partial y^3} \tag{4.108}$$

We assume the transformation $\zeta = x$ and $\eta = ay/\gamma(x)$ and use the method of separation of variables with $\Psi = b \cdot g(\zeta) \cdot f(\eta)$. Equation (4.108)

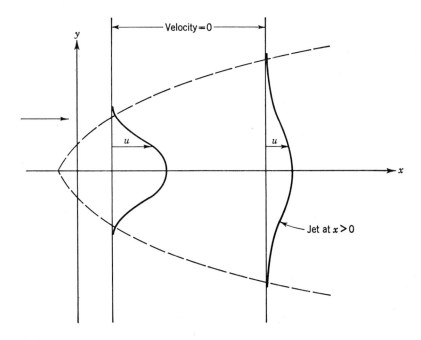

FIG. 4.15

then becomes

$$\gamma g' - \gamma' g = \gamma g' \frac{ff''}{f'^2} + \frac{va}{b} \frac{f'''}{f'^2} \qquad (4.109)$$

This is the same equation which was found for the Blasius problem, Eq. (4.99), since the same partial differential equations apply—only the boundary conditions are different. The boundary conditions corresponding to Eq. (4.106) are

at $\eta = 0$: $bg'f(0) = 0$

at $\eta = 0$: $ba^2 \dfrac{g}{\gamma^2} f''(0) = 0$ (4.110)

at $\eta = \infty$: $ba \dfrac{g}{\gamma} f'(\infty) = 0$

For Eq. (4.109) to be separated, it is necessary that

$$\gamma g' = \text{constant} = c_1$$

A second relation between γ and g can be found by considering Eq. (4.107) (see footnote, p. 188), which can be written as

$$\int_0^\infty u \, dy = \text{constant} = c_2 \qquad (4.111)$$

Now $u = \dfrac{\partial \Psi}{\partial y} = ab \dfrac{g}{\gamma} f'$ and $dy = \left(\dfrac{\gamma}{a}\right) d\eta$; hence Eq. (4.111) becomes

$$\int_0^\infty a^2 b^2 \frac{g^2}{\gamma^2} f'^2(\eta) \frac{\gamma}{a} \, d\eta = b^2 a \frac{g^2}{\gamma} \int_0^\infty f'^2(\eta) \, d\eta = c_2$$

We thus obtain the second relation to be $g^2/\gamma = \text{constant} = c_3$.

Solving the two relations $\gamma g' = c_1$ and $g^2/\gamma = c_3$ simultaneously, we obtain

$$g = [3 c_1 c_3 (x + x_0)]^{\frac{1}{3}}$$

and

$$\gamma = \frac{1}{c_3} [3 c_1 c_3 (x + x_0)]^{\frac{2}{3}}$$

where x_o is a constant of integration. If we now take the arbitrary constants c_1 and c_3 to have the values $c_1 = \sqrt{va/b}$ and $c_3 = \frac{1}{3}$, we obtain the desired natural coordinates. Equations (4.109) and (4.110) can now be written as

$$f''' + ff'' + f'^2 = 0 \qquad (4.112a)$$

with boundary conditions

at $f(0) = 0$: $f''(0) = 0$ $f'(\infty) = 0$ (4.112b)

where

$$\eta = \text{constant} \cdot y/3(x + x_0)^{\frac{2}{3}}$$

The solutions to these equations can be found in closed form and are given, for example, by Pai.[38]

The solution to this problem shows how the integral boundary-condition equation (4.111) is used to obtain the second relation between γ and g necessary to determine the proper similarity variable from the family of possible variables found by considering only the partial differential equation (4.108). In this solution, x_o represents the *potential core* or *starting length*, and could be determined from appropriate data.†

We now turn to some general remarks about similarity variables. First, we discuss the physical meaning. In all three cases studied we have reduced an equation in two independent variables to one with a single independent variable. In Examples 4.13 and 4.14 we found a solution dependent on the new coordinate η alone. However, in Example 4.15 we found the solution for the stream function dependent on the new coordinate η and also on x, since the function $g(x)$ is not a constant in this case, and by construction

$$\Psi = ag(x) \cdot f(\eta)$$

Thus there are at least two distinct cases. Actually, it is instructive to consider three classes. In all cases we have sought solutions in terms of new coordinates purposely constructed so that separation of variables is achieved in the conventional sense. Using coordinates x,y initially, new coordinates ζ,η as above, and a dependent variable Ψ,

1. The most general separated product form is

$$\Psi = ag(\zeta) \cdot f(\eta)$$

where both ζ and η are functions of x and y.

2. The next most general is

$$\Psi = ag(\zeta) \cdot f(\eta)$$

where ζ is a function of x alone (or y alone) and $\eta =$ function x and y.

3. The most restricted is

$$\Psi = Bf(\eta)$$

where $g(\zeta) = B =$ constant, not dependent on either x or y, and $\eta =$ function x and y.

More restricted results (such as $\zeta =$ function of y only and $\eta =$ function x only, or $g =$ constant and $\eta =$ function x only) imply separation or trivial solutions in the original coordinates x and y and need not be considered.

---

† Note in the sketch of Fig. 4.15 that the boundary conditions imply that the jet emerges from a very small hole, so that $x_o = 0$ and starting length can be ignored.

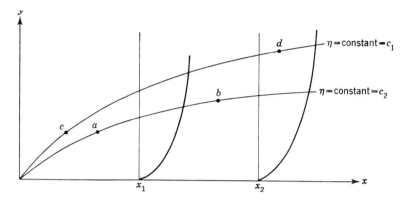

FIG. 4.16

Examination shows that case 3 does express a simple symmetry property. Indeed since we imply that a solution can be given in terms of η alone, it follows that points of constant η will have the same solution. Thus two points with the same value of η can be used to model each other, and we have an internal similitude, as we expected. For example, in the Blasius problem of the laminar incompressible boundary layer on a flat plate, lines of constant η are parabolas through the origin, and the symmetry properties are indicated in Fig. 4.16. As can be seen from Fig. 4.16, expression of the Blasius problem in terms of the coordinate η allows measurement of velocity at one value of x to be used to predict (or model) velocity at any other value of x.

Since $\bar{u} = \bar{u}(\eta)$ only

$$\bar{u}(c) = \bar{u}(d) \qquad \bar{u}(a) = \bar{u}(b) \qquad \text{etc.}$$

Note symmetry does not depend on x,y, but on constancy of η. Velocity profiles at x_1 and x_2 are similar, that is, values of $\bar{u}$ are the same for given η.

The similarity is one-dimensional, and we can call variables such as η in case 3 *one-dimensional similarity variables*, or *homology variables*.

In case 2, which is illustrated by the laminar jet solution of Example 4.15, we still have a symmetry property, but it is less general. In a certain sense it is comparable to the similarity rule of transonic flow given in Example 4.12, that is, the similarity does not give a constant result, but requires a weighting function, in this case $g(x)$. The symmetry property of the laminar jet solution is illustrated in Fig. 4.17.

Case 1 has no symmetry property at all; nevertheless it may provide a solution for much more general boundary conditions than either case 2 or case 3, which so far have been restricted to problems which lack a characteristic length in one of the original coordinates. The bulk of the exact solutions to Prandtl's boundary-layer equations which have been found

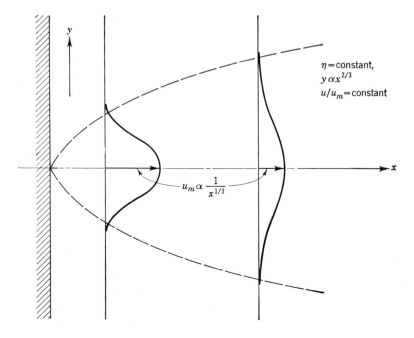

are of type 2 or 3.   However, relatively little investigation of type 1 has been carried out; such work might lead to exact solutions for more general boundary conditions.

It should be emphasized that finding all possible similarity solutions for a given differential equation is by no means a simple matter.   A number of authors have made this claim for Prandtl's boundary-layer equations only to find later that they had not in actuality achieved the stated result.   There are two important reasons for this.   First, in the processes above, two degrees of arbitrariness exist (1) in the definition of the transformation to the new coordinates, that is, in the definitions of ζ and η, and (2) in the definition of the form of separation.   All that can properly be concluded from results like that in Example 4.15 is that under the assumed transformation of variables the coordinates which will give separation in the form of a product have been found.   Different transformations may lead to new similarity variables, and there is no reason why separation cannot be sought in other forms.   Indeed, examples where separation is achieved by a sum form are known, but they have not been widely considered.   The first remark applies with equal force to the transformation methods of Morgan[35] since an assumed transformation is again employed.

The second reason that one cannot find all possible variables readily is best illustrated by considering how one seeks such variables. If we set a well-posed problem, then we write down the complete boundary condition, and, by definition of such problems, only one solution exists. Under these circumstances we can find only one or no similarity variables under a given transformation, since otherwise a contradiction to the existence of a unique solution occurs (barring, of course, functionally dependent transformations, such as from η to η^2). However, if we want to study similarity variables of a given equation with the view toward establishing a number of similarity properties and/or solutions, then we must omit some or all of the boundary conditions. It may then be possible to find an infinite number of different similarity variables for any one assumed transformation of variables. This is the case for the boundary-layer equation under the transformation $\eta = ay/\gamma(x)$ using a product solution. This point can be seen from the footnote of page 188; it shows that the boundary-layer equations are satisfied by an η of the form

$$\eta = \frac{ay}{(ax + b)^p}$$

where p is an arbitrary exponent related to the separation constants c_1 and c_3 of the required differential equations for γ and g. The relation is

$$p = \frac{1}{1 + (c_1/c_3)}$$

There are thus an infinite number of forms of η which will separate Eq. (4.108). The equations in γ and g are relatively simple in the case of the boundary-layer equations, but they can become quite involved.

It follows from the above remarks that the specific form of a suitable similarity variable depends as much on the boundary conditions as on the equations. In all three of the examples above, the form of the similarity variable is really picked out from the boundary conditions—either at the outset by hints, or later on explicitly. Indeed, the possibility of finding a solution, a correlation, or a similarity property in terms of a similarity variable for a given differential equation depends essentially on the boundary conditions. This can be seen from condition (4.87). Consideration of the integrations needed also shows that if the boundary conditions cannot be expressed in terms of the similarity variable η alone, then one of the original coordinates x or y must appear in the limits of integration and a solution in terms of η alone cannot be obtained. A solution in terms of η and a weighting function $g(x)$ may be possible, but this appears highly unlikely. A more promising approach has been adopted by H. Görtler.[16] Görtler has employed separation coordinates to reduce boundary-layer problems in viscous fluid flow to series expansions in just one of the two variables. The convergence properties obtained in the separation variables used by Görtler are definitely superior in many instances to those obtained using rectilinear coordinates. Moreover, the solutions are grouped into classes that can be tabulated, using high-speed computers, into a form which makes quite exact solutions for rather arbitrary boundary conditions quite easy to compute. The details of this method lie beyond the scope of this volume; the interested reader should see the paper by Görtler[16] and underlying references. Here we only note that the generalization of the idea of separation coordinates does have important properties that do not yet seem to have been fully exploited for the fractional analysis and solution of nonlinear partial differential equations.

A few further remarks also need to be made about the excellent work of Morgan.[35] Following a suggestion of A. D. Michal, Morgan investigated in detail the relation between the transformations of the governing equation under Lie groups (continuous one-parameter transformations of variables). He was able to show, on the basis of group theory and some quite original proofs, that the similarity properties of a differential equation in an arbitrary number of independent variables and of an arbitrary order and form are in fact essentially the same as invariance under transformation. Moreover, by use of these methods, Morgan was able to provide a means for finding similarity variables without the need for completing in advance the transformations of variables, which by now the reader will have observed can be quite tedious and tricky in detail even though in theory the procedure is quite straightforward. An excellent example of the power of the method is given by Morgan's discussion of the paper by Hansen.[17]

A full discussion of Morgan's methods lies beyond the scope of the mathematics assumed in this discussion. The reader interested in the investigation of similarity and separation coordinates in complex cases should refer to Morgan's original work.[35,17]

4-11 SUMMARY AND CONCLUSIONS

a. Classification of Types of Similitude—Information Achievable from Fractional Analysis of Governing Equations

Three distinct types of similitude† have been discussed in this chapter. The first is similitude based on constant values of the parameters; it describes external similitude between one system and another in

† The term similitude is used in this section to mean all processes which express similarity, including model laws, similarity rules, analogues, etc.

the same class and can be found from appropriate normalization of the governing equations and boundary conditions. The second type is equivalent to a reduction in the number of independent variables and is based on constant values of the new variables. It describes a purely internal similitude relating two points both inside a single system of the class considered. The third type is based on constant values of a natural coordinate which combines parameters with variables to eliminate one or more of the parameters. It is equivalent to measurement of behavior in units based on the nature of the system itself. The third type of similarity often contains the first type and can be employed to "swap-off" changes in value of parameters for changes in value of the original variables. It thus provides a rigorous basis for distorted models and allows construction of similarity properties which may be impossible from consideration of the parameters alone. Understanding these relations and the concomitant processes in the governing equations provides a more general and more unified picture of similitude than can be achieved from study of the parameters alone.

All three types of similarity can be derived from the normalized governing equations and conditions without need for solution.

When the governing equations and conditions are normalized systematically, a great deal of information can be obtained. This includes establishment of a set of governing dimensionless parameters which is as rigorous and complete as the governing equations and conditions. Governing parameters found in this way are almost invariably particularly useful and they can be made to express directly the ratio of magnitudes of the important effects in the problem if sufficient information is available. However, when this is done one does not usually obtain the standard form of the parameters.

Use of information on magnitudes allows derivation of approximate equations and yields approximate solutions and similarity properties. It thus provides a numerical criterion for when one or more parameters can be dropped from a given correlation or may become unimportant. However, all procedures based on magnitude are more subtle and prone to difficulty than the similarity procedures based on the complete equations and conditions. A sharp distinction should be made between the similarity conditions which can be made as rigorous and complete as the knowledge of the equations and conditions on the one hand, and the approximation-theory procedures for which only relatively weak "rules" can be given on the other hand. It is typical of approximation-theory procedures that many hints about trial procedures are used as well as some information about the general nature of the expected solution.

This philosophy, that is, using available information and hints, and then checking the answer against the complete equation and the physical results, is important in research work.   Indeed, the study of magnitudes in normalized equations, while lacking rigor and elegance, leads directly to the best known means for characterizing solutions over wide ranges of the parameters and to the powerful boundary-layer and expansion procedures.   These two methods provide added insight and form the basis for solution techniques for nonlinear equations.   Essentially the same information on magnitudes of terms forms a sound basis for combinations of physical information and mathematics to achieve maximum information in problems where complete solutions cannot be found.

Study of the form of the governing equations and boundary conditions without solution also can be extremely useful.   Such properties as homogeneity and linearity of the equations, the inherent dependency relations, and the actual combinations of physical properties, constants, and boundary conditions can all be directly used to very good effect. The dependency relations and combinations of physical properties and constants with boundary conditions automatically resolve many questions regarding the proper number of independent nondimensional parameters required.

Study of the various combinations of parameters (by successively normalizing on various terms) leads to construction of the simplest and most instructive parameters for various purposes in a relatively systematic way.   If the equations are homogeneous and the boundary conditions parameter-free, proper normalization can be employed to establish a correlation independent of magnitude of boundary conditions.   Under these conditions, or if only one parameter appears in the equations, estimates of eigenvalues or performance can be made.   When the equations are linear, these estimates can in turn be utilized through the concept of superposition to reach further estimates concerning the system behavior with forcing functions or nonhomogeneous boundary conditions. In such cases the general behavior of systems with complicated boundary conditions can be estimated rapidly and very effectively without need for costly detailed calculations.

Study of the form of the equation and conditions in terms of transformations of variables leads to natural coordinates and similarity coordinates.   Each of these provides a rigorous basis for construction of distorted models.   Similarity variables also form the basis for exact solutions with certain very simple boundary conditions.   The use of natural coordinates provides an extremely powerful basis for deriving similarity rules, for generalizing correlations, and for understanding the physical processes.   The increased generality expressed by such coordinates can sometimes provide a basis for similarity rules and simplification of testing in cases where consideration of the parameters alone would fail to provide useful results.   Such procedures have been employed by aerodynamicists in several problems, but do not seem to have been widely used in other fields.

In fields such as hydrodynamics, where the complete basic equations are intractable to exact solutions, the various methods just enumerated provide the primary basis for calculations. It is probably fair to say that all but a handful of the existing solutions in fluid mechanics depend on one or more of the techniques just discussed. It follows that clear insight into such fields of study and even understanding of the current literature are to a large degree contingent on clear understanding of these processes.

b. *Various Viewpoints—Relations among Invariance, Transformations, and Similitude*

A review of the procedures above shows that all the similitude results demonstrated or indicated can be viewed in either of two equivalent ways. First, they can be considered as a means of describing two or more distinct situations by a single set of equations and conditions. Second, they can be viewed as an invariance under some form of coordinate transformation. Thus we can say that the external similitude of dimensional analysis can be expressed by reducing the equations and conditions for a specified point in each of two distinct problems in a single class to a single normalized equation with constant values of the parameters and variables. We can also view the same property as invariance of the equations for a given point in the system under transformation from the parameters of one system to the parameters of the other in the normalized equation. Thus it can be considered either in terms of reduction of all problems of a given class to a single equation or as constancy in the value of the governing parameters under transformation. These two processes are mathematically equivalent. If substitution of the values of one problem gives the identical result in the normalized equation as that of the other, then by construction both problems can be reduced to the same normalized equation; the difference is only one of viewpoint.

Similarly, the symmetries due to self-similitude embodied in the similarity variables of Sec. 4-10*b* can be viewed either as invariance under transformation of certain coordinates (as Morgan has shown) or as a reduction of all problems of the class with a certain type of boundary condition to a single simpler equation in terms of the same coordinates. Finally, the natural coordinates discussed in Sec 4-10*a* show that problems with different values of the parameters can be brought to the same equation if we can find transformations to new variables which make the equations and boundary conditions parameter-free. This too can be viewed as invariance under coordinate transformation with the given boundary conditions in the natural coordinates.

Birkhoff[5] has expressed many of these ideas. He has preferred to employ the invariance viewpoint and the language of group theory. In most instances the viewpoint of reduction to a single equation has been employed in this discussion, since at present most engineers are not familiar with the formal language of group theory. This viewpoint is assuredly less elegant than group theory, and in some cases it becomes more cumbersome, but it is hoped it will be more readily understood. As the discussion above indicates, it is merely a difference in viewpoint, not one of content.

Indeed, each of the processes summarized in Sec. 4-11a is also subject to other shifts in viewpoint, and these sometimes lead to derivation of different types of results, as has been noted in context. For example, natural coordinates can be viewed as a means for providing improved correlations of data, but the same constancy of value in a natural coordinate can be used to derive a distorted model law by a slight shift in reasoning process. One can use complete equations to derive similarity rules, as in Example 4.12, or, on the other hand, use incomplete equations to establish necessary conditions which must hold if any similarity is to exist and then check the data to see if it does, as in Example 4.6. One can seek to see what terms can be neglected by comparing magnitudes of known terms, or one can study magnitudes to see what data are needed to determine the importance of given terms in a nonhomogeneous equation.

c. *Final Remarks*

As the examples in this chapter show, an amazing amount of information of many types can be extracted from the governing equations and conditions without solving them. An attempt has been made to show that the information gained and assurance in it are both increased if these processes are systematized. It is also hoped that the definitions and catagorizations presented will assist analytical workers in deciding what type of processes may lead to a desired type of information and hence to more widespread use of some of the more powerful techniques than has been the case. Again, direct comparison of the utility of the methods displayed in earlier chapters with those based on systematic use of governing equations and conditions has been deferred to Chap. 5.

While it is hoped that this discussion of methods based on the governing equations is more extensive and comprehensive than those previously available, the author would like to emphasize that it is by no means considered final or complete. The range of examples and even types of problems solvable by techniques of this type is so vast that no treatment of this length can hope to cover them all. Indeed, it is not unlikely that some whole categories have been overlooked, although an attempt has been made to illustrate the various major types. Moreover, there are obvious gaps in the mathematical foundations which one hopes professional mathematicians will fill as time goes on. These include not only existence and uniqueness theorems for specific classes of equations and boundary conditions but also additional theorems for approximation-theory procedures and more adequate rules for anticipating when non-uniform behavior is to be expected as well as its type and probable location. There are also many places where extensions are possible in view of the framework of the subject exhibited by this discussion. Some obvious examples would seem to be applications of the technique of natural coordinates to additional problems as a basis for distorted models, extensions of the investigations of solution of nonlinear partial differential equations by use of separation coordinates for more general boundary conditions than have heretofore been examined,† more systematic investigation of other transformation functions for construction of both separation and similarity variables, and attempts to apply simultaneously the boundary-layer idea with the uniformization idea as a more powerful means for dealing with troublesome singularities. Finally, the rapidly developing theory of integral equations and integral transformations, almost entirely omitted here, can be used with good effect in the context of fractional analysis. The possibilities for systematization and clarification inherent in procedures based on the governing equations by no means appear to be exhausted. On the contrary, only a beginning has been made.

We turn now to a comparison of the available methods in the final chapter.

† Since the first draft of this work, one example of this procedure has been published, see Görtler,[16] pp. 4–187.

5 *Summary and Comparison of Methods*

5-1 INTRODUCTION

Throughout the preceding four chapters, several methods have been developed for solving problems in fractional analysis; these include the pi theorem, the method of similitude, and use of the governing equations. The last method can be divided into at least two parts: use of overall governing equations and use of detailed governing differential equations with boundary conditions. In both instances, either the complete equations or only part of them may be employed. Since the use of the differential equations incorporates all features of the use of overall and algebraic governing equations, as well as additional material, it is sufficient here to compare three distinct methods: the pi theorem, the method of similitude, and use of the governing equations.

202

To make these comparisons as clear as possible, we begin by recapitulating the major steps in the solution method, the primary types of information found, and the input information required for each method.

5-2   SUMMARY OF METHODS

a.   The Pi Theorem

In this method the input information required is a list of the relevant physical quantities including one dependent quantity and a sufficient list of independent physical quantities.   The method shows particularly clearly what can be achieved by using dimensionless groups to reduce the number of independent parameters.   It is the only method that can be used to much effect in discussions of dimensioning, dimensional homogeneity, and the other fundamental concepts involved in the mathematical description of physical quantities.   Insofar as fractional analysis is concerned, the method yields a list of governing pi groups in a purely arbitrary form; only very rarely can more information be found.   It is also subject to a few troublesome exceptions which have been illustrated by examples in Chap. 2.

The procedure involved is to write down, by some method, a list of the important physical quantities.   Application of the pi theorem then leads directly to a set of governing pi groups.   Both formal algebraic methods and heuristic methods are available for application of the pi theorem to the list of secondary quantities.   The underlying mathematics of the theorem is thoroughly understood.   However, within the method itself no means is incorporated either for finding or for checking the list of relevant physical quantities; this must come from some other source, even, if necessary, from pure physical intuition.   The labor involved in the formal procedures is small but appreciable; the only mathematics entirely essential to an understanding of the pi theorem is the fundamental theorem of algebra.

b.   The Method of Similitude

In this method the required input information is the important forces and in some cases also energies and properties which affect the dependent variable in the problem of concern.   These forces and energies can be found by intuition, by inspection of the governing equations, or from estimates of behavior based on sketches of any degree of complexity and sophistication.   In some cases rather difficult questions of dependency among the variables arise.   These can in general be resolved only by study of the governing equations in relatively detailed form. The method provides a list of the governing pi groups. In addition, it gives immediately a physical interpretation for each group together with an indication of the qualitative effect of changes in the value of each pi.

The actual procedure involves the following steps: (1) set relevant forces and energy terms; (2) determine which energies, if any, are independent from the force terms; (3) take the ratio of a sufficient number of independent forces, energies, and properties and write the dependent quantity, in nondimensional form, as a function of the independent nondimensional ratios formed. In some cases it is also necessary to utilize property ratios to express the linking of energy forms through the equation of state or the rate-theory equations. This is usually a subtle and sometimes difficult problem. The labor involved in the method of similitude is very small, and the mathematics required is nominal. The accuracy and power of the method are both considerably improved by using sketches showing free body diagrams, thermodynamic systems, control volumes, etc. Such sketches not only force more careful and detailed thought, but also provide a direct means for incorporating more physical information from any available overall governing equations. The method forms a good basis for systematization and orderly improvement of standard forms of the governing parameters. It is often useful as a basis for simple physical explanations.

c.   Use of Governing Equations

Hopefully, one begins with a complete set of governing equations and appropriate boundary conditions; we discuss this case first.

Use of the governing equations for fractional analysis in this volume has not been based on a single procedure or train of logic. Three distinct types of transformations have been discussed. Reasoning has been introduced concerning a variety of mathematical ideas and their relation to behavior in physical systems.

The first type of transformation is normalization of variables or transformation to nondimensional equations in standard form. Under the conditions given in Sec. 4-3, normalization leads to rigorous solution of several problems: these include (1) the canonical problem of dimensional analysis, (2) rules governing external similitude, and (3) normal model laws. All of these results are found essentially by inspection of the parameters appearing in the normalized equations and boundary conditions.[†] If magnitudes can be provided, then the same normalization procedure also provides a basis for expressing the force and energy ratios of Chap. 3 quantitatively within any finite domain where the magnitudes

[†] Birkhoff[5] indicates that results of types (1), (2), and (3) are merely suggestive; however, he is discussing the case of viscous flow where the requisite existence theo-

hold. Parameters so constructed depend on the boundary conditions, system sizes, and physical constants. They will not usually be in an arbitrary standard form; however, they are usually very instructive and form a powerful basis for correlations.

Consideration of the structure of the normalized governing equations leads to two further types of transformations: formation of *natural coordinates* by absorption of parameters, and reduction of the number of independent coordinates by introducing *similarity variables*.

Natural coordinates allow expression of similarity rules which hold not only between two problems of a given class with the same value of the parameters but also for all values of the parameters for which the normalization is appropriate. It thus provides a basis for both ordinary and distorted model laws; it can provide rigorous model predictions in some cases where no modeling could be achieved by considering the parameters alone.†

Similarity variables lead to construction of exact solutions under restricted, specific types of boundary conditions. When such boundary conditions exist, similarity variables provide the basis for a purely *internal similarity* and allow modeling of behavior at one location in a system by the system behavior at some other point. If a similarity variable can also be expressed in natural coordinates, a still more powerful basis for similarity and correlation is achieved. It relates one point in any system of the class to all other similar points in all problems of the class.

Consideration of the information inherent in the normalized governing equations also leads to approximation theory; this in turn provides the basis for seeking not only approximate governing equations in many cases but also approximate similarity rules and model laws based on these equations. Consideration of the bases of approximation theory also provides information on the rigor of similarity procedures, even though in most cases approximation theory is itself only a trial procedure. Approximation theory also provides a link between normalization procedures and the more powerful mathematical techniques of boundary-layer theory, expansions in the parameters, and uniformization.

All of these types of information can be found from procedures based on invariance, on common equations and conditions, or on transformation of coordinates. These procedures also can be applied when the complete equations or appropriate boundary conditions are not known. The amount of information achievable and the rigor with which it is established depend on the physical completeness of the equations and the

---

rems on the equations are not known. Here we are considering cases where the equations are complete and appropriate. Sedov[46] and Smith[48] have also stated that the conditions can be made rigorous, but did not elaborate.

† See Examples 4.11 and 4.12 in Sec. 4-10.

knowledge of the mathematical conditions required to establish existence of a unique solution. The procedures provide a framework in which data can sometimes be used to replace missing mathematical theorems. Moreover, use of these processes in the absence of complete or appropriate equations often indicates what additional information is needed to supply rigor and thus may provide an important guide to theoretical and experimental researches. Even when complete and appropriate equations are not known, trial procedures can be carried out, and the results checked.

5-3   COMPARISON OF METHODS

It is instructive to compare the methods just summarized on five points:

1. Power—the amount of output information achievable.
2. Rigor—the accuracy inherent in the method.
3. Accuracy—the percentage of correct answers achieved in practice.
4. Simplicity—the effort and knowledge required for use.
5. Input—the amount of information required to utilize the method.

a. Power

Comparison of the total amount of information achievable either in the summary of Sec. 5-2 or in the context of Chaps. 2, 3, and 4 shows that the use of governing equations is far more powerful than either of the other methods. The use of the governing differential equations and boundary conditions provides all the information achievable by the other methods and in addition admits consideration of the following matters which lie entirely beyond the scope of the other methods:

1. Establishment in many cases of rigorous bases for construction of an independent set of nondimensional governing parameters and the various results dependent upon them.
2. Utilization of the specific properties of the governing equations to improve correlations. (Homogeneity in the dependent variable leads to correlations independent of the magnitude of the boundary conditions, etc.)
3. Study of the detailed dependency relations among the parameters and variables in the system of equations for a given problem.
4. Determination of the possibility of grouping two or more conventional governing parameters into a smaller number of groups in a given problem.
5. Construction of governing parameters which express in detailed quantitative form the physical ratios of concern as opposed to conventional expression of the parameters in arbitrary form.

6. Derivation of internal similarity properties and exact solutions for special boundary conditions based on similarity variables.
7. Generalization of the concept of similarity to include distorted models found by a swap-off between values of the parameters and variables in terms of constancy in the value of a natural coordinate.
8. Provision of a basis for solutions and modeling by use of mathematical and physical analogues.
9. Construction of approximate governing equations, approximate model laws based on them, and a connection to the extended mathematical procedures involved in improved approximations.

This list can be extended, but further comment on the power of use of the governing equations relative to the simpler methods would seem superfluous. A comparison of power between the method of similitude and dimensional analysis shows that they are roughly the same, but the method of similitude has perhaps a slight advantage. The method of similitude does provide some information on the physical meaning of the pi groups found and on the effects of qualitative changes in the pi groups that are not normally directly available from dimensional analysis. In addition, the method of similitude can be considerably extended by inclusion of information from the governing overall equations.

In a sense these remarks should not be surprising. They all follow from a fact that has already been stated several times; it is impossible in general to achieve more physical information in an answer than is somewhere fed into the analysis, explicitly or implicitly. Thus if we hope to obtain the maximum amount of output information, it is clear that we should strive to utilize all the available physical information. This in turn strongly suggests use of carefully prepared sketches and of the most detailed and complete governing equations available.

The real difficulty with the pi theorem method, insofar as power is concerned, would seem to be that the rationale of the method provides no direct or systematic way for including any physical information except a list of secondary quantities, and this is very scant information when viewed in terms of the totality of information we would like to achieve by fractional analysis. A similar but less stringent remark applies to the method of similitude; in that case means do exist for utilizing governing overall equations directly, and this is a considerable advantage.†

---

† Birkhoff[5] has noted that the Buckingham method is limited to linear transformations of variables, while use of the governing equations also allows introduction of other transformations, such as affine and conformal mappings. This is certainly true, and provides part of the basis for the extensions of the concept of similarity in Sec. 4-10. However, it does not, by itself, explain a number of other factors, such as ability to derive similarity properties for all problems in a class independent of the magnitude of the parameters or construction of approximate models through approximation theory.

It is worthwhile to repeat in this context earlier remarks concerning the quantities used to form pi's.   If the best answer is desired in the sense of fractional analysis, it is never sufficient or even adequate to form the requisite number of pi's from any quantities in the problem that happen to have the necessary dimensions.   On the contrary, it is of first importance to use the specific form of the parameters that represent the controlling physical effects as precisely as possible.   Consider, for instance, the boundary-layer problem of Example 4.5.   The whole burden of Prandtl's derivation is based on appropriate distinction between the two lengths δ and L.   If no distinction is made between these lengths, the entire meaning of the analysis is lost.   (Moreover, this is a key derivation; it is widely recognized as one of the primary foundations of the advances in fluid mechanics during the twentieth century.)   Without use of the quantitative organization provided by governing equations, such derivations are difficult or impossible.

b. *Rigor*

Essentially the same comparison exists for rigor as for power.   Use of the differential equations can be made as rigorous as the equations and the state of mathematical and physical knowledge about them.   On the other hand, exceptions occur to the pi theorem method even when the list of quantities is correct.   In fact, it seems fair to say that the establishment of the list of quantities for solution by the pi theorem and the list of forces and energies employed in the method of similitude both represent arguments to plausibility rather than rigorous procedures.   As such they are particularly liable to error and difficult to check without additional procedures.   Undoubtedly, some of the governing differential equations we use are incorrect in some of the problems we now believe they cover.   However, this is a matter that has at least had the careful attention of many workers and is thus subject to a minimum of suspicion.   Moreover, it is a matter on which the accumulated empirical evidence of the scientific method can be brought to bear increasingly as time passes; it is subject to continuous and controlled improvement.

c. *Accuracy*

It is noted again that accuracy is used to indicate the fraction of correct answers actually achieved, as differentiated from the inherent rigor of the methods employed to reach these answers.

For a number of years the writer has given successive first-year graduate classes problems to work by each of the three methods under discussion.   The results achieved were fairly striking in regard to accuracy, although this was not the original purpose of the assignments.

Using the pi theorem, the bulk of the class was never able to solve problems in fractional analysis properly. On problems where the answer was not known to the class in advance or readily found in the literature, the percentage of correct† answers achieved in finding a list of governing pi's was in the range of 10 to 30 percent in all classes. Using similar standards, the percentage of correct answers employing the method of similitude was 25 to 60 percent, and using the governing differential equations, 70 to 90 percent. Results found by students from the pi theorem invariably showed very large scatter in the number of groups found. For example, in a problem where external similarity can be specified by use of two independent nondimensional groups, typical answers would be received with one to eight or ten groups. Moreover, plots of frequency of occurence of the number of groups found by the students failed to reveal a cluster about some single number. The plots were typically irregular, thus suggesting basic inability to cope with the problems by such a technique rather than a consistent error of some sort. It is possible that the writer's bias affected these results, but this is considered unlikely for three reasons: (1) after early instances of such results, every attempt was made to eliminate the author's opinion from the remarks on the pi theorem for two consecutive years; no noticeable change in results occurred; (2) the majority of the students had used only the pi method in prior classes, and some of them invariably were initially biased in its favor and said so; (3) similar results have been reported to the author by instructors at several other universities; unfortunately no statistics from these other sources are available.

Further discussion of the possible reasons for these results on accuracy may be useful in order to illuminate comparisons regarding the rationale of the various methods. On the surface the methods of similitude and dimensional analysis appear accurate in the main, even though some troubling exceptions occur now and then. However, study of the many published examples from which this appearance stems shows that most of these examples are not new solutions to research problems, but are merely formalizations of previously known information from experiment or from more powerful theory. Study of the literature reveals relatively few new problems in fractional analysis actually worked for the first time by the pi theorem. Moreover, as already mentioned, the real difficulty in employing the pi theorem for fractional analysis does not appear to be the exceptions which now and then occur, but is instead the failure of the method to provide any means for direct inclusion of the full physical information available. The impact of this deficiency on accuracy can be seen in part by examining the types of questions which the analytical

---

† The word "correct" here is used to mean obtaining the minimum number of pi's including the proper physical quantities in any form whatsoever.

worker must face in using the pi theorem for fractional analysis. Within the rationale of the pi theorem, one proceeds to seek directly a list of secondary quantities representing the parameters. The analytical worker is therefore forced to ask, "What are the physical quantities of importance in this problem?" Thus in Example 2.2 (laminar flow in a pipe) he must ask, "Does the viscosity act independently from density in this problem, or should only their ratio, the kinematic viscosity, be employed in the list of physical quantities?" In Example 2.3 (on heat-exchanger analysis) the question that arises is, "Does the specific heat act in this problem independently of the flow rate of the fluid, or can a single product or ratio be used to represent them?" As has been shown by examples, this type of question does not hinge on independence in the sense of ability to vary the value of one of these physical quantities and hold the other constant, but depends instead on the specific form in which the parameters combine in a particular problem. *Consequently these questions can be answered with assurance only when the form of the relations, that is, the equations governing behavior, are known.*

Thus inside the framework of analysis using the pi theorem there are two choices. The first is to operate under the assumption that nothing is known about the form of the functional relation among the variables and parameters. This was until recently† and probably still is the accepted view in the English-language literature. If nothing is known about the *form* of the relation among the variables and parameters, then it must follow that it is unreasonable to expect even an able worker to answer questions like those posed in the preceding paragraph correctly a large percentage of the time. Under this first assumption, using the pi theorem alone, the answers to such questions lie outside of the framework as well as the details of the knowledge available; they are essentially "unknowable."

The reader can check his own reactions on this point by comparing the solutions to the beam-vibration problem achieved in Examples 2.6 and 4.3, respectively. He should ask himself, "In reading Example 2.6, did I *at that point* discover that Poisson's ratio was irrelevant to the oscillation of simple transverse beams with small deflections?‡ Did I see how to reformulate the *five groups* of Example 2.6 into the *one more powerful group* of Example 4.3?" Finally, in reading Example 2.6, "Was I aware of the significance of altering the boundary conditions from homogeneous to nonhomogeneous on the required method of correlation?" (Compare Example 4.4.) The tests with classes in several instances used

---

† Since the preparation of the first draft of this work, the treatise of Sedov[46] has been made available in English; it clearly espouses a different view.

‡ The reader's indulgence is asked for this small booby-trap regarding Poisson's ratio; experience suggests such a device is necessary to counterbalance the effects of 20-20 hindsight.

beam problems of this general type; the students usually achieved answers like that of Example 2.6 (or worse ones) using the pi theorem. On the other hand, the majority of students using the governing equations at least found the one group of Example 4.6 and the resulting similarity implications, although many of them failed to carry the implications of just one group through to its logical conclusions.

The second choice in using the pi theorem has recently been pointed up by Sedov.[46] It consists of using the governing equations and boundary conditions to formulate the list of secondary quantities for the pi theorem, and sometimes to use added properties such as linearity of the equations. As Sedov has shown, this method is certainly better than using the pi theorem alone, but it contains what this author believes is a fundamental contradiction. If one knows the governing equations and boundary conditions, then the list of secondary quantities taken from them will be accurate only up to the extent that the equations are complete and appropriate; it follows that completeness and appropriateness need to be examined. Even more important, if the equations and conditions are known, then there is no need for the pi theorem at all; the processes discussed in Chap. 4 will provide the results obtainable by the pi theorem and a great deal more besides.

In the method of similitude the situation is a little better than for the pi theorem. In Example 2.2 the analytical worker must ask himself, "Is the inertia force important in the solution to this problem?" In Example 2.3 he asks, "What heat flow is important in determining the value of the specific dependent variable of interest, and what quantities characterize this particular heat flow?" Questions of this sort are still difficult, but are usually more manageable on an intuitive basis than those which arise in using the pi theorem. They relate much more directly to the prior experience of the analytical worker both with actual systems and with calculations, and they at least set in motion a train of thought which deals with the pertinent physical effect instead of isolated secondary quantities. Questions of independence can be very subtle and difficult, but within the framework of the method of similitude means are directly available to employ at least simple governing force and energy equations to resolve such problems when required.

When the governing equations are employed, most of the troublesome questions of the simpler methods are directly resolved. Assuredly, the use of the governing equations does not provide a foolproof method; the author agrees with his former colleague E. P. Neumann who was fond of stating, "There is no system so foolproof that a really good fool cannot muck it up." Nevertheless, the use of governing equations and boundary conditions, apparently by forcing attention to the more detailed structure of the mathematics, does appear less subject to error. Another way of viewing this same point is the following.   As many writers have very properly stressed, the mathematical procedures of dimensional analysis *alone* yield very little; a clear understanding and use of physical behavior in the analysis are essential.   Direct introduction of the governing equations and boundary conditions is one method for supplying as much of this physical information as is available in the general literature.

d. Simplicity

From the previous discussion it is clear that the simplest procedure is the method of similitude, the next simplest is the pi theorem, and the most complex is the use of governing equations.   These remarks apply to the mathematics needed and also to the amount of manipulation involved in solving a given problem.   However, this comparison is misleading in one sense and needs comment to that extent.

Even though use of the governing equations is more complex and shows more steps in a finished solution, it does not follow that it always takes longer for a given fractional analysis; in fact, the contrary is often true.   Since the method of similitude to some extent and the use of the pi theorem to an even greater degree both involve answering relatively imponderable questions, the time spent can become much larger than indicated by the finished steps on paper.   In using the governing equations, once a relatively formal method is mastered, frequently far less time can be spent pondering the steps required.

e. Input Information

In this category lies the only real advantage of the methods of similitude and dimensional analysis visible from the present study.   In some problems it is clear that we cannot write a single differential equation with appropriate boundary conditions, or even a set of differential equations that will accurately describe all the important behavior of the system under study.   Even more frequently we cannot supply mathematical theorems demonstrating existence of a unique solution for a prescribed set of equations and boundary conditions.

Examples of instances where we cannot write complete equations include the flow through complex machinery, such as compressors and turbines, highly irreversible processes (as in combustion) where complex particles are in states far removed from local equilibrium, and the physiological and social processes of human beings.   There are many others.   In such cases we must resort to the simpler but less powerful techniques of dimensional analysis and similitude or plain judgment in any attempts to construct similarity rules of correlations governing behavior.

Indeed, the general rule seems to be that the less we know about the mathematical models for a given system the simpler the correlation methods we are forced to use. Thus in highly complex turbomachinery we can use ideas of geometric similarity and force ratios with governing overall equations relatively successfully. In highly irreversible processes we can only state certain limited mathematical symmetry properties. In individual biological organisms we can make statements like "birth processes of mammals are generally similar." Finally in the interactions we call human affairs we still must rely, unfortunately, on the art of politics as embodied in the often fallible judgment of individual statesmen.

When the equations and boundary conditions are known, but existence theorems guaranteeing a unique solution are not available, it is still almost always profitable to employ procedures based on the equations. A number of such examples have been given in Chap. 4; they show that more information is obtained, a better basis provided for direct use of physical data, and sometimes even information on missing data or theory is revealed. The governing equations of viscous fluid flow fall in this class. Indeed, since these equations are inherently nonhomogeneous, since few exact solutions have been found, and since parameter-dependent solutions dependent on stability considerations are so common, it is not surprising that the main trend of advance in fluid mechanics in this century has been based on various processes relating to fractional analyses of the differential equations. Thus we find the bases of the whole field of boundary-layer analysis, the methods employed in testing high-speed aircraft, the construction of similarity solutions, and a number of other results and techniques all emerging as different aspects of fractional analysis of the governing differential equations and boundary conditions. These methods and solutions are clearly useful even though mathematical uniqueness still cannot be proved.

It is again emphasized that direct data must play a distinct role when the equations are nonhomogeneous and the complete solution cannot be established. To proceed effectively in such cases requires some knowledge, or a shrewd guess, about the overall form of the solution.

5-4　CONCLUDING REMARKS

a.　*Utility of Various Methods*

In Table 5.1 a summary of the comparison of the three methods just presented is tabulated for ready reference. If the results of Table 5.1 are correct, then the important conclusion is that it would seem foolish from the point of view of fractional analysis to use either the method of similitude or dimensional analysis if the governing equations are available in any reasonably detailed form.   In the present state of knowledge this is far more often than not the case in macroscopic engineering systems.

There is sometimes a temptation to use the simpler methods as a means for minimizing the input with the idea that this allows the analyst to get something for nothing.   Indeed, dimensional analysis has sometimes been presented with much of this flavor.   However, in fractional analysis this is not the fruitful approach.   As in all engineering and scientific analysis, the profitable game is not to minimize input but rather to maximize output; this implies the use of all available input knowledge.

Table 5.1   Comparison of Three Methods of Fractional Analysis

Method	Power	Rigor	Accuracy	Simplicity	Input
Dimensional analysis	Least	Least	Least	Intermediate	Least
Method of similitude	Intermediate	Intermediate	Intermediate	Greatest	Intermediate
Systematic use of differential equations†	Far greater than others	Much better than others	Greatest	Most complicated	Greatest

† Applies also to use of governing overall equations in sense discussed in Chap. 4.

If we remember not only that a surprising amount of information can be obtained from relatively complete and detailed governing integral and/or algebraic equations but also that considerable information can be obtained from even very crude and incomplete governing equations, then it must also follow that such equations should be employed whenever they are available and the differential equations and boundary conditions are not.   These equations can be utilized through a normalization, in combination with the method of similitude, or in combination with the pi theorem, as indicated by Sedov.[46]

As Prof. S. H. Crandall has noted, one can consider engineering analysis as composed of three levels.   Keeping in mind Lord Kelvin's dictum that we know little about a problem until we can express it quantitatively, we can describe three levels as follows.   The first is dimensional organization based solely on a qualitative recognition of the physical quantities involved.   The second is dimensional organization after a statement of the quantitative relations among the physical quantities is known.   The third is some form of complete solution, numerical or analytical.   In this framework we see that the pi theorem and its associated processes, as well as the method of similitude, fall into the first group. Derivation of similarity rules and model laws from governing equations fall into the second group. Approximation theory procedures overlap, and provide some relations between, the procedures of the second and third groups.

Moreover, as time progresses, we will develop complete equations for more situations, and we will solve the easy problems in more and more fields. Under these conditions the procedures of approximation theory and more rigorous similitude processes must necessarily tend to become more and more important.

Since we will never reach the situation where complete and appropriate governing equations can be written for all problems of concern, we will always need the more qualitative procedures of the pi theorem and the method of similitude. It is well to bear in mind, however, that they are qualitative in applying them in research problems where the situation is not really understood in advance. This is one reason why the method of similitude is useful as a semi-independent check on pi theorem procedures. It also implies that any result found by these methods should be viewed with a healthy scientific scepticism until empirical evidence sufficient to justify results is in hand.

b. *Implications in Teaching*

The author is well aware that the conclusions expressed in Sec. 5.4*a* are not in accord with those held by many writers and teachers in this area. A number of authors have stated that the pi theorem is the beginning and end of dimensional analysis and some of these authors have used the term dimensional analysis to mean something quite close to what has been called fractional analysis in the present volume. The vast majority of published examples of fractional analysis employ the pi theorem, and very little has been written on the methodology of fractional analysis based on use of the governing equations. Some authors have even gone to the extreme of using the pi theorem to "check" results obtained from governing equations.† In many current undergraduate courses the pi theorem is presented and the other methods are not. This is a considerable weight of history and opinion. Nevertheless, if the conclusions above are correct, or even partially correct, then the English-language literature particularly has been relying too much on the method of dimensional analysis alone and this method has often been pushed beyond its useful limits. A reconsideration of the utility of the various methods in both published works and undergraduate courses would seem to be in order.

---

† In the author's opinion this is analogous to calibrating a micrometer with a yardstick.

Certainly, the average undergraduate is taught the governing equations in at least some form in many fields today, and assuredly he is capable of dividing variables by appropriate parameters to make them nondimensional. He is certainly also capable of grasping the method of similitude, which is in essence simpler than the pi theorem. The author hopes that this treatment will encourage some instructors to reassess the merits of the pi theorem in undergraduate instruction, at least to the extent of including some discussion of other methods. It is also hoped that graduate instructors will point up more frequently the many implications of normalization procedures.

c. Possible Further Development

Since the present volume is concerned with the development and use of fractional analysis as a tool for the analytical worker in science and engineering, it is appropriate to make a few closing remarks in an attempt to assess what remains to be accomplished.

Dimensional Analysis

Use of the pi theorem appears to be extremely well developed in the literature. Six books in English, devoted almost entirely to dimensional analysis, are available, in addition to a number of articles. A treatment suited to virtually any level of mathematical sophistication and of any length can be found. Most of these treatments are clear, and they contain a great variety of carefully worked examples. While it is always risky to make statements of this nature, nevertheless, the author believes that the method is now developed to nearly its full limits in the literature and that startling improvements in the near future are not too likely. In fact, the author believes that in the recent past too much reliance has been placed on this method, as a method, for solution of problems in fractional analysis. This has probably contributed to the lack of systematic developments of other methods.

The Method of Similitude

Since the late nineteenth century this method seems to have been largely neglected. As is shown by the examples, it is a very simple technique. In addition, it provides a good basis for systematizing and utilizing physical intuition, and it provides a useful cross-check on answers obtained from dimensional analysis. It would certainly seem profitable for workers in various fields to prepare additional reference material of the sort given in Tables 4.1 and 4.2 to make the method more readily applicable to their specific specialties. Such tables not only serve as an aid in dimensional analysis, but also are of basic value in providing a systematic basis for improved understanding of the dimensionless parameters employed.

The obvious present gap in the available structure of the method of similitude is a clear and precise treatment of the independence of the various effects and of the fundamental governing equations in the many common forms. This topic has had little direct study. It is not simple, but further careful discussions would very probably be highly profitable. Such discussions carried out by skilled research workers for their own particular field as well as additional discussion of the general problems appear to be needed.

Use of Governing Equations

The neglect of this technique *as a systematic method* for solution to problems in fractional analysis seems to be very widespread. In view of the truly vast number of published ad hoc examples of the method and the great variety of types of problems these include, this neglect seems surprising. One can make a good case for the view that most of the advances of the current century in fields such as viscous fluid flow are directly related to such procedures; nevertheless, the existence of such a method does not even seem to be generally recognized, nor does it have an accepted name.

While Chap. 4 hopefully provides some progress toward construction of systematic methodology, provision for basic theorems, and categorization of various types of similarity, the author is all too well aware of its shortcomings and omissions. Many questions still remain unanswered. Among these are the following. Can more complete criteria be found to indicate whether a given problem is amenable to simplification and generalization by combinations of pi's and formation of natural coordinates? What other less stringent conditions than those of Rule 3 but more specific than those of Rule 4 can be found for approximation theory in a relatively general framework? How and in what instances can physical data be better integrated in approximation theory in the case of nonhomogeneous differential equations? What new transformations will generate further useful similarity variables, and separation variables for exact or approximate solutions of nonlinear partial differential equations? Can the idea of *separation variables* be used to find more exact solutions to nonlinear partial differential equations with general types of boundary conditions? Can better indications be found which will tell us when nonuniform behavior and boundary layers must be expected? Can the boundary-layer ideas be joined more profitably with the expansion methods due to Lighthill and others? The whole question of a firm mathematical foundation for these expansion methods still seems quite unsatisfactory as noted by Tsien.[49]   The same is true of the method of zonal estimates.   Numerous specific problems exist where a study of natural coordinates would seem appropriate in order to attempt simplification of testing procedures and generalization of correlations by trade-off of variables for parameters in numerical value.   Only a few examples of application of this very powerful method seem to exist.   The implications of the various ways in which approximation theory can fail (infinite limits of integration, singular behavior in the limit of large and small values of a parameter, and infinite values of the integrand) seem to have had little study or even distinction within the framework of similarity and approximation theory procedures.   Similarly, the implications of nonhomogeneity in the boundary conditions as opposed to nonhomogeneity in the equations, indeed, the whole question of parameters in the boundary conditions as opposed to the equations, seems to have no clear interpretation in physical meaning regarding correlations.

In addition, the whole topic of approximation theory in cases involving improper integrals has been essentially omitted from the present volume.   There appears to be a real need for skilled applied mathematicians to discuss the considerable available knowledge on these more advanced problems in a framework suitable for direct application to approximation theory, that is, with more attention than is usually given to what sort of procedures can be tried when rigorous methods are lacking. The sort of questions which naturally arise are, Can the now considerable knowledge of Fourier and related transforms be used to provide a basis for approximation methods in problems with complicated boundary conditions and infinite domains?   Can a reasonably compact summary be given of the rules for convergence of improper integrals and for uniformly valid expansions which are more accessible to the engineer than existing materials?

This list of open questions is very long and involves many difficult problems; no doubt even further questions will have occurred to many readers before this point.   Since we have already concluded that the use of governing equations for similitude procedures and approximation theory must, in the nature of things, increase in importance as time goes on, it would seem that much more work on the method of governing equations, as a method, could be done with profit.

d.   Final Remark

It seems appropriate to end this discussion by reiterating the comment that any solution to a problem in similitude may be subject to improvement by defining new variables, new parameters, or a new combination of parameters and variables which express a higher order of generality for the class of problems under study. We can state this as a nonuniqueness theorem:

> It may be possible to obtain a simpler and more general similitude property for any given problem if we are shrewd enough to find it.

Apparently this theorem will be with us for some time, since it seems unlikely that we shall be able to be more precise until considerably more general information is available on governing equations, appropriate boundary conditions, existence and uniqueness theorems for nonhomogeneous and nonlinear partial differential equations, and the transformation properties of differential equations. Thus our nonuniqueness theorem presents a challenge to the research engineer, the scientist, and the mathematician. The challenge to the research engineer and scientist is to find new coordinates which provide increased simplicity and generality in various classes of problems. The challenge to the mathematician is to increase the theoretical foundations for approximation theory, for boundary layer and expansion methods, and for the transformation properties of complex sets of differential equations.

References

1. Abbott, D. E., and S. J. Kline: Simple Methods for Construction of Similarity Solutions of Partial Differential Equations, AFOSR TN60-1163, Report MD-6, Department of Mechanical Engineering, Stanford University (1960).
2. Bentley, B. V.: Singular Perturbation Problems of Ordinary Differential Equations, M.S. thesis, Stanford University (1955).
3. Bieberbach, L.: "Theorie der gewöhnlichen Differential Gleichungen auf Funktionen theoretischer Grundlagen dargestellt," Springer-Verlag OHG, Berlin, 1953.
4. Birkhoff, G.: Dimensional Analysis of Partial Differential Equations, *Elec. Eng.*, **67**: 1185 (1948).
5. Birkhoff, G.: "Hydrodynamics," chap. III, Princeton University Press, Princeton, N.J., 1950.
6. Bridgman, P. W.: "Dimensional Analysis," Harvard University Press, Cambridge, Mass., 1921.
7. Buckingham, E.: On Physically Similar Systems: Illustrations of the Use of Dimensional Equations, *E. Phys. Rev.*, **4**: 345 (1914).

8. Carrier, G. F.: Boundary Layer Problems in Applied Mechanics, *Advan. Appl. Mech.*, **3**: 1–19 (1953).
9. Clauser, F. H.: *Advan. Appl. Mech.*, **4** (1956).
10. Crandall, S. H.: "Engineering Analysis," McGraw-Hill Book Company, New York, 1956.
11. Courant, R., and D. Hilbert: "Methoden der mathematischen Physik," vol. II, Springer-Verlag OHG, Berlin, 1937.
12. Den Hartog, J. P.: "Mechanical Vibrations," 4th ed., McGraw-Hill Book Company, New York, 1956.
13. Duncan, W. J.: "Physical Similarity and Dimensional Analysis," Edward Arnold (Publishers) Ltd., 1953.
14. Einstein, H. A., and H. Li: Shear Transmission from a Turbulent Flow to Its Viscous Boundary Layer, Heat Transfer and Fluid Mechanics Institute, UCLA (1955).
15. Fourier, J. B. J.: "Théorie Analytique de Chaleur," Paris, 1822, English translation by Freeman, Cambridge, 1878.
16. Görtler, H.: A New Series for the Calculation of Steady Laminar Boundary Layer Flows, *J. Rational Mech.*, **6**: 1–65 (1957).
17. Hansen, A. G.: Possible Similarity Solutions of the Laminar Incompressible Boundary Layer Equations, *Trans. ASME*, **80** (1958).
18. Hudson, D. E.: Scale Model Principles in Vibration Analysis, in Harris and Crede (eds.), "Shock and Vibration Handbook," McGraw-Hill Book Company, New York, 1961.
19. Huntley, H. E.: "Dimensional Analysis," McDonald and Company, London, 1953.
20. Ipsen, D. C.: "Units, Dimensions, and Dimensionless Numbers," McGraw-Hill Book Company, New York, 1960.
21. Jacobsen, L. S., and R. S. Ayre: "Engineering Vibrations," McGraw-Hill Book Company, New York, 1958.
22. Jeffreys, H., and B. S. Jeffreys: "Methods of Mathematical Physics," 3d ed., Cambridge University Press, New York, 1956.
23. Kays, W. M., and A. L. London: "Compact Heat Exchangers," McGraw-Hill Book Company, New York, 1958.
24. Kline, S. J., and F. O. Koenig: The State Principle, *Trans. ASME, J. Appl. Mech.*, **24** (March, 1957).
25. Kline, S. J., and P. W. Runstadler: Some Preliminary Results of Visual Studies of the Flow Model of the Wall Layers of the Turbulent Boundary Layer, *J. Appl. Mech.*, **26**(2): (June, 1959).
26. Kraichnan, R. H.: The Closure Problem of Turbulence Theory, Res. Report HSN-3, Institute of Mathematical Science, New York University (January, 1961).
27. Langer, R. E.: On the Connection Formulas and the Solutions of the Wave Equation, *Phys. Rev.*, **51**(8): 669–676 (1937).
28. Langhaar, H.: "Dimensional Analysis and Theory of Models," John Wiley & Sons, Inc., New York, 1951.
29. Latta, G.: Singular Perturbations, Diss. Calif. Inst. Tech. (1951).

30. Liepmann, H. W., and A. Roshko: "Elements of Gasdynamics," John Wiley & Sons, Inc., New York, 1957.
31. Lighthill, M. J.: A Technique for Rendering Approximate Solutions to Physical Problems Uniformly Valid, *Phil. Mag.*, **7**(40): 1179 (1949).
32. McAdams, W. H.: "Heat Transmission," 3d ed., McGraw-Hill Book Company, New York, 1954.
33. Michal, A. D.: Differential Invariants and Invariants Under Continuous Transformation Groups in Normed Linear Spaces, *Proc. Nat. Acad. Sci.*, **37**(9): 623-627 (September, 1952).
34. Moody, L. M. F.: Friction Factors for Pipe Flow, *Trans. ASME*, **66**: 671 (1944).
35. Morgan, A. J. A.: Reduction by One of the Number of Independent Variables in Some Systems of Partial Differential Equations, *Quart. Appl. Math.*, Oxford, (2)**3**(12): 250–259 (December, 1952).
36. Morse, P. M., and H. Feshbach: "Methods of Theoretical Physics," McGraw-Hill Book Company, New York, 1953.
37. Murphy, G.: "Similitude in Engineering," The Ronald Press Company, New York, 1950.
38. Pai, S. I.: "Viscous Flow Theory," vol. I, p. 62, D. Van Nostrand Company, Inc., Princeton, N.J. (1956).
39. Poincaré, H.: "Les Méthodes Nouvelles de la Mécanique Céleste," vol. I, chap. II, Paris, 1892.
40. Prandtl, L.: Article on Viscous Flow, in Aerodynamic Theory, W. F. Durand (ed.), **3** (1934).
41. Prandtl, L.: "Essentials of Fluid Dynamics, with Application to Hydraulics, Aeronautics, Meteorology and Other Subjects" (transl.), Hafner, New York, 1953.
42. Rayleigh, L.: *Nature*, 66 and 694 (1915).
43. Riabouchinsky, M.: *Nature*, 591 (1915).
44. Ruark, A. E.: Inspectional Analysis: A Method Which Supplements Dimensional Analysis, *J. Elisha Mitchell Sci. Soc.*, **51**: 127–133 (1935).
45. Schlichting, H.: "Boundary Layer Theory," 4th ed., Series in Mechanical Engineering, McGraw-Hill Book Company, New York, 1960.
46. Sedov, L. I.: "Dimensional and Similarity Methods in Mechanics" (transl.), Academic Press Inc., New York, 1960.
47. Sellars, J. R., M. Tribus, and J. S. Klein: Heat Transfer to Laminar Flow in a Round Tube or Flat Conduit—The Graetz Problem Extended, *Trans. ASME*, **78** (February, 1956). (The reader is cautioned that while the methods in this paper are satisfactory, the tabulated numerical results are erroneous.)
48. Smith, L. H.: Dimensionless Reasoning Needs More Emphasis, Prepared by Flight Propulsion Division, General Electric Co., Evendale, Ohio, for National Science Foundation Conference on Teaching Fluid Mechanics, Galen Hall, Pa. (September, 1960). (Copies obtainable from the author.)
49. Tsien, H. S.: The Poincaré-Lighthill-Kuo Method, *Advan. Appl. Mech.*, **4** (1956).

50. Van Driest, E.: On Dimensional Analysis and the Presentation of Data in Fluid-Flow Problems, *J. Appl. Mech., Trans. ASME*, **13**: A-34 (1946).
51. Van Dyke, M.: Higher Approximations in Boundary Layer Theory, *J. Fluid Mech.*, part I, **14**: 161(1962); part II, **14**: 481 (1962); part III, **19**: 145 (1964).
52. Vennard, J. K.: "Elementary Fluid Mechanics," 2d ed., John Wiley & Sons, Inc., New York. 1948.
53. von Kármán, T.: Mechanical Similitude and Turbulence, NACA TM 611 (1931).
54. Wecker, N. S., and W. D. Hayes: Self-Similar Solutions, AFOSR TN, 60-894, Air Force Office of Scientific Research (1960).
55. Wilson, E. B.: "Introduction to Scientific Research," McGraw-Hill Book Company, New York, 1952.
56. Yang, K. T.: Possible Similarity Solutions for Laminar Free Convection on Vertical Plates and Cylinders, *J. Appl. Mech.*, **27**(2): (June, 1960).

Name Index

225

Subject Index